Explore se

Scottish Gardens
open for charity

RATHBONES

Incorporating
Investec Wealth &
Investment (UK)

Contents

Scotland's
GARDENS
Scheme

Welcome from our Chair

One of the best things about being semi-retired is that I now get weekends off, rather than working in the garden centre! As a result, many of my summer weekends have been filled with the pleasure of visiting gardens open for charity, far and near, with my wife Lesley, fortunately a fellow garden lover. We've visited gardens by arrangement on our travels north, village gardens of all shapes and sizes in the Lothians and even city gardens that are micro-havens teeming with wildlife in urban areas.

What is striking is the sheer range of different types of gardens now opening for charity with Scotland's Gardens Scheme. Perhaps due to the changes in fashion and attitudes shown by gardeners these days, and we do see this in the garden centre too, people are increasingly keen to welcome wildlife into their gardens. The smallest gardens may leave an area of grass uncut, while larger gardens and estates cultivate wildflower meadows. Whether large or small, it's good to see these gardens buzzing with life and there is no doubt that our Scottish gardeners play a hugely important part in giving nature a home.

There is other inspiration to be gained from open gardens too; there's always a new plant to be spotted; planting and colour combinations in the generous and vibrant herbaceous borders, not to mention garden design features and art in the garden. There's always something new to see and ideas to take home.

Best of all, it's always wonderful to meet the people behind the gardens, the gardeners who are so generous in sharing their gardens, and often their plants, and the volunteers who are so generous with their time, advice and support – all raising funds for charity.

Over 200 causes are supported through garden openings each year, including our core charity partners, the Queen's Nursing Institute Scotland, the gardeners' benevolent charity, Perennial, and Maggie's. We also launched the Cattanach horticultural training bursary last spring and following a successful first year, are planning to run it again this year – you can read more about it on the following pages.

To carry on doing what we do, we need help. Could you join in and make a difference? We're always welcoming new people to share their time or their gardens and there are lots of ways you can get involved. Whether it's by opening your garden, helping at an event, baking a cake or pouring a cup of tea or two – or even just bringing a friend to enjoy an open garden for the first time, we would love to welcome you to a garden this year. Sharing a love of gardening is indeed a wonderful way to raise funds for charity and you will make a difference.

Dougal Philip

Dougal Philip
Chair, Scotland's Gardens Scheme

About our charity

Scotland's Gardens Scheme is powered by hundreds of garden owners and volunteers all around Scotland, who work incredibly hard to organise and support garden openings. We are so grateful to everyone involved – the life and soul of our charity!

We have a small Head Office team to support our volunteers, who are in turn governed by our Board of Trustees, all of whom bring their specialist skills and interests to support the charity.

Meet our Trustees

Dougal Philip
Chair & Garden
Centre Owner

Sarah Landale
Vice Chair, Garden
Owner & District
Organiser for
Dumfriesshire

Peter Yellowlees
Honorary Treasurer,
Accountant (retired)

David Buchanan-Cook
Board Secretary,
District Organiser
& Treasurer, Fife &
Garden Owner

Jonathan Cobb
Investment Specialist
& Author

Colin Crosbie
Horticulturist
& Garden Owner

Charlotte Halliday
Marketing Specialist

Charlotte Hunt
Honorary Vice
President

Stephen McCallum
Horticulturist
& Garden Opener

Helen McMeekin
Charity Specialist
& Horticulturist

Front cover image: Amulree, Wigtownshire
© Ray Cox
rcoxgardenphotos.co.uk

Back cover image: West Bank, East Lothian
© Delia Ridley-Thomas

Artwork: Matt Armstrong – Serious Artworker, Jessica Taylor, Hazel Reid

Maps: Alan Palfreyman Graphics

Contains OS Data © Crown Copyright and Database 2023

Printed by Belmont Press

ISBN13: 9780901549396

MIX
Paper from
responsible sources
FSC® C015185
www.fsc.org

Scotland's Gardens Scheme Head Office
2nd Floor, 23 Castle Street, Edinburgh EH2 3DN
T: 0131 226 3714   E: info@scotlandsgardens.org
W: scotlandsgardens.org

Charity no: SC049866

Staff:

Liz Stewart – Chief Executive
Jessica Taylor – Communications Manager
Hazel Reid – Office Manager
Kate Allan – Volunteer Support Officer

Read more about our staff & trustees here:
scotlandsgardens.org/about-us/

Our impact

Scotland's Gardens Scheme exists to raise funds for a host of good causes and we are proud to have supported over **225 charities and good causes** in 2023. However, the impact of what we do is so much more. Our roots are deep, our relationships are longstanding, and we are proud of our loyal and established community of garden openers and volunteers across Scotland, involving over 1000 people in 2023.

Grow

Scotland's Gardens Scheme enables people to come together, share unique and memorable experiences and have a positive impact within and beyond their communities. People reap the benefits of spending time in nature and the wellbeing gained through connecting with others.

Give

Together, we enable funds to be raised for many charities and causes, close to the hearts of our garden owners. In 2023, over £230k was distributed to charities and good causes chosen by our garden owners.

Inspire

We are open to all, welcoming both seasoned gardeners and the next generation of gardeners, sharing good gardening practice and inspiration along the way. In 2023, we estimated that over 70,000 people came along to enjoy our open gardens.

We are also proud to support our three amazing charity partners again in 2024 and the important work they do to promote wellbeing.

MAGGIE'S
Everyone's home of cancer care

Qnis
THE QUEEN'S
NURSING
INSTITUTE
SCOTLAND

Helping people
in horticulture
Perennial

Your garden visits make a difference – every garden gate ticket bought, cup of tea sipped, slice of cake eaten – goes towards supporting charities. Here's how some of our garden openers have supported local causes that help improve the lives of others.

Garden owner Eric Wright presenting a cheque to the Rio Community Centre

Willowhill Garden in Fife raised £5,505 in 2023, with 50% going to support SGS and charity partners, with the remainder going to a cause close to the owners' heart, local organisation the Rio Community Centre, in Newport-on-Tay, which provides support for all members of the local community, particularly children and families.

"We did amazing things with the cheque we received last year including popular and well-attended holiday clubs during school breaks." says the Centre's Betty Martin. "Over 100 families enjoyed hearing about a variety of animals and why we need to plant trees, make ponds and grow vegetables and flowers. A pumpkin competition involving local schools and nurseries was popular and a sunflower seed competition attracted great interest from all over."

With thanks to garden owners, Sally Lorimore and Eric Wright.

Bruckhills Croft in Aberdeenshire has raised £735 for Befriend A Child charity in Aberdeen.

"Funds donated will assist with our volunteer's monthly allowance which covers the costs of activities and outings arranged with their befriendee, including – swimming lessons, horse riding, ice skating, visits to trampoline parks, cinema trips, and going out for meals. Many of the children we support are not given the same chances in life that most of us take for granted, but our befriending projects ensure they can enjoy the same opportunities as their friends and grow up having fun."

With thanks to garden owner Helen Rushton.

"A donation such as yours is a blessing for a small church in a deprived area, as ours is. It enables us to make a material difference to our community in a way that would be otherwise impossible. Thank you so much." St Salvador's Scottish Episcopal Church Food Initiative.

With thanks to garden owners Anna Buxton of Redcroft and Vicki Reid Thomas of Riccarton Mains, who raised over £5,300 for the Church through their garden open days.

Volunteer with us

If you love garden visits, why not consider getting involved by volunteering with us? We have lots of roles to suit everyone, all around Scotland – for example, you could:

 Use your admin skills to help update our database with garden open days or to plan and support garden openings

 Use your financial skills as a local treasurer, keeping the fundraising accounts up to date and paying charities

 Help out at open days as an event volunteer – putting up signs, staffing the entry gate, surveying visitors

 Helping with the teas – baking cakes!

 Showcase your social media and PR talents to promote open days in your local area

The best bit is that you will get to meet other like-minded gardeners and garden lovers, see beautiful gardens and make a difference by raising funds for charity.

Interested? We would love to hear from you! Find out more:
W: scotlandsgardens.org/our-volunteers/
T: 0131 226 3714
E: info@scotlandsgardens.org

Through the year we will be sharing stories of how our brilliant volunteers and garden owners, open gardens and raise funds for charity. Look out for stories on our social media channels and in our e-newsletters.

THE QUEEN'S NURSING INSTITUTE SCOTLAND

Scotland's Gardens Scheme was founded in 1931 to raise money for the Queen's Nursing Institute Scotland. The Institute has been generously supported by garden owners and visitors in Scotland's communities ever since.

Thank you.

Today, funding from Scotland's Gardens Scheme goes directly to supporting Scotland's community nurses so they can be agents for health improvement and catalysts for social change.

Together, we can drive positive action. Two charities working together to make Scotland's communities

Healthier, Kinder, Fairer & Greener.

Email: office@qnis.org.uk

Web: www.qnis.org.uk

Phone: +44 (0)131 229 2333

Diana Macnab Award for outstanding service

Vicki Reid Thomas
District Organiser

Edinburgh, Midlothian & West Lothian

Each year we ask our community of garden openers and volunteers to nominate someone who they feel is worthy of recognition. This year, we received the following resounding nomination for Vicki Reid Thomas from her Edinburgh, Midlothian and West Lothian Team and so are delighted to make this award to her, with our thanks.

Vicki has been a District Organiser for 25 years. This year, she is finally stepping down, after an extraordinary and energetic tenure that has taken her District from strength to strength, with 23 gardens and groups of gardens opening in 2023 – doubling the number of just six years ago. Funds raised have increased progressively, making over £100,000 in the last three years. The District has also enlarged by taking in Midlothian, which was previously separate. Vicki has devoted enormous amounts of time and energy over the past quarter century to making this large and busy District such a success and has gone above and beyond to bring more gardens in and keep the gardeners and her team on board.

Vicki has been a generous and hands-on leader. She hosts committee meetings and events for garden openers in her house, and in the season has a car boot that seems constantly full of SGS materials she is transporting to wherever they are needed.

She is present at many of the openings in the District and knows every gardener and every garden individually, supporting and encouraging them. She frequently helps out at group openings in person and at plant sales, and also contributes many plants from her own garden.

She personally visits all new garden openers and is encouraging of all types of garden, large and small. Her wide personal network means she is able to help new group openers make additional connections with new gardens. Vicki is persuasive in bringing new people on to the District committee, and highly supportive of new committee members. As well as facilitating so many gardeners to open for SGS, Vicki also finds time to open her own stunning garden.

As members of her District committee, we are delighted to nominate her for the Diana Macnab Award.

Find your way through cancer

Come to Maggie's

Maggie's offers the best possible psychological and emotional support for free to anyone with cancer and their families.

Built in the grounds of NHS hospitals, our centres are warm and welcoming places, with professional staff on hand to offer the support you need to find your way through cancer.

Our centres are open Monday to Friday, 9am – 5pm, and no referral is required. We are also online at maggies.org.

Maggie's centres across Scotland receive vital funds from every garden opening. Our heartfelt thanks go to everyone who supports Scotland's Gardens Scheme by opening their garden, volunteering or visiting a garden.

Scotland's
GARDENS
Scheme
OPEN FOR CHARITY

maggies.org

Maggie Keswick Jencks Cancer Caring Centres Trust (Maggie's) is a registered charity, no. SC024414

MAGGIE'S
Everyone's home of cancer care

Pass on your love of gardens with a gift in your will

Leaving a gift to Scotland's Gardens Scheme will help us to continue to share the joy of garden visiting and inspire the next generation of gardeners.

To find out more about leaving a gift in your will to Scotland's Gardens Scheme, please email **info@scotlandsgardens.org** or visit **scotlandsgardens.org/gift-in-will/**

We're here for all seasons

We need the people behind the flowers, plants trees and grass, and sometimes they need us. We're here for everyone, working and retired, to help grow their wellbeing physically, mentally and financially. Please support the people behind our beautiful gardens.

" Our wellbeing benefits from gorgeous gardens. However, all of us working in horticulture need more than nature's support. Please spread the word that Perennial is here, helping those in need bloom again. "

Carole Baxter,
Charity Trustee, BBC Scotland
Beechgrove Garden, presenter.

Find out more or donate
perennial.org.uk

Helping people in horticulture
Perennial

Scotland's Gardens Scheme is seeking new gardens – why not open yours?

Join our community of like-minded individuals passionate about gardens and open your garden to raise money for charity.

Our collection of gardens is wide and varied. We welcome country estates, walled gardens and stately homes, alongside cottage gardens, tropical paradises and urban oases. We are also pleased to welcome community gardens, school gardens and allotments. So, whatever its size or style, if your garden has quality, character and interest, we would love to hear from you.

To find out more about opening your garden:

Call us on: **0131 226 3714**

Email the office: **info@ scotlandsgardens.org**

Visit our website: **scotlandsgardens.org/ open-your-garden/**

SGS Ambassador Lizzie Schofield has opened her garden for Scotland's Gardens Scheme, so why not join her and open yours?

Dogs are welcome in many of our gardens, but keep them on a short lead!

Look out
for this icon

At Queen Victoria Park
one's vistors always get a royal welcome.

Queen Victoria Park is an exclusive residential neighbourhood for the over 55s within a 100-acre garden paradise at Inchmarlo Retirement Village near Banchory in Aberdeenshire on Royal Deeside.

Queen Victoria Park is next to Inchmarlo Golf Centre and the River Dee, and comprises an active community of like-minded people with round-the-clock security and support services.

- 1 bed apartments with balconies from £65,000
- 2 bed apartments with balconies from £79,000

To find out more or to arrange viewings:
please call Fenella Scott on 01330 824981 or
email fenella.scott@inchmarlo-retirement.co.uk

INCHMARLO
RETIREMENT VILLAGE

Where Gracious Living
Comes Naturally

inchmarlo-retirement.co.uk

Discover how Queen Victoria Park might be just your type of place.

West Linton Village Gardens © Kathy Henry

Gardens open by arrangement

Did you know we have hundreds of beautiful gardens where visitors can get in touch with the garden owners and book a private visit?

Many gardens welcome visits from groups, such as gardening clubs, U3A and even ramblers and cycling groups planning days out around garden visits. Or perhaps you'd like to visit as a couple or small group of garden-loving friends looking for a special day out. Many of our gardens even provide teas and sometimes there are plants to buy!

Booking a visit is easy:

 Browse the guidebook or website and look for the 'by arrangement' gardens in the opening details for each listing

 Contact the garden owner to arrange a time to visit – contact details or booking links will be in the book and on the website

Our garden owners would love to hear from you and you will be sure of a very warm welcome! Please tell them that you heard about their garden through Scotland's Gardens Scheme.

RHS Membership

Get closer to the world you *love*

SAVE
25%
TODAY*

JOIN TODAY

Grow your love of gardens with free days out, season-by-season inspiration, expert gardening advice and a year of possibilities.

Call **020 3176 5820**, scan the **QR code** or visit **rhs.org.uk/4498**

Your membership supports our work as a charity.

New horticultural training bursary

Scotland's Gardens Scheme's Cattanach Fund supports Scotland's gardening sector

In 2023, Scotland's Gardens Scheme piloted a new bursary scheme to support people working or training in horticulture in Scotland. The aim of the fund was to support personal and professional development training relating to horticulture, to support our horticultural sector in Scotland.

We had a successful first year of the fund, which was administered by the team at the Professional Gardeners' Trust, with the results as follows.

13 Awards Made so far

£6975 Total value of SGS awards

Status of bursary holder:

 5 employed in a horticultural institution (NTS, RBGE etc)

 4 employed by a private garden

 2 students

 1 self-employed

 1 community project worker

Courses supported:

Chainsaw **(3)**

Spraying **(3)**

Design **(2)**

Herbology **(2)**

 1 Certificate in Arboriculture
1 Nursery Management
1 Social & Therapeutic Horticulture

This was made possible by a legacy made by Mr Albert Cattanach and we hope to build on this fund in the future with legacies received by Scotland's Gardens Scheme.

We will be launching the next round of the fund in early 2024 so please keep an eye on our website, social media and e-newsletters.

scotlandsgardens.org/bursaries/

We would also like to take this opportunity to thank the following for their generous bequests to Scotland's Gardens Scheme:

The Estate of Helen Tabor

The Estate of Kathleen Brownlie

The Estate of June Reid

Thank you to the first three of our Cattanach Candidates for reporting back on their training experiences in 2023.

"I am so thankful for the support of Scotland's Gardens Scheme in helping me with the funding costs of my PA1 and PA6 tests. Without this support I would have really struggled to gain this qualification that allows me to be better prepared for any future employment. It is my hope to work in an indoor glasshouse team where this will be of great use to me and I have a real passion for working outside as well. I have been retraining as a horticulturist and this qualification is another goal off my checklist. Thank you so much to the Scotland's Gardens Scheme for helping me achieve it! I am now one step closer towards my future in horticulture."

Stella Jardine

"I am currently a gardener for the National Trust for Scotland at Kellie Castle, already holding an HND in Horticulture with Plantsmanship from the Royal Botanic Garden in Edinburgh/SRUC. Thanks to this generous award, I had the opportunity to undergo professional chainsaw training for tree felling. This training has equipped me with a highly valuable skill that I can now apply in the garden and use to propel my career to a senior position. I am now thrilled to apply my newly acquired chainsaw proficiency at the garden and look forward to advancing my career within the organisation, securing a more senior position in the near future."

Aline Abreu

"I'm writing this report to express my deepest gratitude for the £900 that I received as a donation funded by Scotland's Gardens Scheme (SGS) Cattanach. I was successful on assessment day and passed the course. This will have a positive impact on my current job as a gardener at Threave Gardens (National Trust for Scotland) as I will be able to use the skills I have acquired as part of tree maintenance and take down on site at Threave."

Alec Cook

With thanks to our friends at the Professional Gardeners' Trust for administering the fund on behalf of Scotland's Gardens Scheme.

Professional Gardeners' Trust

Welcome to our gardens

We hope you have a fabulous season ahead, exploring the gardens on the following pages.

Don't forget to:

Plan ahead

Things can change, so please do check the website and our social media for any cancellations, changes to timing or new garden openings being added.

Book a visit

Did you know that many of our gardens are open by arrangement? Contact the garden owner to plan a visit; just call or email using the contact details in the garden listing – they will be delighted to hear from you. Don't forget to mention Scotland's Gardens Scheme!

Share your visit

Tell a friend about Scotland's Gardens Scheme or share your pictures on social media and tag us *#lovescotlandsgardens*

Enjoy your visits and we look forward to seeing you in the garden.

The art of sitting
comfortably

Snowdrops & Winter Walks

In the depths of winter there is nothing more uplifting than the sight of snowdrops peeping through the winter leaves. Explore the gardens below for carpets of snowdrops or curated collections of the rare and unusual. Full details may be found on the garden's listing later on in this book and on our website *scotlandsgardens.org*.

You can also find more places to visit at *discoverscottishgardens.org* for gardens taking part in the Scottish Snowdrop Festival, **24 January – 11 March 2024**.

Aberdeenshire
- Laundry Cottage, **by arrangement**
- Bruckhills Croft*, **by arrangement from 3 February**

Angus, Dundee & The Mearns
- Kinblethmont House, **24 & 25 February**
- Ecclesgreig Castle, **3 March**
- Lawton House, **29 February – 2 March**

Dumfriesshire
- Tinnisburn Plants, **17 & 18 February**
- Craig, **18 February**

Dunbartonshire
- Stuckenduff, **25 February**

East Lothian
- Shepherd House, **Sunday 18 February and Tues/Thurs from 6 – 29 February**

Edinburgh Midlothian & West Lothian
- Preston Hall Walled Garden, **17 & 18 February**

Fife
- Madeira, **by arrangement**
- Cambo Gardens*, **open through the season**
- Dunimarle Castle, **10 & 11 February**
- Lindores House, **24 February**

Inverness, Ross, Cromarty & Skye
- Dunvegan Castle & Gardens, **10, 15 & 20 February**
- Abriachan Garden & Nursery, **from 1 February**

* National Plant Collection of Galanthus

Kirkcudbrightshire
- Barhill (NEW), **by arrangement**
- Brooklands, **by arrangement**
- Kings Grange House, **by arrangement**
- Barholm Castle, **by arrangement**
- Danevale Park, **Sunday 18 February**

Lanarkshire
- Cleghorn, **Sunday 3 March**

Moray & Nairn
- Burgie Arboretum, **from 24 January**
- 10 Pilmuir Road West, **by arrangement**

Peeblesshire & Tweeddale
- Kirkton Manor House, **Wednesdays from 14 February**
- Kailzie Gardens, **Sunday 3 March**

Perth & Kinross
- Fingask Castle, **22 January – 7 March (NOT Friday, Saturday, Sunday)**
- Braco Castle, **from 1 February**
- Cloan, **18 February**
- Scone Palace Garden, **24 February**

Stirlingshire
- Gargunnock House Garden, **from 1 February by arrangement**
- Duntreath Castle, **from 1 February by arrangement**
- Kilbryde Castle, **from 1 February by arrangement**

Wigtownshire
- Glenwhan Gardens & Arboretum, **open through the season**
- Craichlaw, **by arrangement**
- Logan Botanic Garden, **Saturdays & Sundays in February**
- Castle Kennedy Gardens, **3 February - 31 March (Saturday & Sunday)**

Plant Sales & Special Events

Some of our most popular events include plant sales. Everyone loves a bargain!

We've also highlighted a few events that are a bit different, and we will publicise further details of these and more as we go through the year, so do sign up for our e-newsletter on our website and keep an eye on our social media.

● Angus, Dundee & The Mearns

Angus Plant Sale at Pitmuies, **18 May**

● Argyll & Lochaber

Ardchattan Priory Garden Fête, **9 June**

● Dunbartonshire

James Street Community Garden Plant Sale, **1 September**

● East Lothian

Winton Castle Daffodils – Garden Fair, **14 April**

● Edinburgh Midlothian & West Lothian

Redcroft Plant Sale & Garden Open Day, **11-12 May**

● Fife

SGS Autumn Plant Sale at St Andrews Botanic Garden, **6 October**

● Glasgow & District

A Soiree in September, **14 September**

● Inverness, Ross, Cromarty & Skye

Glenkyllachy Plant Sale & Garden Open Day, **16 June**

● Kirkcudbrightshire

Threave & SGS Garden Open Day, **6 May**

● Perth & Kinross

Snowdrops at Scone, **24 February**

Bradystone House Plant Sale, **15 June**

Drummond Castle Garden Fair, **4 August**

● Renfrewshire

SGS Kilmacolm Plant Sale, **27 April & 14 July**

Unique Opportunity

Culzean Guided Tour, with NTS Head Gardener and Gardens & Designed Landscapes Manager. Spaces will be limited.

The dates and further information of this special event will be posted on our website scotlandsgardens.org and in our e-newsletter.

New gardens for 2024

It's always exciting to receive an enquiry from a new garden owner wishing to open with Scotland's Gardens Scheme and the variety of gardens is ever changing; we have educational and community gardens, urban oases and country retreats, eco-gardens and tropical paradises, castles and even a bowling club. This year, we are delighted to welcome over 50 new gardens to our opening programme and we can't wait to share them with you. Please do come along and support these new gardens and make their first opening a day to remember!

Angus, Dundee & The Mearns:
Carnoustie's Tropical Garden

East Lothian:
Amisfield Walled Garden

Fife:
Pitlochie House

Glasgow & District:
SWG3 Community Garden

Inverness, Ross, Cromarty & Skye:
Aldourie Castle Garden

Kirkcudbrightshire:
Barhill

Perth & Kinross:
Tomandroighne

Stirlingshire:
Bannockburn House Garden

Wigtownshire:
Barlockhart Lodge

New gardens by district NEW

Aberdeenshire

- Norton House

Angus, Dundee & The Mearns

- 1 Castle Street
  (Brechin Gardens in July)
- Carnoustie's Tropical Garden
- Charleston Forest Garden
- Heather's Garden (West End Trio)

Argyll & Lochaber

- Ilha de Deus

Dumfriesshire

- The Hewke

Dunbartonshire

- Brantwoode
  (opening with High Glenan)
- Linn Botanic Gardens*

East Lothian

- Amisfield Walled Garden
- Blackdykes Garden

Edinburgh, Midlothian & West Lothian

- 20 Blackford Road*
- 77 Kirk Brae
- Fountainbank
- Pentland Crescent Gardens
- Regent, Royal and Carlton
  Terrace Gardens
- Whitehouse & Grange Bowling Club

Fife

- Blanerne
- Dawson's Garden
- Edenhill*
- Kirkbrae House
- Moonzie House
- Pitlochie House

Glasgow & District

- SWG3 Community Garden

Inverness, Ross, Cromarty & Skye

- Aldourie Castle
- Monarda House
- Struanbridge

Kirkcudbrightshire

- Barhill
- Tal-y-Fan

Lanarkshire

- Covington Gardens
- Stobwood Cottage

Moray & Nairn

- The Biblical Garden
- Ruthven Cottage Hardy Plant Nursery
- Sunflower Dreams*

Peeblesshire & Tweeddale

- Kirkhouse

Perth & Kinross

- Auchterarder Allotments
- Beech Cottage
- Birnam Bank Walled Garden
- Mouse Cottage
- Tomandroighne*

Renfrewshire

- Barnbeth House
- North Newton Farm

Roxburghshire

- Larch House
- Southdean Mill

Stirlingshire

- Southfield Crescent
- 18 Buchany
- Bannockburn House Gardens
- Brahead Community Garden Oakmore
- Tiny Farm

Wigtownshire

- Barlockhart Lodge
- Lutra Holt

*Featured as a late 'Pop-up' opening in 2023
but not in 2023 Guidebook

Groups & Villages

Visiting a series of group or village gardens presents the very best opportunity for a peep behind the garden gate. Discover a range of gardens to suit every taste, from vibrant veg plots and herbaceous borders, to gardens for socialising and havens for wildlife. You'll definitely find something to inspire you and these garden groups are amongst our garden visitors' favourites.

If you enjoy group or village gardens, why not join in with your neighbours and open your own garden?

Aberdeenshire
- Two Gardens in Banchory Devenick

Angus, Dundee & The Mearns
- Brechin Gardens in June*
- Brechin Gardens in July*
- West End Trio, Dundee*

Argyll & Lochaber
- Ardverikie with Aberarder

Caithness, Sutherland, Orkney & Shetland
- Old Granary Quoy and the Quoy of Houton

Dunbartonshire
- Brantwood (NEW) and High Glenan

East Lothian
- Dirleton Village
- Inveresk Village
- Longniddry Gardens
- Tyninghame House and The Walled Garden

Edinburgh, Midlothian & West Lothian
- Dean Gardens
- Moray Place and Bank Gardens
- Pentland Crescent Gardens
- Stockbridge Gardens

Fife
- Auchtermuchty Village
- Blebo Craigs Village Gardens
- Crail: Gardens in the Burgh
- Pittenweem: Gardens in the Burgh

Glasgow & District
- Kilsyth Gardens
- The Gardens of Milton of Campsie*

Inverness, Ross, Cromarty & Skye
- Kiltarlity Gardens

Lanarkshire
- Covington Gardens (NEW)

Peeblesshire & Tweeddale
- Gattonside Village Gardens
- Macbiehill Gardens

Stirlingshire
- Bridge of Allan Gardens

*Group includes new gardens

Covington Mill Farmhouse

Tips & key to symbols

By Arrangement

This is a great way to see a garden when it's quiet and garden owners will be delighted to hear from you to book a visit. Many gardens welcome visits from larger groups or clubs such as horticultural societies, as well as individuals or couples. Do get in touch.

Photography

Most of our gardens are privately owned so any photographs taken must be for private use only. The garden owner's permission must be sought if images are to be included in publications. Our Volunteer Photographers may take photos on the open day. Please notify them if you don't wish to appear in our promotional materials.

Gardening Advice

Our garden openers love to chat about their gardens. If there's a bit of advice you're after, please do ask!

Extra Assistance

Carers are offered free entry to our gardens and Assistance Dogs are always welcome.

Children & Families

Children are welcome with an accompanying adult, unless otherwise stated, but must be supervised at all times. Some openings offer children's activities – look for the children's activities symbol.

Group Visits

Many of our gardens are pleased to have groups visiting. Get in touch with the garden or contact the local District Organiser for more information.

Toilets

Private gardens do not normally have outside toilets. For security reasons, our Openers have been advised not to admit visitors into their homes.

Cancellations & additional openings

All cancellations and new dates will be posted on our website, scotlandsgardens.org, under the garden listing.

Please bring cash

While some gardens have card readers, please help our garden owners by bringing cash.

Key to symbols

Always check our website before setting out for any cancellations, last-minute changes to opening details or booking arrangements.

Gardens open for the first time, or after a long break

Dogs on short leads welcome

Full or partial wheelchair accessibility

Locally-grown plants for sale

Children's activities

Snowdrops & Winter Walks

Accessible by public transport

Champion Trees, from the UK Tree Register

National Plant Collection®, from Plant Heritage

Gardens & Designed Landscapes by Historic Environment Scotland

Basic teas

Cream teas

Homemade teas

Refreshments

Accommodation available at the garden

Our districts

Aberdeenshire

Sponsored by

RATHBONES

Incorporating
Investec Wealth &
Investment (UK)

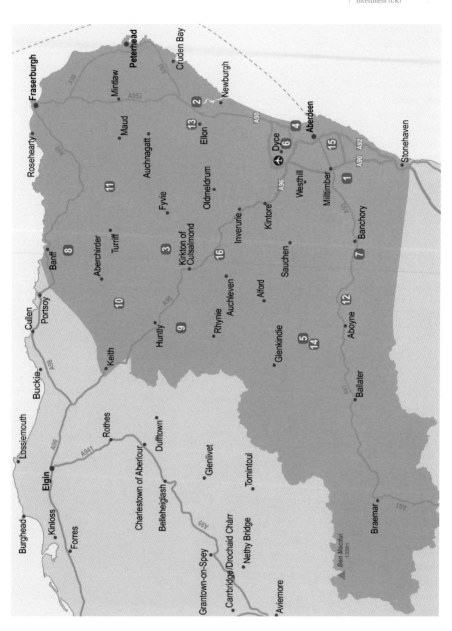

Aberdeenshire

OUR VOLUNTEER ORGANISERS

District Organiser:	Verity Walters	Tillychetly, Alford AB33 8HQ info@scotlandsgardens.org
Area Organisers:	Catherine Nichols	Westerton Steading, Dess, Aboyne AB34 5AY
	Jennie Gibson	6 The Chanonry, Old Aberdeen AB24 1RP
	Denise Jones	Smiddy House, Glenkindie, Alford AB33 8SS
	Julie Nicol	Cedarwood Lodge, Rhu-Na-Haven Road, Aboyne AB34 5JB
	Helen Rushton	Bruckhills Croft, Rothienorman AB51 8YB
	Madeleine Fraser	
	Anne Fettes	
	Gill Cook	
District Photographer:	Andy Leonard	Parkvilla, 47 Schoolhill, Ellon AB41 9AJ
Treasurer:	Ann Doyle	South Cottage, Fisherford, Inverurie AB51 8YS

GARDENS OPEN ON A SPECIFIC DATE

Auchmacoy, Ellon	Sunday, 7 April
Westhall Castle, Oyne, Inverurie	Sunday, 21 April
Middle Cairncake, Cuminestown, Turriff	Sunday, 5/Sunday, 12 May
Inchmarlo Retirement Village Garden, Inchmarlo, Banchory	Sunday, 19 May
Norton House, 1 North Deeside Road, Kincardine O'Neil, Aboyne	Sunday, 2 June
Bruckhills Croft, Rothienorman, Inverurie	Sunday, 30 June
Douneside House, Tarland	Sunday, 7 July
Two Gardens in Banchory Devenick, Banchory Devenick	Saturday/Sunday, 20/21 July
Tarland Community Garden, Tarland, Aboyne	Sunday, 11 August
Mayen Estate, Rothiemay, Huntly	Date to be confirmed
Altries, Maryculter, Aberdeenshire	Date to be confirmed

GARDENS OPEN REGULARLY

Middle Cairncake, Cuminestown, Turriff	30 June - 14 July

Aberdeenshire

GARDENS OPEN BY ARRANGEMENT

Laundry Cottage, Culdrain, Gartly, Huntly	1 January - 31 December
Bruckhills Croft, Rothienorman, Inverurie	3 February - 17 March
Chaplains' Court, 20 The Chanonry, Old Aberdeen, Aberdeen	1 March - 30 September
Grandhome, Danestone, Aberdeen	1 April - 31 October
Two Gardens in Banchory Devenick, Banchory Devenick	1 June - 31 July
Kemplemyres Farmhouse, Alvah, Banff	29 June - 30 June, 27 July - 28 July & 24 August - 25 August
Parkvilla, 47 Schoolhill, Ellon	6 July - 29 September
Middle Cairncake, Cuminestown, Turriff	15 July - 31 July

Inchmarlo Retirement Village Garden

Aberdeenshire

1 ALTRIES
Maryculter, Aberdeenshire AB12 5GD
Mr and Mrs Melfort Campbell

The Altries garden has been redesigned to give a feeling of space and to let in the light. The house itself is surrounded by a terraced area, borders and lawns. There is an exceptional view looking west up the River Dee, a woodland walk, a slate sphere sculpture using the original slates of the house following the refurbishment, a striking ten-foot wall making use of the down-takings of the house, a small new greenhouse with rose arbour path and further use of granite, and the original walled garden which has vegetables, fruit, and a picking garden. Each area of the garden has its own feeling of being a separate destination. Beautiful mature beech trees surround the area, giving a great sense of privacy.

Open: Opening date to be confirmed, admission £10.00, children free. Disabled parking at the house.

Directions: From Bridge of Dee, follow the South Deeside road, B9077. Half a mile after Maryculter House Hotel, turn left at yellow SGS sign, and follow signs to car park. For SatNav follow AB12 5GJ.

Opening for: River Dee Trust

2 AUCHMACOY
Ellon AB41 8RB
Mr and Mrs Charles Buchan
E: sharon@buchan.co.uk

Auchmacoy House's attractive policies feature spectacular displays of thousands of daffodils.

Open: Sunday 7 April, 1pm - 4pm, admission £4.00, children free. Please, NO dogs. The Buchan Pipe Band will play.

Directions: A90 from Aberdeen. Turn right to Auchmacoy/Collieston.

Opening for: St Mary On The Rock Episcopal Church Ellon & Saint James Church Cruden Bay

3 BRUCKHILLS CROFT
Rothienorman, Inverurie AB51 8YB
Paul and Helen Rushton
T: 01651 821596 E: helenrushton1@aol.com

An informal country cottage garden extending to ¾ of an acre with a further acre as wildflower meadow and pond. There are several distinct areas which include a white border, a butterfly alley, kitchen garden with polytunnel, greenhouse and fruit cage, an orchard, and a blue and yellow border. Relax on one of the many seats in the garden and soak up the atmosphere. Awarded National Collection status for *Galanthus* (snowdrops) in 2021.
National Plant Collection: *Galanthus*.

Open: by arrangement 3 February - 17 March for Snowdrops and Winter Walks. Also open Sunday 30 June, noon - 5pm. Admission £5.00, children free.

Directions: From Rothienorman take the B9001 north for 2½ miles. On the S-bend turn left. When you reach the Bruckhills Farm turn off, yellow signs will direct you to the Croft.

Opening for: Plant Heritage (3 February - 17 March) & Befriend A Child Ltd (Sunday 30 June)

Aberdeenshire

4 CHAPLAINS' COURT
20 The Chanonry, Old Aberdeen, Aberdeen AB24 1RQ
Irene Wischik
T: 01224 491675 E: irene@wischik.com

This historic walled garden has a long, well-stocked herbaceous border offering a succession of vivid colour from early spring to winter. It is divided by an ornamental pergola, a perfect place to sit and enjoy the garden. Large trees of ash, beech, horse chestnut, oak and sycamore give this garden a mature feel. A specimen Camperdown elm sits in the centre of the lawn, which in spring is covered in a carpet of crocuses, snowdrops and *Scilla*. Vegetables and herbs produce plentiful crops, together with newly-planted espalier and fan-trained apple and pear trees.

Open: by arrangement 1 March - 30 September, admission £6.00, children free.

Directions: Bus 1 or 2 from Aberdeen city centre to St Machar Drive, and head towards St Machar Cathedral. Or drive down St Machar Drive, turn into The Chanonry and drive down until the junction with Don Street.

Opening for: SSAFA Forces Help

Douneside House

5 DOUNESIDE HOUSE
Tarland AB34 4UD
The MacRobert Trust
W: www.dounesidehouse.co.uk

Douneside is the former home of Lady MacRobert, who developed these magnificent gardens in the early to mid-1900s. Ornamental borders, an Arts and Crafts themed terraced garden and water gardens surround a spectacular infinity lawn overlooking the Deeside hills. The walled garden houses a large ornamental greenhouse and supplies organic fruit, vegetables, herbs and cut flowers to Douneside House which is a multi-award winning hotel. All areas of the garden will be open and there will be a pipe band, teas and plants for sale.

Open: Sunday 7 July, 2pm - 5pm, admission £6.00, children free.

Directions: On the B9119 towards Aberdeen. Tarland one mile.

Opening for: Perennial

Aberdeenshire

6 **GRANDHOME**
Danestone, Aberdeen AB22 8AR
Mrs WJB Paton
T: 01224 722202 E: admin@grandhome.co.uk

Eighteenth-century walled garden incorporating a rose garden and policies with daffodils, tulips, rhododendrons, azaleas, mature trees and shrubs.

Open: by arrangement 1 April - 31 October, admission £5.00, children free. Please, no dogs. We would prefer three working days' notice of your visit when booking.

Directions: From the north end of North Anderson Drive, continue on the A92 over Persley Bridge, turning left at the Tesco roundabout. After 1 ¾ miles, turn left through the pillars on a left-hand bend.

Opening for: All proceeds to SGS Beneficiaries

7 **INCHMARLO RETIREMENT VILLAGE GARDEN**
Inchmarlo, Banchory AB31 4AL
Skene Enterprises (Aberdeen) Ltd
T: 01330 826242 E: info@inchmarlo-retirement.co.uk
W: www.inchmarlo-retirement.co.uk

Beautiful five-acre woodland garden filled with azaleas and rhododendrons beneath ancient Scots pines, Douglas firs and silver firs (some over 140 feet tall). Also beeches, rare and unusual trees including pindrow firs, Pere David's maple, Erman's birch and a mountain snowdrop tree. The Oriental Garden features a Karesansui, a dry slate stream designed by Peter Roger, a *RHS Chelsea* gold medal winner. The keyhole-shaped garden houses a purple *Prunus cerasifera* hedge and a herbaceous border, and has been designed by Billy Carruthers of Binny Plants, an eight-times gold medal winner at Gardening Scotland and a regular at the RHS Chelsea Flower Show.

Open: Sunday 19 May, 1:30pm - 4:30pm, admission £5.00, children free.

Directions: From Aberdeen via North Deeside Road on the A93, one mile west of Banchory turn right at the main gate to the Inchmarlo Estate.

Opening for: Alzheimer Scotland & The Forget-Me-Not Club

8 **KEMPLEMYRES FARMHOUSE**
Alvah, Banff AB45 3UR
Jane Duffield
T: 07778 083759 E: janeduffield@hotmail.co.uk

A large wildlife garden, still in the making. Starting from a completely blank canvas 15 years ago, we wanted the garden to blend sympathetically into the wider, natural landscape. We're constantly learning how to garden creatively, in order to live harmoniously alongside the visiting deer and badgers! Areas of interest include a rose garden, stone circle garden, dell garden, two wildlife ponds, mixed shrub beds and our current project, a small, walled kitchen garden.

Open: by arrangement 29 - 30 June, 27 - 28 July & 24 - 25 August, admission £5.00, children free.

Aberdeenshire

Directions: From Turriff, take the B9025, signposted to *Aberchirder*. Approximately five miles out of Turriff, turn right, on to the B9121, signposted *Banff* and *Whitehills*. After approximately two miles, take the right hand turn, signposted *Alvah*. The road passes farm buildings on your left. Just past these, at the bottom of the hill, take the left hand turn, signposted *Kirktown of Alvah*. The road dips down to a small bridge over a burn, with a short, steep climb up the other side. Our drive is on the right-hand side, by the big beech tree, with double wooden gates, signposted *Kemplemyres Farmhouse and the Bothy*.

Opening for: *Macmillan Cancer Support*

Kemplemyres Farmhouse

9 LAUNDRY COTTAGE
Culdrain, Gartly, Huntly AB54 4PY
Judith McPhun
T: 01466 720768 E: judithmcphun@icloud.com

An informal, cottage-style garden of about 1½ acres by the River Bogie. Two contrasting steep slopes make up the wilder parts. The more intensively gardened area around the cottage includes a wide variety of herbaceous plants, shrubs and trees, an orchard area and fruit and vegetable plots, making a garden of year-round interest.

Open: by arrangement 1 January - 31 December, admission £5.00, children free. Snowdrops during February and March. Groups of up to 12 welcome.

Directions: Four miles south of Huntly on the A97.

Opening for: *Amnesty International UK Section Charitable Trust*

10 MAYEN ESTATE
Rothiemay, Huntly AB54 7NL
Mr and Mrs A Cheyne
W: www.mayenestate.com

The Mayen Estate walled gardens are two acres in size and were built in 1997. They feature a large octagonal glasshouse, and the space is broken into small themed ornamental gardens and vegetable beds by tall yew hedges. We use permaculture growing methods and enjoy growing our plants from seed. Highlights include the large herbaceous border and highly scented rose garden.

Open: Admission £8.00. No disabled toilets. Opening date to be confirmed.

Aberdeenshire

Directions: From the A96 towards Inverness, take the B9002 just north of Huntly towards Portsoy. After six miles turn right, for Rothiemay, alongside the river. Entering the village, turn left, past the church then turn right for Aberchirder, on the B9117. After two miles along the valley, you will go round a sharp left corner and our gate lodge is on the right. It has navy iron gates and a signpost for *Mayen House*.

Opening for: Deveron, Bogie and Isla Rivers Charitable Trust

 ## MIDDLE CAIRNCAKE
Cuminestown, Turriff AB53 5YS
Nick and Penny Orpwood
T: 01888 544432 E: orpwood@hotmail.com

The garden here surrounds the traditional farmhouse and steading in a rural landscape. We enjoy a series of gardens, all interlinked and with different character and planting: roses, heathers, ponds, borders and beds, wild area plus a large vegetable plot with polytunnel for self-sufficiency. We grow annuals from seed collected from our own plants. The spring open afternoons will show a colourful garden getting ready for the summer planting. Refreshments will be served in our winter garden which houses tender plants such as begonias, passion flowers and brugmansia.

Open: Sundays 5 & 12 May, 11am-4pm. Also open 30 June - 14 July, 1pm - 4pm. And open by arrangement, 15 - 31 July. Admission £7.00, children free. Please bring cash as we cannot accept cards. Homemade refreshments at additional charge. We welcome prebooked visits from groups.

Directions: Middle Cairncake is on the A9170 between New Deer and Cuminestown. It is clearly signposted.

Opening for: Parkinsons UK

Mayen Estate © Clare Lou Photography

Aberdeenshire

12 NORTON HOUSE

1 North Deeside Road, Kincardine O'Neil, Aboyne, Aberdeenshire AB34 5AA
Andrew and Nicola Bradford

Norton House, on the edge of historic Kincardine O'Neil village, is a detached Victorian property dating back to 1840. The garden is new to Scotland's Gardens Scheme but the owners are not, as Andrew and Nicky have moved from nearby Kincardine Castle into what was once Andrew's grandmother's home. Happily the intervening owners were keen gardeners and this is a mature garden with trees, shrubs, herbaceous borders and a small orchard. An area that has been neglected for decades is being chain-sawed into submission as a woodland - work in progress!

Open: Sunday 2 June, 2pm - 5pm, admission £10.00, children free. £10 entry includes price of tea. Children's free entry to include juice and biscuits, homemade tea available for children by donation. The Open Day will include a well-stocked plant stall with lots of super plants and knowledgeable helpers.

Directions: Situated on the A93 at the eastern end of Kincardine O'Neil. Accessible by bus, the Stagecoach 201 service.

Opening for: Children 1st

13 PARKVILLA

47 Schoolhill, Ellon AB41 9AJ
Andy and Kim Leonard
T: 07786 748296 E: andy.leonard@btinternet.com

A south-facing Victorian walled garden, lovingly developed from a design started in 1990 to give colour and interest all year. Enjoy densely planted herbaceous borders, pause under the pergola clothed in clematis, honeysuckle and rambling roses, continue on to the bottom of the garden where three ponds and wildflower beds reflect a strong focus on wildlife. This is a hidden gem of a garden that has won awards including *Ellon Best Garden* and with plants rarely seen in north-east Scotland.

Open: by arrangement 6 July - 29 September, admission £5.00, children free. Please, NO dogs, except guide and assistance dogs by prior arrangement.

Directions: From centre of Ellon head north towards Auchnagatt. Schoolhill is third left. From Auchnagatt head into Ellon along Golf Road, Schoolhill is first right after the golf course. Limited on-street parking, car parks in Ellon (five minutes walk) and Caroline's Well Wood. Public toilets in Ellon town centre.

Opening for: St Mary On The Rock Episcopal Church Ellon, Alzheimer Scotland & Ellon Men's Shed

14 TARLAND COMMUNITY GARDEN

Tarland, Aboyne AB34 4ZQ
The Gardeners of Tarland

Tarland Community Garden opened in 2013 and is a Tarland Development Group project. It provides an inclusive and accessible community growing space for local residents. It has indoor (polytunnel) and outdoor raised beds for members based on availability, plus communal planting areas including a soft fruit cage, fruit trees and a herb garden. It is a place for members to grow produce, learn, share and have fun.

Aberdeenshire

Open: Sunday 11 August, noon - 4pm, admission £3.00, children free.

Directions: Take the B9094 from Aboyne or the A96 and B9119 from Aberdeen. Arriving at the village square the gardens will be clearly signposted.

Opening for: Tarland Development Group

15 TWO GARDENS IN BANCHORY DEVENICK
Banchory Devenick AB12 5XR
Angela and Derek Townsley & Jane and Terry O'Kelly
T: text 07712 528450 E: janeokelly868@gmail.com

Pinetrees Cottage Banchory Devenick AB12 5XR (Angela and Derek Townsley): A mature garden set in three-quarters of an acre, filled with a wide range of hardy plants including rhododendrons, azaleas, acers, topiary and roses, with two ponds. An alpine house is fronted by stone troughs filled with rock plants. Set in a backdrop of mature pine trees to the north and open fields to the south.
Whin Cottage Ardoe, Aberdeen AB12 5XT (Jane and Terry O'Kelly): A cottage garden of just under half an acre surrounded by farmland. It features a border of rhododendrons and azaleas, several mixed borders, two formal rose beds, a wildlife pond and four raised beds growing a variety of vegetables and flowers for the house. The garden reflects a love of colour and structure and an interest in wildlife.
Open: Saturday/Sunday, 20/21 July, 2pm - 5pm. Also open by arrangement 1 June - 31 July. Admission £6.00, children free. Plants for sale at Pinetrees Cottage. Teas available at Whin Cottage.

Directions: Pinetrees Cottage: Banchory Devenick is four miles from Bridge of Dee. Turn off B9077 at Banchory Devenick church. Follow to T-junction, turn right. Next right is Butterywells Steading. Turn into opening and follow track, go around the back of farmhouse (Lochend) and continue on track to Pinetrees.
Whin Cottage: Take the B9077 out of Aberdeen. After approximately two miles turn left immediately after Banchory Devenick Church, signposted Banchory Devenick. (There is parking available along the verge on the left.) Turn right after 100 metres. Whin Cottage is on the right immediately after you have turned. There is limited parking outside the cottage.

Opening for: Fighting For Sight Aberdeen

16 WESTHALL CASTLE
Oyne, Inverurie AB52 6RW
Mr Gavin Farquhar
T: 01224 214301 E: enquiries@ecclesgreig.com

Set in an ancient landscape in the foothills of the impressive and foreboding hill of Bennachie, is a circular walk through glorious daffodils with outstanding views. This interesting garden is in the early stages of restoration, with large groupings of rhododendrons and specimen trees. Westhall Castle is a 16th-century tower house, incorporating a 13th-century building of the bishops of Aberdeen. There were additions in the 17th, 18th and 19th centuries. The castle is semi-derelict, but stabilised from total dereliction. A fascinating house encompassing 600 years of alteration and additions.

Open: Sunday 21 April, 1pm - 4pm, admission £5.00, children free.

Directions: Marked from the A96 at Old Rayne and from Oyne Village.

Opening for: 1st Insch Scout Group

Angus, Dundee & The Mearns

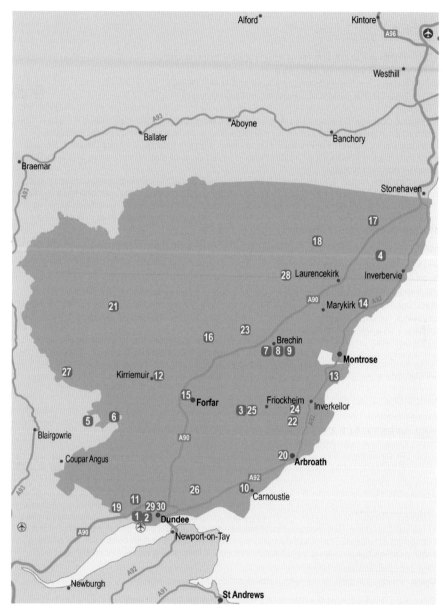

Angus, Dundee & The Mearns

OUR VOLUNTEER ORGANISERS

District Organisers:	Debbie Butler	Top Croft, Arniefoul, Angus DD8 1UD
	Frances Dent	12 Glamis Drive, Dundee DD2 1QL
		sgsangusdundee@gmail.com
Area Organisers:	Pippa Clegg	Easter Derry, Kilry, Blairgowrie PH11 8JA
	Moira Coleman	Templeton House, Arbroath DD11 4QP
	Catherine Cowie	Allardyce Castle, Inverbervie DD10 OST
	Jan Crow	Lower Duncraig, 2 Castle Street, Brechin DD9 6JN
	Terrill Dobson	Logie House, Kirriemuir DD8 5PN
	Claire Tinsley	Ethie Mains, Inverkeilor DD11 5SN
Treasurer:	James Welsh	Dalfruin, Kirktonhill Road, Kirriemuir DD8 4HU

GARDENS OPEN ON A SPECIFIC DATE

Kinblethmont House, by Arbroath, Angus	Saturday/Sunday, 24/25 February
Lawton House, Inverkeilor, by Arbroath	Thursday - Saturday, 29 Feb - 2 March
Ecclesgreig Castle, St Cyrus	Sunday, 3 March
17a Menzieshill Road, Dundee	Saturday/Sunday, 20/21 April
Forfar Open Garden, 36 Lochside Road, Forfar	Sunday, 28 April
17a Menzieshill Road, Dundee	Saturday/Sunday, 4/5 May
Inchmill Cottage, Glenprosen, near Kirriemuir	Thursday, 9 May
Balhary Walled Garden, Balhary, Alyth, Blairgowrie	Saturday, 11 May
Angus Plant Sale, House of Pitmuies, Guthrie, by Forfar	Saturday, 18 May
Dalfruin, Kirktonhill Road, Kirriemuir	Sunday, 19 May
Gray Cottage, 23 Church Road, Liff, Dundee	Saturday/Sunday, 25/26 May
Brechin Castle, Brechin	Sunday, 26 May
Inchmill Cottage, Glenprosen, near Kirriemuir	Thursday, 30 May
West End Trio, 3 & 12 Glamis Drive and 5 Glamis Terrace, Dundee	Saturday/Sunday, 1/2 June
Balhary Walled Garden, Balhary, Alyth, Blairgowrie	Saturday, 8 June
Arbuthnott House Gardens, Arbuthnott House, Laurencekirk	Sunday, 9 June
Tillytoghills Steading, Fettercairn	Sunday, 9 June
Inchmill Cottage, Glenprosen, near Kirriemuir	Thursday, 13 June
St Bride's Cottage, South Kingennie, Broughty Ferry	Saturday/Sunday, 15/16 June
Kirkside of Lochty, Menmuir, by Brechin	Sunday, 16 June
Brechin Gardens in June, Locations across Brechin	Sunday, 23 June
The Old Schoolhouse, Kilry	Sunday, 30 June
Inchmill Cottage, Glenprosen, near Kirriemuir	Thursday, 4 July
Balhary Walled Garden, Balhary, Alyth, Blairgowrie	Saturday, 13 July
Charleston Forest Garden, 43 Gourdie Terrace, Dundee	Saturday, 20 July
Gardeners Cottage, Fern, Brechin	Sunday, 21 July
Brechin Gardens in July, Locations across Brechin	Sunday, 28 July

Angus, Dundee & The Mearns

Glenbervie House, Drumlithie, Stonehaven	Sunday, 4 August
Balhary Walled Garden, Balhary, Alyth, Blairgowrie	Saturday, 10 August
Inchmill Cottage, Glenprosen, near Kirriemuir	Thursday, 15 August
Glensaugh, Glensaugh Lodge, Fettercairn, Laurencekirk	Sunday, 18 August
Forfar Open Garden, 36 Lochside Road, Forfar	Sunday, 25 August
Carnoustie's Tropical Garden, 28 Prosen Bank, Carnoustie	Saturday, 31 August
Inchmill Cottage, Glenprosen, near Kirriemuir	Thursday, 5 September
Braidestone Farm, Meigle, Blairgowrie	Sunday, 8 September
Balhary Walled Garden, Balhary, Alyth, Blairgowrie	Saturday, 14 September
Hospitalfield Gardens, Hospitalfield House, Westway, Arbroath	Saturday, 28 September
Westgate, 12 Glamis Drive, Dundee	Saturday/Sunday, 19/20 October

GARDENS OPEN REGULARLY

Pitmuies Gardens, House of Pitmuies, Guthrie, by Forfar	1 April - 30 September
Dunninald Castle, Montrose	1 May - 31 August (Monday, Tuesday & Sunday)

GARDENS OPEN BY ARRANGEMENT

10 Menzieshill Road, Dundee	20 April - 2 June
Glenbervie House, Drumlithie, Stonehaven	1 May - 15 September

Angus, Dundee & The Mearns

1 10 MENZIESHILL ROAD
Dundee DD2 1PW
Frances Tait
T: 01382 665719

On a sloping site facing the river, No 10 is home to one of the nine wells in this part of the west end of Dundee. At one time, the well provided drinking water for a nearby farmhouse and two cottages. It was also the first and last water available to carriers' horses on their way to and from Dundee. Now it feeds rhododendrons and camellias, many of which came from the Rothschilds' garden at Exbury, Hampshire. Of particular interest are magnolia 'Manchu Fan' and rhododendrons 'Loderic King George' and 'Lady Chamberlain'. More recently, an area near the well has been given over to bulbs and small herbaceous plants, various irises and primulas.

Open: by arrangement from 20 April - 5 May, 2 - 5pm and from 6 May - 2 June, 2 - 5pm and 7 - 9pm. Admission £5, children free. All visitors welcome including groups of up to 15 people. Please phone 01382 665719 to arrange a visit. Due to the sloping site, access involves steps but there are handrails and seats.

Directions: Turn off A85/Riverside Ave at the roundabout towards Dundee Botanic Garden. Pass the Botanic Garden to where it joins Perth Road. Turn left then 1st right onto Invergowrie Drive and 1st left onto Menzieshill Road. Bus 5 takes you to the foot of Glamis Road; Buses 5A and 19 to Hazel Drive. Walk west along Perth Road until you come to Invergowrie Drive.

Opening for: Cancer Research UK

2 17A MENZIESHILL ROAD
Dundee DD2 1PS
Mr and Mrs John Stoa
W: www.johnstoa.com

This Dundee garden is on a fairly steep slope with steps and paths. It features a riot of colour in April/May with thousands of tulip bulbs planted over the years. This display continues with azaleas and rhododendrons. There is a large fig tree and a grapevine 'Brant' growing on south facing walls. In the greenhouse John grows four grapevines, 'Phoenix', 'Seigerrebe', 'Muller Thurgau' and 'Solaris', used for his Muscat flavoured wines, and three varieties of tomato. John is a horticulturist, evidenced by some unusual fruit varieties including Saskatoon. John is also an artist and his art gallery will be open to visitors .

Open: Saturday/Sunday, 20/21 April & Saturday/Sunday, 4/5 May, 11am - 4pm, admission £5.00, children free.

Directions: Turn off the A85/Riverside Avenue at the roundabout towards Dundee Botanic Gardens. Pass the Botanics, road bears left and becomes Perth Road. Right onto Invergowrie Drive and first left on Menzieshill Road. Buses 5 and 5A to the foot of Glamis Road and walk west to Invergowrie Drive. In Menzieshill Road look for the garden with the prominent white stemmed birch tree.

Opening for: Cancer Research UK

Angus, Dundee & The Mearns

3 ANGUS PLANT SALE
House of Pitmuies, Guthrie, by Forfar DD8 2SN
SGS Angus & Dundee Organisers

A change of venue for our ever popular annual plant sale. By kind permission of Ruaraidh and Jeanette Ogilvie we are moving to Pitmuies (see separate garden entry for description). Coffee and cakes will be available. There will be a good selection of plants sourced from private gardens and some local nurseries. Please bring boxes and trays if you can. Donations of plants in advance or on the day will be welcome.

Open: Saturday 18 May, 10am - 1pm, admission £5.00, children free. Entrance fee covers the sale and the garden and includes refreshments.

Directions: From Forfar take the A932 east for seven miles and gardens are signposted on the right. From Brechin take the A933 south to Friockheim and turn right onto the A932. The gardens are signposted on the left after 1½ miles.

Opening for: All proceeds to SGS Beneficiaries

4 ARBUTHNOTT HOUSE GARDENS
Arbuthnott House, Laurencekirk AB30 1PA
Chris and Emily Arbuthnott
E: arbuthnotthouse@gmail.com
W: www.arbuthnott.co.uk

Arbuthnott House is the seat of the Viscount of Arbuthnott, whose family has lived here since 1190. The five-acre garden was laid out in the 17th century and comprises a walled garden with some 1920s Arts and Crafts planting. Thought to be one of the oldest gardens in Scotland, it runs down a steep, south-facing slope that is divided by three main broadwalks which run horizontally and are intercepted with diagonal pathways. The vegetables and soft fruit are contained within beds which are bound by topiary, herbaceous borders, rose beds and long beds for cut flowers.

Open: Sunday 9 June, 2pm - 5pm, admission £5.00, children free. The nearby Grassic Gibbon Centre and Cafe will be open and has toilet facilities.

Directions: Located at the heart of Arbuthnott Estate, just off the B967 Inverbervie to Fordoun. Three miles off the A90.

Opening for: Pickups for Peace SCIO

5 BALHARY WALLED GARDEN
Balhary, Alyth, Blairgowrie PH11 8LT
Teri and Paul Hodge-Neale
W: www.facebook.com/balharywalledgarden/

This two-acre, organic, working walled garden is being lovingly restored back to full production with the development of the 'no dig' method to grow many heritage and new varieties of vegetables with impressive results. The maturing herbaceous borders have the space to encourage drifts of colour and interest throughout the seasons. An opportunity to follow the garden throughout the growing season from late spring to autumn harvest, and to discuss and learn about the benefits of 'no dig'. Paul and Teri will also open their own private Therapy Garden which is a beautiful contemplative space with serene water features, statuary, stonework and unusual plants.

Angus, Dundee & The Mearns

Open: Saturday 11 May, Saturday 8 June, Saturday 13 July, Saturday 10 August & Saturday 14 September, 1pm - 5pm, admission £5.00, children free. Please approach the gardens at low speed due to resident wildlife. Please no dogs.

Directions: Situated between Alyth and Meigle on the B954 opposite the sign to *Jordanstone*.

Opening for: Perennial

6 BRAIDESTONE FARM
Meigle, Blairgowrie PH12 8RE
Leslie and William Robertson

Braidestone is situated in the Valley of Strathmore with views of the Sidlaw Hills, Grampians and surrounding countryside. The garden has year-round interest with a selection of shrubs, perennials, bulbs and annuals. There is a walled garden for vegetables, an orchard with a variety of fruit and nut trees and a garden, with several flower borders, surrounding the house. A large Wellingtonia tree stands in the centre of the garden next to a small woodland walk. Seating areas are available to relax and enjoy the views.

Open: Sunday 8 September, 2pm - 5pm, admission £5.00, children free. Parking is available at the Farm Steading. Teas available in nearby Meigle.

Directions: From Forfar/A90 take the A94 west to Eassie. Turn right at the crossroads. Turn left at T junction and continue along the road for approximately 1¼ miles. From Coupar Angus take the A94 to just before Meigle, follow signs to *Kirriemuir*. The garden is approximately three miles along the road.

Opening for: Blairgowrie Players

7 BRECHIN CASTLE
Brechin DD9 6SG
The Earl and Countess of Dalhousie
T: 01356 624566 E: mandyhendry@dalhousieestates.co.uk
W: www.dalhousieestates.co.uk

The uniquely-curving walls are just one of many delightful surprises in store as you wander around Brechin Castle's renowned walled garden. Find charm and splendour in the wide gravelled walks, secluded smaller paths and hidden corners, whilst you take in the stunning blend of ancient and modern plantings. May sees the rhododendrons and azaleas hit the peak of their flowering to wonderful effect throughout the month, with complementary underplanting and a framework of beautiful trees to further heighten your experience. This is a lovely garden to visit at any time of year, but it is really something to behold in the spring.

Open: Sunday 26 May, 2pm - 5pm, admission £6.00, children free.

Directions: A90 southernmost exit to Brechin, one mile past Brechin Castle Centre, castle gates are on the right.

Opening for: The Dalhousie Centre Day Care For The Elderly & The Attic SCIO

Angus, Dundee & The Mearns

 8 **BRECHIN GARDENS IN JUNE**
Locations across Brechin DD9 6JL
The Gardeners of Brechin

....

9 Pearse Street Brechin DD9 6JR (James Mackie): Opening in memory of its creator Irene Mackie, the well-known plantswoman whose love of plants is reflected in every inch of this beautiful, tranquil garden. There's a secluded and rural feel to this town garden. A huge collection of ferns is a unique feature of the garden, unusually planted to mingle with other colourful herbaceous plants.
Bishops Walk 11A Argyll St, Brechin DD9 6JL (Steff and Mike Eyres): A collection of acers grown successfully for years in large pots greets you as you access the unexpected door after viewing several different planting areas. You will find a hidden, walled garden planted with scented climbing and shrub roses, lavenders, perennials and evergreen shrubs and conifers including an established Wollemi, the prehistoric tree recently discovered.
Dalhousie Estate Allotments Brechin Bridge, Arbroath Road, Brechin DD9 6TJ (George Garden): Fourteen varied plots in a beautiful setting making use of reclaimed materials including a wind-powered generator, raised beds and sheds of all shapes and sizes!
Hoodston House Findowrie DD9 6RF (Kat and Aaron Robertson): A work-in-progress family garden and wildlife haven created from scratch, on a tight budget. The garden includes wildlife (and child!) friendly lawns, vegetables and herbs, fruit cage, perennials and shrubs.
Kirkton Cottage Aberlemno DD8 3PE (George Henry and Susan Norris): Nestled in a dip beside a stream, this country cottage garden is packed with plants. Mown grass paths meander among mature trees, shrubs and perennials in borders, island beds and rockeries. Rustic steps lead to raised vegetable beds, greenhouse and a prolific nursery area.
Rosehill West 15C North Latch Road, Brechin DD9 6LF (Robert and Jenny Martin): An acre of newly-planted garden, formerly a field, featuring mature original trees, herbaceous areas, fruit trees (quince and crab apple), and a path through recently planted trees. A work in progress!

Open: Sunday 23 June, noon - 5pm, admission £8.00, children free. Tickets and teas available at St Andrews Episcopal Church, Argyll Street, Brechin, DD9 6JL

Directions: Most gardens are located around the town of Brechin. Look for the SGS yellow signs. A map with directions will be provided with tickets.

Opening for: St Andrews Scottish Episcopal Church

 9 **BRECHIN GARDENS IN JULY**
Locations across Brechin DD9 6JL
The Gardeners of Brechin

....

1 Castle Street (NEW) 1 Castle Street, Brechin DD9 6JN (Bob and Pam Thomson): A mature, south facing, town garden featuring a variety of shrubs, including various hydrangeas, as well as colourful perennials.
24 North Latch Road Brechin DD9 6LE (Alistair and Mary Gray): Learn how the owners grow and show vegetables and how these can be a spectacular display of colourful, bedding-full greenhouses.
Bishops Walk 11A Argyll St, Brechin DD9 6JL (Steff and Mike Eyres): A collection of acers grown successfully for years in large pots greets you as you access the unexpected door after viewing several different planting areas. You will find a hidden, walled garden planted with scented climbing and shrub roses, lavenders, perennials and evergreen shrubs and conifers including an established Wollemi, the prehistoric tree recently discovered.

Angus, Dundee & The Mearns

Brechin Cathedral Allotments Chanory Wynd, Brechin DD9 6EU (Brechin Cathedral Allotments Gardeners): Eleven varied plots reflect the interests and personalities of each plot holder and include fruit, vegetables and herbs. A unique feature is the historical 'College Well' used by medieval monks.

Kirkton Cottage Aberlemno DD8 3PE (George Henry and Susan Norris): Nestled in a dip beside a stream, this country cottage garden is packed with plants. Mown grass paths meander among mature trees, shrubs and perennials in borders, island beds and rockeries. Rustic steps lead to raised vegetable beds, greenhouse and a prolific nursery area.

Latchlea 17A North Latch Road, Brechin DD9 6LE (Pamela Stevens): A new garden begun as a way of coping with bereavement. Inspired by Queen Elizabeth II saying that 'everyone should plant as many trees as possible', 100 trees are newly planted along The Old Lady Walk. Features include some fine stonework, shrubs, herbaceous plants and bulbs and also a courtyard garden.

Lower Duncraig 2 Castle Street, Brechin DD9 6JN (Jan and Andrew Crow): A densely planted, small town garden including rambling roses and a small wildlife pond.

Open: Sunday 28 July, noon - 5pm, admission £8.00, children free. Tickets and teas available at St Andrews Episcopal Church, Argyll Street, Brechin, DD9 6JL

Directions: Most gardens are located around the town of Brechin. Look for the SGS yellow signs. A map with directions will be provided with tickets.

Opening for: St Andrews Scottish Episcopal Church

 10 ## CARNOUSTIE'S TROPICAL GARDEN
28 Prosen Bank, Carnoustie DD7 6GS
Colin Wilson

A small tropical garden in Carnoustie. You'll be met by a stunning circular wall with a Brazilian slate seat to keep you cosy among Musa basjoo, tree ferns, Tetrapanax papyrifer rex and bamboos. You'll find a small collection of palms, including the spectacular Brahea armata, 'Mexican Blue Palm', Chamaerops humilis cerifera, a breathtaking palm, Trachycarpus fortunei, Trachycarpus wagnerianus and Chamaerops vulcano. The garden has elegant curves at every turn, creating a botanical wonderland. A jungle curved path is surrounded by tree ferns, Fatsia japonica and zebra grasses. At journey's end you'll find a beautiful Betula jacquemontii, Schefflera taiwaniana and macrophylla, Pink China, ferns, cannas, fatsias and Trachycarpus fortunei, in a hidden suntrap patio, accessed through the enchanting moon gate.

Open: Saturday 31 August, 2pm - 5pm, admission £5.00, children free. No dogs, please.

Directions: Buses 73 & 73C from Dundee/Arbroath. Prosen Bank is found by a path via Newton Road. No parking in Prosen Bank. Parking at football pitches on Newton Road or in adjacent streets.

Opening for: Alzheimer Scotland

Angus, Dundee & The Mearns

11 CHARLESTON FOREST GARDEN
43 Gourdie Terrace, Dundee DD2 4QT
L Wakefield

A young forest garden in Dundee, practising permaculture principles. Perennial vegetables are scattered throughout the garden, along with medicinal herbs, fruit trees, edible hedges and ornamental edible plants. A small flock of chickens contribute to a composting system and there is also a 'chop and drop' approach being used. This garden is home to some Scottish heirloom vegetable varieties, with the intention to save seeds to share. There is a small patch of alpines and a number of roses throughout, along with some purely ornamental herbaceous perennials, mostly grown with pollinators and wildlife in mind.

Open: Saturday 20 July, 11am - 4pm, admission £5.00, children free.

Directions: In the centre of Charleston, Dundee, with some parking on Gourdie Terrace and Balgarthno Road. The number 28 bus stops around the corner at the community centre.

Opening for: Dementia UK

12 DALFRUIN
Kirktonhill Road, Kirriemuir DD8 4HU
Mr and Mrs James A Welsh

A well-stocked, connoisseur's garden of about ⅓ acre situated at the end of a short cul-de-sac. There are many less common plants like varieties of trilliums, meconopsis (blue poppies), tree peonies (descendants of ones collected by George Sherriff and grown at Ascreavie), dactylorhiza and codonopsis. There is a scree garden and collection of ferns. The vigorous climbing rose, Paul's Himalayan Musk, grows over a pergola. Interconnected ponds encourage wildlife.

Open: Sunday 19 May, 2pm - 5pm, admission £4.00, children free. Sorry, no dogs.

Directions: From the centre of Kirriemuir turn left up Roods. Kirktonhill Road is on the left near the top of the hill. Park on Roods or at St Mary's Episcopal Church. Disabled parking only in Kirktonhill Road. Bus 20 (from Dundee) getting off at either stop on the Roods.

Opening for: Kirriemuir Day Care Ltd

Dalfruin

Angus, Dundee & The Mearns

13 DUNNINALD CASTLE

Montrose DD10 9TD
The Stansfeld family
T: 01674 672031 E: estateoffice@dunninald.com
W: www.dunninald.com

We welcome our visitors to explore our 100 acres of woods, wild garden, policies and a walled garden. From January to May, the main interest is the wild garden and policies where snowdrops in January are followed by daffodils and finally bluebells in May. In June, the emphasis turns to the walled garden, rich in interest and colour throughout the summer. Situated at the bottom of the beech avenue, the walled garden is planted with rose borders, traditional mixed borders, vegetables, herbs, soft fruits and fruit trees and there is a greenhouse.

Open: 1 May - 31 August (Monday, Tuesday & Sunday), 1pm - 5pm, admission £5.00, children free. See website for Castle Tours.

Directions: Three miles south of Montrose, ten miles north of Arbroath, signposted from the A92.

Opening for: Donation to SGS Beneficiaries

14 ECCLESGREIG CASTLE

St Cyrus DD10 0DP
Mr Gavin Farquhar
T: 01224 214301 E: enquiries@ecclesgreig.com
W: www.ecclesgreig.com

Ecclesgreig Castle, Victorian Gothic on a 16th-century core, is internationally famous as an inspiration for Bram Stoker's *Dracula*. The snowdrop walk (over 150 varieties of snowdrops) starts at the castle, meanders around the estate, along woodland paths and the pond, ending at the garden. In the Italian balustraded gardens, there is a 140-foot-long herbaceous border, classical statues and stunning shaped topiary with views across St Cyrus to the sea. Started from a derelict site, development continues. Also to be found in the grounds is the ancient well of St Cyrus.

Open: Sunday 3 March, 1pm - 4pm for Snowdrops and Winter Walks, admission £5.00, children free.

Directions: *Ecclesgreig* will be signposted from the A92 Coast Road and from the A937 Montrose/Laurencekirk Road.

Opening for: Girlguiding Montrose District

Angus, Dundee & The Mearns

15 FORFAR OPEN GARDEN
36 Lochside Road, Forfar DD8 3JD
T: 07763842407 E: forfaropengardens@gmail.com

Now into its 8th year, this therapeutic and tranquil space consists of a walled garden and woodland. The garden contains a diversity of herbaceous planting, food growing areas, greenhouse, polytunnel and the old well. The woodland is more informal with a cosy bothy room and an abundance of wildlife. As a charity, we support volunteers and aim to promote the benefits of working alongside others in natural surroundings. We sell plants (mostly perennials) to raise funds. The main garden is fully accessible, with toilet facilities.

Open: Sunday 28 April & Sunday 25 August, 1pm - 4pm, admission £5.00, children free.

Directions: Lochside Road is situated opposite Tesco, with the Factory Shop on the corner. The garden is found towards Forfar Loch on the right, with a large parking bay opposite. Bus 117 stops directly outside the garden.

Opening for: Forfar Open Garden

16 GARDENERS COTTAGE

Fern, Brechin DD8 3FF
Nick and Michelle Tonge

This former two-acre Victorian kitchen garden is undergoing a slow transition from its previous owners (H.M. Prisons) after a decade of neglect. With some restoration and a little repurposing, Michelle and Nick are beginning to open up beds and restore lawns, old and new. They are creating smaller areas of formal, herbaceous, woodland and seasonal planting mixed between the orchards, soft fruits, hedges, paths and pagodas. This is complemented by a ten-acre woodland bursting with wild flowers, ferns and foxgloves, and is undergoing a transformation after the Arwen and Corrie storms. The replanting of the more commercial forestry with native species has opened up opportunity to create a fun element in this amenity space for the campsite, with lots of benches and footpaths to explore and unusual things to find.

Open: Sunday 21 July, noon - 5pm, admission £5.00, children free. Teas served until 4pm.

Directions: On the road between Fern and Noranside.

Opening for: Diocese of Brechin: St Andrews Church Brechin Soup Initiative

17 GLENBERVIE HOUSE

Drumlithie, Stonehaven AB39 3YA
Mr and Mrs A Macphie

The nucleus of the large garden at Glenbervie is the traditional Victorian walled garden. It slopes south east for 1½ acres, divided essentially into four sections, including vegetables punctuated by annuals, roses and lawn, surrounded by fruit and perennials. At the top of the garden is an extensive heated greenhouse, well worth exploring. A lovely woodland garden can be found in other parts of the garden, also around the house, lawns with herbaceous and shrub borders.

Angus, Dundee & The Mearns

Open: Sunday 4 August, 2pm - 5pm. Admission £6.00, children under 12 free. Teas and Plants and Bakery stall. Open by arrangement from 1 May - 15 September. Please apply in writing. Please note some steep pathways and tree roots can make walking difficult in places. Gravel pathways are not accessible for electric wheelchairs. Please no dogs.

Directions: Drumlithie one mile. Garden is 1½ miles off the A90.

Opening for: Scotland's Charity Air Ambulance

---

18 GLENSAUGH
Glensaugh Lodge, Fettercairn, Laurencekirk AB30 1HB
Donald and Sue Barrie

The twenty-year development of the hillside garden at Glensaugh, with its fine outlook over the Howe of the Mearns, continues as lawn evolves into wildflower meadow and borders are replanted. Trees, species rhododendrons and other shrubs provide year-round interest while herbaceous planting extends colour into the autumn. Yew hedges and well-placed natural stone give structure in the lower garden where a productive kitchen garden and polytunnel exist alongside informal borders and a sunken pond.

Open: Sunday 18 August, 1:30pm - 4:30pm, admission £6.00, children free. No teas, but you are welcome to bring a picnic.

Directions: Three miles north of Fettercairn on the B974, turn right at the Clatterin Brig and follow minor road signed Glensaugh for ½ mile, then turn right into the Glensaugh farm steading (parking) and follow beech avenue from the steading to Glensaugh Lodge.

Opening for: Kincardine And Deeside Befriending

---

19 GRAY COTTAGE
23 Church Road, Liff, Dundee DD2 5NN
Graham Haddow

With wonderful views over Dundee, open farmland and the Tay across to Fife, Gray Cottage sits on the edge of Liff village. Built in 1886 for the Land Steward of Gray Estate, its half-acre, mature garden has a wide variety of shrubs and trees and is particularly colourful in May/June when rhododendrons, azaleas and pieris are at their best. The peaceful garden is one to explore with a number of corners and hidden areas which are linked and connected by hedge tunnels and natural 'windows'. One fascinating feature is a very large rhododendron with its interior branches fully exposed to give an almost mystical quality. Red squirrels, pheasants, woodpeckers, jays and the occasional fox are all regular visitors to Gray Cottage Garden where James McIntosh Patrick painted 'The Elm Tree, Perthshire'.

Open: Saturday/Sunday, 25/26 May, 10am - 4pm, admission £5.00, children free.

Directions: Liff village is two miles north west of Dundee. Gray Cottage is next to the only church in Liff. The church steeple is the landmark and the cottage is down the track to the left.

Opening for: MND Scotland

Angus, Dundee & The Mearns

Glensaugh

 20 ## HOSPITALFIELD GARDENS
Hospitalfield House, Westway, Arbroath DD11 2NH
Hospitalfield Trust
E: info@hospitalfield.org.uk
W: www.hospitalfield.org.uk

In 2021 the walled garden at Hospitalfield was comprehensively redeveloped to a design by celebrated garden designer and plantsman, Nigel Dunnett. The new garden tells the 800-year horticultural story of this extraordinary site from its monastic origins in the 13th century through to the Victorian passion for ferns. You will be able to explore the garden in its first few years after planting as it continues to grow into its inspirational design; full of diverse textures and striking colours. The house that overlooks the garden was remodelled in the 19th century by Elizabeth Allan-Fraser and her husband, the artist Patrick Allan-Fraser, who designed their home in the Arts and Crafts style. Their fernery, which sits within the walled garden, has been restored and re-planted with ferns from all over the world and will also be open for visitors. Hospitalfield celebrated the opening of its Physic Garden in June of 2023, a project which introduced over 30 new medicinal plants to the garden along with an illustrated guided walk exploring Hospitalfield's herbal history and the garden's themes. For more information about Hospitalfield and its international cultural programme rooted in contemporary visual arts, please visit the website.

Angus, Dundee & The Mearns

Open: Saturday 28 September, 11am - 4pm, admission £6.00, children free. Admission is for the walled garden and fernery and Angus residents will receive an annual pass with their admission. The new glasshouse café offers excellent refreshments.

Directions: Comprehensive directions can be found on the website at hospitalfield.org.uk/visit/location/.

Opening for: Donation to SGS Beneficiaries

21 INCHMILL COTTAGE
Glenprosen, near Kirriemuir DD8 4SA
Iain Nelson
T: 01575 540452

This is a long, sloping and terraced garden at over 800 feet in the Braes of Angus, developed to be a garden for all seasons. Half is dominated by bulbs, rhododendrons, azaleas, primulas, meconopsis and clematis. The other half is mainly later summer bulbs, herbaceous plants and roses. There is also a rockery/scree.

Open: Thursday 9 May, Thursday 30 May, Thursday 13 June, Thursday 4 July, Thursday 15 August & Thursday 5 September, 2pm - 5pm, admission £5.00, children free.

Directions: Please DO NOT use SatNav. From Kirriemuir take the B955 (signposted *The Glens*) to Dykehead (about five miles). From there follow the *Prosen* sign for about five miles. Inchmill is the white-fronted cottage beside the phone box in the village. There is car parking beside the church (50 yards away) and by the village hall opposite.

Opening for: The Archie Foundation

22 KINBLETHMONT HOUSE
by Arbroath, Angus DD11 4RW
The Ramsay family
E: info@kinblethmont.com
W: www.kinblethmont.com, www.facebook.com/kinblethmont

Kinblethmont is an historic estate which, with its advantageous elevated position, has been settled since Pictish times. In the centre is the Victorian mansion house surrounded by beautiful policy woodlands where specimen trees and snowdrops abound. Paths take you through the woods past the old pet cemetery and to the walled garden with children's play area. A longer walk will take you up around the solar park with spectacular views over to the Angus hills and the North Sea.

Open: Saturday/Sunday, 24/25 February, 10am - 4pm for Snowdrops and Winter Walks, admission £5.00, children free. The estate has some lovely holiday cottages for anyone wanting to make a weekend of it. House tours will also be available, please see website or Facebook for details.

Directions: From Forfar/Brechin, take the A933 towards Arbroath, turn left to Friockheim. Drive through Friockheim and continue along the road, past the crematorium, until you reach a T-junction. Turn right and continue along this road, past a crossroads, until you enter Kinblethmont estate on your left.

Opening for: Friockhub

Angus, Dundee & The Mearns

23 KIRKSIDE OF LOCHTY

Menmuir, by Brechin DD9 6RY
Ed and Fi Troughton
T: 01356 660431

This garden, designed by renowned local plantswoman Irene Mackie over 20 years ago, is now nurtured by the current owners. There are four distinct areas each with their own character. Along the short drive and to the east of the house is a spring woodland spot full of bulbs, leading to the new gravel garden, a sheltered spot to enjoy late summer sunshine amongst the agapanthus and grasses. The hot, sunny courtyard parterre is full of herbaceous perennials with high summer interest and from there, one is drawn through the beech hedge into a wilder area of three island beds with mixed planting, as well as a meadow loved by wildlife and bees. More recently the garden has been enhanced by careful reduction in the perimeter tree canopy opening up the westerly views to grazings and allowing the pollarded willow hedge to be back-lit by winter sun.

Open: Sunday 16 June, 1pm - 5pm, admission £5.00, children free. Teas available nearby.

Directions: From the A90, take Careston/Fern/Menmuir turn just south of Brechin. Proceed towards Menmuir for about 2 miles. The garden is on the left behind beech hedge.

Opening for: St Andrews Scottish Episcopal Church & Pitt Hopkins UK

24 LAWTON HOUSE

Inverkeilor, by Arbroath DD11 4RU
Cate and Simon Dessain

Woodland garden of beech trees, carpeted with snowdrops, aconites and crocuses in spring, set around a 1755 house. There is also a walled garden planted with fruit trees and vegetables. The property was owned for many years by Elizabeth and Patrick Allan-Fraser who remodelled Hospitalfield House in Arbroath.

Open: Thursday 29 February, Friday 1 March & Saturday 2 March, 10am - 5pm for Snowdrops and Winter Walks, admission £5.00, children free.

Directions: Take the B965 between Inverkeilor and Friockheim, turn right at the sign for *Angus Chain Saws*. Drive approximately 200 metres, then take the first right.

Opening for: Siobhan's Trust

25 PITMUIES GARDENS

House of Pitmuies, Guthrie, by Forfar DD8 2SN
Jeanette and Ruaraidh Ogilvie
T: 01241 828245 E: ogilvie@pitmuies.com
W: www.pitmuies.com

Two renowned, semi-formal walled gardens adjoin an 18th-century house and steading, sheltering long borders of herbaceous perennials, superb old-fashioned delphiniums and roses, together with pavings rich with violas and dianthus. An extensive and diverse collection of plants, interesting kitchen garden, spacious lawns, and river, lochside and woodland walks beneath fine trees. A wide variety of shrubs with good autumn colour and a picturesque turreted doocot and a 'Gothick' wash house. Myriad spring bulbs include carpets of crocus following massed snowdrops and daffodils.

Open: 1 April - 30 September, 10am - 5pm, admission £5.00, children free.

Angus, Dundee & The Mearns

Directions: From Forfar take the A932 east for seven miles and gardens are signposted on the right. From Brechin take the A933 south to Friockheim and turn right onto the A932. The gardens are signposted on the left after 1½ miles.

Opening for: Donation to SGS Beneficiaries

Pitmuies Gardens

26 **ST BRIDE'S COTTAGE**
South Kingennie, Broughty Ferry DD5 3PA
Alison and Donald Gordon

This half-acre garden was started from scratch in 2002 and now provides year-round interest. Planting several trees and making a wildlife pond and stream were the first priorities, as birds were sadly rare visitors to the garden. Parts of the perimeter of the garden are left semi wild with dense shrubs to provide cover and nesting areas, while the area visible from the house is planted for viewing, with a mixture of shrubs, perennials and bulbs. Some features are inspired by visits to gardens around the world, including a Japanese-themed area with island bed. There is a small bog garden with a lovely early summer display of *Iris sibirica* and many plants justify their existence by attracting a wide variety of bees and butterflies.

Open: Saturday/Sunday, 15/16 June, 1pm - 5pm, admission £5.00, children free. Plants will also be for sale, for the benefit of Dundee Botanic Garden.

Directions: From Kellas take the minor road signed *Murroes Church* for approximately one mile to some steading houses and turn left up the farm track immediately before them. St Bride's is the first house on the left with the conservatory and solar panels.

Opening for: Diabetes UK

Angus, Dundee & The Mearns

27 THE OLD SCHOOLHOUSE

Kilry PH11 8HU
Carol and Richard Till

The garden extends to ⅔ acre and comprises two distinct areas. Firstly, the original cottage-style garden with lawn and borders of mixed shrubs, perennials and annuals, enhanced by a variety of trees. The second area is a recently acquired paddock which is home to a polytunnel, a fruit cage, a Finnish BBQ hut with decking and a riverside deck on the bank of Kilry Burn which runs along the southern edge of the garden.

Open: Sunday 30 June, 2pm - 5pm, admission £5.00, children free.

Directions: From Perth take A94 to Coupar Angus and just before Meigle take the B954 and follow signs to Glen Isla and then to Kilry, signed to the left. Follow road past Kilry Church then downhill, past former Kilry Primary School and continue for ½ mile until reaching The Old Schoolhouse on the left. **From Dundee** take the A923 to Muirhead and then B954 to Meigle, turn right up B954 towards Glen Isla and then follow signs as above.

Opening for: The Rotary Club of the Angus Glens Charitable Trust

28 TILLYTOGHILLS STEADING

Fettercairn AB30 1YJ
Veronica and Steve Engel

A large country garden with established herbaceous borders, new shubbery borders, a paddock with native trees and a large pond with fish, waterlilies and other water plants. Veronica and Steve have made a productive vegetable and fruit garden with a vine in the greenhouse and tender vegetables in the polytunnel. There are also espaliered apple trees and soft fruit, with free-range chickens roaming close by.

Open: Sunday 9 June, 2pm - 5pm, admission £5.00, children free. Refreshments available nearby.

Directions: On the B966 half way between Edzell and Fettercairn.

Opening for: Edzell Village Improvement Society: Garden Group

Dunninald Castle © John Carracher

Brechin Castle © S Whittaker

Angus, Dundee & The Mearns

 29 WEST END TRIO
3 & 12 Glamis Drive and 5 Glamis Terrace, Dundee DD2 1QL
Elaine Lowe, Frances and John Dent, and Heather MacLean

These gardens are opening with fond memories of Frances Shepherd; she had planned to include her garden at Windyridge, 10 Glamis Drive.

Greengaites 3 Glamis Drive, Dundee DD2 1QG (Elaine Lowe): A cottage-style garden with small trees, herbaceous borders and rockeries. Interest throughout the seasons is provided with magnolia blossom and bulbs in the spring, followed by wisteria, clematis and roses climbing up the walls of this pretty 1920s house. Further colour is provided in the summer and autumn by the herbaceous borders and rockeries.

Heather's Garden (NEW) 5 Glamis Terrace DD2 1NA (Heather MacLean): This mature suburban garden has a lovely south-facing aspect giving glimpses of the Tay and Fife coastline. The perennial herbaceous borders have been loosely planted with wildlife in mind. There are mature trees and shrubs, and a small wildlife pond provides a home for lots of frogs! A vegetable garden, with polytunnel and greenhouse, sits at the top of the garden where there is also a summerhouse.

Westgate 12 Glamis Drive, Dundee DD2 1QL (John and Frances Dent): This established garden, with many mature trees, occupies a south-facing site overlooking the River Tay and Fife hills. The tennis court lawn is surrounded by herbaceous plants and shrubs. A short woodland walk reveals a miniature knot garden, a bower and other surprise features. There are also rose beds and two oriental-themed water gardens.

Open: Saturday/Sunday, 1/2 June, 2pm - 5pm, admission £7.00, children free. Teas at Westgate and Heather's Garden and plant stall at Greengaites. No dogs in any of the gardens please.

Directions: Buses 5, 22 or 73 from Dundee city centre to the far end of Blackness Road. Glamis Drive is straight ahead and Glamis Terrace is a few yards down the hill, parallel to Glamis Drive. Please note there is no roadside parking on Glamis Drive.

Opening for: Cancer Research UK

 30 WESTGATE
12 Glamis Drive, Dundee DD2 1QL
John and Frances Dent

This established garden, with many mature trees, occupies a south-facing site overlooking the River Tay and Fife hills. The tennis court lawn is surrounded by herbaceous plants and shrubs. A short woodland walk reveals a miniature knot garden, a bower and other surprise features. There are also rose beds and two oriental-themed water gardens. All the areas will be displaying their autumn colours and, as darkness falls, they will be further enlivened by a variety of lighting techniques.

Open: Saturday/Sunday, 19/20 October, 3pm - 7pm, admission by donation. Children's activities and a variety of floodlighting effects. Torches recommended. Also open with the West End Trio of gardens on 1/2 June. No dogs, please.

Directions: Buses 5, 22 or 73 from Dundee city centre. Please note there is no roadside parking on Glamis Drive. Limited disabled parking is available at the house.

Opening for: Dr Graham's Homes Kalimpong (UK)

Argyll & Lochaber

Sponsored by

RATHBONES

Incorporating
Investec Wealth &
Investment (UK)

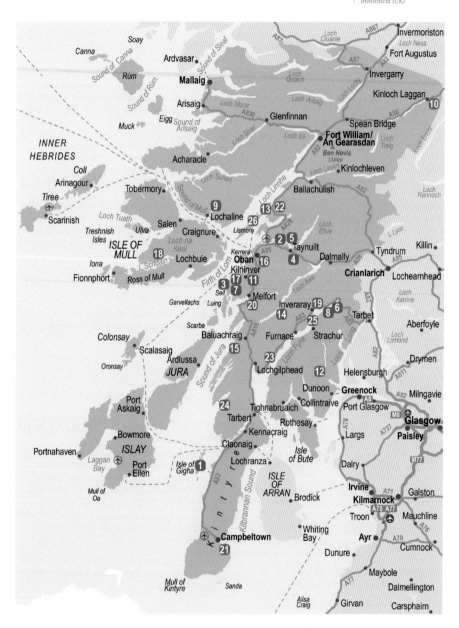

Argyll & Lochaber

OUR VOLUNTEER ORGANISERS

District Organiser:	Minette Struthers	Camasmaddy, Ardmaddy, by Oban PA34 4QY
Area Organisers:	Grace Bergius	Craignish House, Ardfern, by Lochgilphead PA31 8QN
	Shian Carlow	Balliemore, Loch Striven, Dunoon PA23 8RH
	Mary Lindsay	Dal an Eas, Kilmore, Oban PA34 4XU
District Photographer:	Maurice Wilkins	Dunrobian, Laurel Road, Oban PA34 5EA
Treasurer:	Shelagh Cannon	Kames Bay, Kilmelford, By Oban PA34 4XA

GARDENS OPEN ON A SPECIFIC DATE

Achamore Gardens, Isle of Gigha	Saturday, 4 May
Ilha de Deus, Tiroran, Isle of Mull	Sunday, 5 May
Knock Newhouse, Lochgair	Saturday/Sunday, 11/12 May
Braevallich Farm, by Dalmally	Sunday, 12 May
Strachur Flower & Woodland Gardens, Strachur	Sunday, 12 May
Strachur Flower & Woodland Gardens, Strachur	Sunday, 19 May
Braevallich Farm, by Dalmally	Sunday, 2 June
Knock Newhouse, Lochgair	Sunday, 2 June
Ardverikie with Aberarder, Kinloch Laggan, Newtonmore	Sunday, 2 June
Ilha de Deus, Tiroran, Isle of Mull	Sunday, 2 June
Ardchattan Priory, North Connel	Sunday, 9 June
Ilha de Deus, Tiroran, Isle of Mull	Sunday, 7 July
Benmore Botanic Garden, Benmore, Dunoon	Sunday 29 September

GARDENS OPEN REGULARLY

Angus's Garden, Barguillean, Taynuilt	1 January - 31 December
Ardmaddy Castle, by Oban	1 January - 31 December
Ardkinglas Woodland Garden, Cairndow	1 January - 31 December
Achnacloich, Connel, Oban	1 January - 31 December (Saturday only)
Ardtornish, by Lochaline, Morvern	1 January - 31 December
Kinlochlaich Walled Garden, Appin	3 March - 31 October
Inveraray Castle Gardens, Inveraray	28 March - 28 October
Crinan Hotel Garden, Crinan	29 March - 31 October
Ardchattan Priory, North Connel	1 April - 31 October (Wednesdays only)
An Cala, Ellenabeich, Isle of Seil	1 April - 31 October

Argyll & Lochaber

GARDENS OPEN BY ARRANGEMENT

The Secret Garden, Isle of Lismore, Oban, Argyll	1 January - 1 December
Berandhu, Appin, Argyll	1 April - 31 October
Kames Bay, Kilmelford	16 April - 16 June
Barochreal, Kilninver, Oban, Argyll	1 May - 30 September
Dal an Eas, Kilmore, Oban	1 May - 30 September
Eas Mhor, Cnoc-a-Challtuinn, Clachan Seil, Oban	1 May - 31 October
Kildalloig, Campbeltown	1 May - 31 October
Ardno, Cairndow	1 May - 30 September
Braevallich Farm, by Dalmally	1 May - 30 September
Ilha de Deus, Tiroran, Isle of Mull	1 May - 31 July
Ormsary Gardens, Ormsary, Lochgilphead, Argyll	1 June - 30 September

Ilha de Deus

Argyll & Lochaber

1 ACHAMORE GARDENS

Isle of Gigha PA41 7AD
The Isle of Gigha Heritage Trust
E: gardens@gigha.org.uk
W: www.visitgigha.co.uk/Achamore-Gardens

Created by Colonel Sir James Horlick with the assistance of Gardener Kitty Lloyd Jones in 1944, Achamore Gardens is the home of Horlick's renowned rhododendron and camellia collection. Flourishing in Gigha's warm microclimate, the 54-acre gardens host many notable and unusual plants and trees from around the world. The woodland walks with rhododendrons, azaleas, camellias, New Zealand tree ferns, hydrangeas and fuchsias complement the walled garden's tender exotics, herbaceous borders and bamboo maze. The garden viewpoint has stunning views over to Islay and Jura while the pond area offers a secluded oasis. After years of decline, The Isle of Gigha Heritage Trust is now actively working to restore and develop Achamore Gardens.

Open: Saturday 4 May, 10am - 4pm, admission £7.00, children free. The garden is also open to visitors through the season; visit the garden website for details.

Directions: Access to Gigha is via CalMac ferry. Gigha can be explored by foot or bicycle so you can choose to leave your vehicle for free at the Tayinloan ferry car park and help to avoid congestion of traffic on Gigha's single track roads. The garden is three-quarters of a mile from the ferry.

Opening for: Gigha Village Hall

2 ACHNACLOICH

Connel, Oban PA37 1PR
Mr T E Nelson
T: 01631 710223 or or Gardener David Field 07929 336217
E: davefield6@hotmail.co.uk & cassandhu@gmail.com

The 20-acre woodland garden overlooking Loch Etive has been planted over the last century with a wide range of trees and shrubs from Asia, China, Japan, North America, Chile and New Zealand. Many have grown to considerable size. The light woodland canopy consists of native oaks and a number of magnificent 150-year-old Scots pines and European larch. Amongst these are open glades, carpeted with bluebells and numerous other bulbs. Two ponds and streams are planted with primulas, iris species, lysichitum, and astilbes. The woodland contains innumerable species of rhododendron and azalea, of which the triflorums and yunnanense are outstanding. Amongst these are species of acer, betula, camellia, cercidiphyllum, cornus, crinodendron, drimys, embothrium, enkianthus, eucryphia, hoheria, magnolia, malus, nothofagus, pieris, sorbus, stewartia, telopea and viburnum. Beside the house is a giant Douglas fir from Douglas' original introduction. One of the first Dawyck beeches stands beside the drive. Fine autumn colours.

Open: 1 January - 31 December (Saturday only), 10am - 4pm, admission £6.00, children free.

Directions: On the A85 two miles east of Connel. The car park is at the bottom of the drive.

Opening for: Macmillan Cancer Support

Argyll & Lochaber

3 AN CALA
Ellenabeich, Isle of Seil PA34 4RF
Mrs Sheila Downie
W: www.gardens-of-argyll.co.uk/view-details.php?id=447

A wonderful example of a 1930s designed garden, An Cala sits snugly in its horseshoe shelter of surrounding cliffs. A spectacular and very pretty garden with streams, waterfall, ponds, many herbaceous plants as well as azaleas, rhododendrons and cherry trees in spring. Archive material of Thomas Mawson's design was found recently and is available to visitors.

Open: 1 April - 31 October, 10am - 6pm, admission £6.00, children free.

Directions: Proceed south from Oban on Campbeltown Road for eight miles, turn right at the *Easdale* sign, a further eight miles on the B844; the garden is between the school and the village. Bus Oban – Easdale.

Opening for: Cancer Research UK

4 ANGUS'S GARDEN, BARGUILLEAN
Taynuilt PA35 1HY
The Josephine Marshall Trust
T: 01866 822333 E: info@barguillean.co.uk
W: www.barguillean.co.uk

Created in 1957 as a memorial garden by Betty Macdonald of Barguillean for her son Angus, this picturesque nine acre woodland garden is set around the tranquil shores of Loch Angus in historic Glen Lonan. Whilst famous for its extensive collection of hybrid rhododendrons and azaleas, this glorious garden cleverly retains the natural atmosphere of the landscape. Visitors can enjoy an informal network of paths, lined with spring flowering shrubs and bulbs, through native woodland and by shoreland whilst surrounded by the magnificent views of Ben Cruachan and the mountains of Glen Etive. This unspoilt natural setting attracts a wide range of wildlife, and the eleven acre loch is home to swans and ducks. On the north-west side of the garden overlooking the loch stands Betty's bell paying tribute to her 40 years of work creating this magical garden. The garden reaches its full glory between April and the end of June but is a place of special tranquillity and charm at all times of the year. Three marked, circular walks from the car park taking between 30 minutes and 1.5 hours. Not suitable for wheelchairs.

Open: 1 January - 31 December, 9am - dusk, admission £5.00, children under 16 free. Coach tours welcome by appointment.

Directions: Off A85 Crianlarich/Oban road at Taynuilt, road marked *Glen Lonan*, three miles up a single track road, turn right at the sign opposite Barguillean Farm.

Opening for: SSAFA Forces Help

Argyll & Lochaber

5 ARDCHATTAN PRIORY

North Connel PA37 1RQ
Mrs Sarah Troughton
T: 01796 481355 E: admin@ardchattan.co.uk
W: www.ardchattan.co.uk

Overlooking Loch Etive, Ardchattan Priory Garden has a mature rockery and extensive herbaceous and rose borders to the front of the house. On either side of the drive, shrub borders, numerous roses and ornamental trees, together with bulbs, give colour throughout the season. The Priory, founded in 1230, is now a private house. The ruins of the chapel and graveyard are in the care of *Historic Environment Scotland* and open with the garden.

Open: Open 1 April - 31 October (Wednesdays only) 9.30am - 5.30pm. Garden Fête Sunday 9 June 12 - 4pm. Admission £6 each day, children under 16 free.

Directions: Oban 10 miles. From north, turn left off the A828 at Barcaldine onto the B845 for six miles. From east or from Oban on the A85, cross Connel Bridge and turn first right, proceed east on Bonawe Road.

Opening for: Donation to SGS Beneficiaries

6 ARDKINGLAS WOODLAND GARDEN

Cairndow PA26 8BG
Ardkinglas Estate
T: 01499 600261
W: www.ardkinglas.com

In a peaceful setting overlooking Loch Fyne, the garden contains one of the finest collections of rhododendrons and conifers in Britain. This includes the mightiest conifer in Europe – a silver fir – as well as many other Champion Trees. There is a gazebo with a unique scriptorium based around a collection of literary quotes. For younger visitors, the garden features a Fairy Trail, Gruffalo Trail and Snakey Slide. It is a *VisitScotland* 3-star garden.
Champion Trees: The mightiest conifer in Europe and others.

Open: 1 January - 31 December, dawn to dusk. Admission £5.00, children over 3 £2.50. Tickets available online at www.ardkinglas.com or pay on arrival. All admission fees go to helping maintain and preserve the garden, as well as a donation to SGS charities.

Directions: Entrance through Cairndow village off the A83 Loch Lomond/Inveraray road.

Opening for: Donation to SGS Beneficiaries

Ardmaddy Castle

Argyll & Lochaber

7 ARDMADDY CASTLE

by Oban PA34 4QY
Mr and Mrs Archie Struthers
T: 01852 300353 E: minette@ardmaddy.com
W: www.ardmaddy.com

The gardens lie in a most spectacular setting in the centre of a horseshoe valley sheltered by mixed mature woodlands and the elevated castle standing on a volcanic mound to seaward. The walled garden is full of magnificent rhododendrons, a collection of rare and unusual shrubs and plants, the clock garden with its cutting flowers, the crevice garden, a NEW border with grasses and coastal theme, fruit and vegetables grown with labour saving formality, all within dwarf box hedging. Beyond, a woodland walk, with its 60-foot *Hydrangea petiolaris*, leads to the water garden which in spring has a mantle of bluebells and daffodils and in early summer a riot of *Primula candelabra*, irises, rodgersias and other damp-loving plants and grasses. Lovely autumn colour. A plantsman's garden for all seasons.

Open: 1 January - 31 December, 9am - dusk, admission £6.00, children free. Holiday cottages available sleeping 4 - 12. Find out more at www.ardmaddy.com

Directions: Take the A816 south of Oban for eight miles. Turn right onto the B844 to Seil Island/Easdale. Four miles on, turn left to Ardmaddy (signposted) and follow for a further two miles.

Opening for: Donation to SGS Beneficiaries

8 ARDNO

Cairndow PA26 8BE
Denzil How
T: Rob Backhouse Gardener 01499 302304 E: denzil.how@btconnect.com

From the rich, varied landscape, a romantic garden has been created from scratch over the past 25 years. Visitors can stroll in the walled garden near the house, or explore the old oak wood planted with many interesting shrubs. These are growing up fast, adding shape and colour. Across the burn is the gorge and a wonderful waterfall. The woodland garden ends in the meadow, planted with irises and a collection of unusual trees, which continues down to the beach and a magnificent huge rock. My garden is a place to be peaceful in. Come and enjoy, but be prepared as some of the paths are steep with lots of steps and are unfortunately not suitable for wheelchairs.

Open: by arrangement 1 May - 30 September, admission £6.00, children free. Small groups of up to 6 people by application to the Gardener, Robert Backhouse, Ardno Cottage T: 01499 302304 from May – September.

The Rediweld Foundation supports charities in London and the west coast of Scotland that are primarily but not exclusively involved with children's educational activities.

Directions: Situated at the top end of Loch Fyne between Cairndow and St Catherines, off the A815.

Opening for: Rediweld Foundation

Argyll & Lochaber

9 ARDTORNISH
by Lochaline, Morvern PA80 5UZ
Mrs John Raven
W: www.ardtornish.co.uk

Ardtornish Estate spreads out around Loch Aline, a huge, wooded, U-shaped bay, a natural haven. Wonderful gardens of interesting mature conifers, rhododendrons, deciduous trees, shrubs and herbaceous plantings, set amid magnificent scenery. Much of the garden is covered by native birch, alongside extensive planting of exotic species, under mature groups of larch, firs and pine, whose strong form and colour complement the pink sandstone towers and gables of Ardtornish House.

Open: 1 January - 31 December, 10am - 6pm, admission £5.00, children free. Groups must be pre-booked.

Directions: Three miles from Lochaline along the A884.

Opening for: Donation to SGS Beneficiaries

10 ARDVERIKIE WITH ABERARDER
Kinloch Laggan, Newtonmore PH20 1BX
The Fielden family, Mrs P Laing and Mrs E T Smyth-Osbourne
T: 01528 544300 E: amanda@ardverikie.com

Ardverikie
Kinloch Laggan, Newtonmore PH20 1BX (Mrs P Laing and Mrs E T Smyth-Osbourne):
Lovely setting on Loch Laggan with magnificent trees. Walled garden with large collection of acers, shrubs and herbaceous plants. Architecturally interesting house (not open) featured in *Monarch of the Glen* and *The Crown*.

Aberarder
Kinloch Laggan, Newtonmore PH20 1BX (The Fielden Family): The garden has been laid out over the last 20 years to create a mixture of spring and autumn plants and trees, including rhododendrons, azaleas and acers. The elevated view down Loch Laggan from the garden is exceptional.

Open: Sunday 2 June, 2 - 5.30pm, admission £8 for both gardens, children under 16 free

Directions: On the A86 between Newtonmore and Spean Bridge.
Ardverikie House entrance is at the east end of Loch Laggan via the bridge by Gatelodge
Aberarder Lodge entrance is about 200 metres west of the Ardverikie entrance, next to the small cottage.

Opening for: Laggan Parish Church & Highland Hospice

Argyll & Lochaber

11 BAROCHREAL
Kilninver, Oban, Argyll PA34 4UT
Nigel and Antoinette Mitchell
T: 01852 316151 E: antoinettemitchell1946@gmail.com
W: www.barochreal.co.uk

The garden was started in 2006. Fencing and stone walling define it from the rest of Barochreal land. Every year an area has been added, resulting in the gardens you will see today. There are rhododendron banks, a water feature, waterfalls and burns, a pond, a walled rose garden, active beehives (now housed in a purpose-built bee shelter built in 2021), tiered areas, a greenhouse and wild garden across the burn. Maintained walking tracks in the fields lead to viewpoints. Biodiversity studies revealed that rare butterflies inhabit the small glen by the waterfall, there are forty different species of moths including rare micro moths and over seventy species of wildflowers in the fields, including three types of wild orchid. There is an abundance of wildlife including red squirrels, pine martens and a wide range of birds can be seen. This garden is a haven of tranquillity, as seen in episode 9 of 2022 *Beechgrove Garden*.

Open: by arrangement 1 May - 30 September, admission £5.00, children free. Visiting by arrangement allows the owners to personally show visitors around if they wish, and explain the history around Barochreal, a village in the 1700s before Oban existed.

Directions: Fifteen minutes south of Oban. On the main A816 Oban to Lochgilphead road just to the south of the village of Kilninver on the left-hand side of the road. Bus Oban – Lochgilpead stops at Kilninver School, short walk after. Please disregard SatNav and use what3words address instead www.w3w.co/albums.forest.tinned

Opening for: Scottish SPCA

12 BENMORE BOTANIC GARDEN

Benmore, Dunoon PA23 8QU
A Regional Garden of the Royal Botanic Garden Edinburgh
T: 01369 706261 E: benmore@rbge.org.uk
W: www.rbge.org.uk

Benmore's magnificent mountainside setting is a joy to behold. Its 120 acres boast a world-famous collection of plants from the Himalayas, China and Japan to North and South America, as well as an impressive avenue of giant redwoods, one of the finest entrances to any botanic garden. Established in 1863, these majestic giants stand over 150 feet high. Seven miles of trails throughout lead to a restored Victorian Fernery and a dramatic viewpoint at 420 feet looking out to surrounding mountains and Holy Loch. There are also traditional Bhutanese and Chilean pavilions and the magnificent Golden Gates. Keep an eye out for red squirrels and other wildlife as you explore the garden.
National Plant Collection: Abies, South American Temperate Conifers, Picea.
Champion Trees: Many rare trees and giant conifers.

Open: Sunday 29 September, 10am - 5pm, admission details can be found on the garden's website.
Also see website for details of regular opening times – www.rbge.org.uk

Directions: Seven miles north of Dunoon or 22 miles south from Glen Kinglass below Rest and Be Thankful pass. On the A815. Bus service is limited.

Opening for: Donation to SGS Beneficiaries

Argyll & Lochaber

13 BERANDHU

Appin, Argyll PA38 4DD
John and Fiona Landale
T: 01631 730585 mobile 07900 377414 E: johnllandale@gmail.com

A sheltered one-and-a-half acre coastal garden in a scenic setting offering fabulous views over Loch Laich to Loch Linnhe, Castle Stalker and the Morvern hills beyond. Craggy limestone abounds on the undulating site, some of which forms natural rockeries. Native trees mix with introduced firs and conifers. A variety of rhododendrons and azaleas provide spring and early summer colour. A mix of limestone overlaid with peat gives an unusual mix of wild flowers. This well-tended garden also has lovely wild areas of bog garden and woodland.

Open: by arrangement 1 April - 31 October, admission £5.00, children free.

Directions: In Appin turn off the A828 Connel to Ballachulish road at Gunn's Garage signposted for *Port Appin*. After one mile when the road turns uphill, it's the first entrance on the right, half way up the hill.

Opening for: The Appin Village Hall & Alzheimer Scotland

14 BRAEVALLICH FARM

by Dalmally PA33 1BU
Mr Philip Bowden-Smith
T: 01866 844246 E: philip@brae.co.uk

Discover two gardens, one at the farm and an upper garden further up the hill. The former is approximately one and a half acres and developed over the last 40 years. Its principal features include dwarf rhododendron, azaleas (evergreen and deciduous), large drifts of various primula and meconopsis and bluebells, and mixed herbaceous perennials/shrubs; there is also quite a serious kitchen garden. The second garden has been developed over the last 30 years out of a birch and sessile oak wood and is a traditional west coast glen garden intersected by two pretty burns with waterfalls. The garden has been extended over the last few years and now covers nearly ten acres with extensive new paths, and a suspension bridge over the ravine. Whilst the plants are important, many say that it is the topography with its differing vistas which make this garden such a peaceful and special place.

Open: Sunday 12 May & Sunday 2 June, 12:30pm - 5:30pm. Also open by arrangement 1 May - 30 September. Admission £6.00, children free. Dogs must be on leads.

Directions: South-east of Loch Awe on the B840, 15 miles from Cladich, seven miles from Ford.

Opening for: Mary's Meals

Argyll & Lochaber

15 CRINAN HOTEL GARDEN

Crinan PA31 8SR
Mrs N Ryan
T: 01546 830261 E: nryan@crinanhotel.com
W: www.crinanhotel.com

A small, mature garden behind the Crinan Hotel which has been open with SGS for over 25 years. It is 100 years old and was originally the walled vegetable garden for the Hotel. In 1980 it was cleared and reinstated with azaleas, rhododendrons and herbaceous beds. Approached from a patio under ancient griselinia boughs, the garden catches the afternoon sun and is a peaceful escape!
The garden is open from Easter until October.

Open: 29 March - 31 October, dawn - dusk, admission by donation. Raffle of signed, limited edition fine art print by Frances Macdonald. Tickets available at the coffee shop, art gallery and hotel. Cream teas at the coffee shop by the canal basin at a very special garden rate.

Directions: Take the A83 to Lochgilphead, then the A816 to Oban, then the A841 Cairnbaan to Crinan. Daily bus.

Opening for: Alzheimer Scotland & Guide Dogs

16 DAL AN EAS

Kilmore, Oban PA34 4XU
Mary Lindsay
T: 01631 770246 E: dalaneas@live.com

An informal country garden with the aim of increasing the biodiversity of native plants and insects while adding interest and colour with introduced trees, shrubs and naturalised perennials. There is a structured garden round the house and beyond there are extensive flower-filled 'meadows' with five different species of native orchid. Grass paths lead to waterfalls, vegetable plot, woodland garden, views and ancient archaeological sites.

Open: by arrangement 1 May - 30 September, admission £5.00, children free. Teas on request.

Directions: From Oban take the A816 to Kilmore three-and-a-half miles south of Oban. Turn left on the road to Barran and Musdale. Keep left at the junction for Connel. Dal an Eas is approximately one mile on the left before the big hedges.

Opening for: All proceeds to SGS Beneficiaries

Dal an Eas © Nick Edgington

Argyll & Lochaber

17 EAS MHOR

Cnoc-a-Challtuinn, Clachan Seil, Oban PA34 4TR
Mrs Kimbra Lesley Barrett
T: 01852 300469 E: kimbra1745@gmail.com

All the usual joys of a west coast garden plus some delightful surprises! A small contemporary garden on a sloping site – the emphasis being on scent and exotic plant material. Unusual and rare blue Borinda bamboos (only recently discovered in China) and bananas. The garden is at its best in mid to late summer when shrub roses and sweet peas fill the air with scent. The delightful, sunny deck overlooks stylish white-walled ponds with cascading water blades. Recent additions include a 20-foot citrus house, Chinese pergola walk and peony border.

Open: by arrangement 1 May - 31 October, admission £6.00, children free.

Directions: After arranging a visit and agreeing a time, you will be met at the Tigh An Truish car park by the Atlantic Bridge, Isle of Seil. Or if travelling by bus, you will be met off the bus and taken to Eas Mhor. Please inform Mrs Barrett the time of your arrival. The bus stops at the bottom of Cnoc-a-Challtuinn Road.

Opening for: ABWA: Argyll & Bute Woman's Aid – support for domestic abuse – Oban Branch

18 ILHA DE DEUS

Tiroran, Isle of Mull PA69 6ET
John Innes
T: 01681705022 E: johninnes2009@hotmail.com

Half-acre garden with stunning views of Loch Scridain, the Ross of Mull, and surrounded by mountains and community forest. The current owner has been developing the garden over the last 3 years with a collection of rhododendrons, camellias, fruit trees, roses, ferns, peonies, lilies and a few exotics from the southern hemisphere, together with three small ponds. Dogs welcome on leads. Small selection of plants for sale. Kindly walk on gravel paths and grassy areas only.

Open: Sunday 5 May, Sunday 2 June & Sunday 7 July, 2pm - 6pm. Also open by arrangement 1 May - 31 July. Admission £5.00, children free.

Directions: From A849 (Craignure to Fionnphort) turn right at Kinloch junction onto B8035 "Scenic route to Salen". Garden on left after 4.5 miles immediately opposite Balevulin. The Saltire is flying when wind is below 30mph.

Opening for: North West Mull Community Woodland Company Ltd & Open Doors with Brother Andrew

Argyll & Lochaber

19 INVERARAY CASTLE GARDENS

Inveraray PA32 8XF
The Duke and Duchess of Argyll
T: 01499 302203 E: manager@inveraray-castle.com
W: www.inveraray-castle.com

With Inverary Castle as an imposing backdrop, the 16 acre garden has formal, meadow, park and woodland areas and is one of the most important designed landscapes in Scotland. The formal gardens consist of vivid green manicured lawn; the Flag Borders, historically laid out in the shape of the St Andrew's cross; a spectacular rose garden and herbaceous borders. A number of significant trees, including notable specimens of *Magnolia acuminata* and *Oxydendrum arboreum*, provide structure and form in this section of the garden. Colour is abundant from April until well into the autumn. The wildflower meadow is managed with native flora and fauna in mind and links the formal and informal parts of the garden. The carpet of fragrant bluebells is a feast for the senses throughout the spring, following straight on from thousands of narcissi. With views over Loch Fyne and the majesty of the West Highlands, the garden holds numerous rhododendrons, hydrangeas and other plants known to flourish in the Argyll climate.

Open: 28 March - 28 October, 10am - 5pm, admission £9.00 (garden only), children under five free. Tearoom and shop on site. Free parking with castle and garden entrance. Pre-booking via website recommended. Tours with the Head Gardener can be arranged in advance. Only assistance dogs within the castle and garden. **Please check the website** for opening days (currently shut Tuesdays and Wednesdays) and times, further information and accessibility. www.inveraray-castle.com

Directions: Inveraray is 60 miles north of Glasgow and 45 miles from Oban. Regular bus services from Glasgow, Oban and Campbeltown. SatNav PA32 8XF.

Opening for: Donation to SGS

20 KAMES BAY

Kilmelford PA34 4XA
Stuart Cannon
T: 07770 877817 E: kamesbay@talk21.com

Kames Bay garden has evolved from two acres of scrub and bracken on an exposed lochside hill into a natural, almost wild garden spread over 13 acres, which blends into the contours of the coastal landscape. A garden where visitors can wander at peace on the woodland walk, or the hillside walk edged with wild primroses and violets, or around the pond edged with hydrangeas. Relax on hidden benches to enjoy the magnificent views over Loch Melfort and the islands to the west. An enchanting garden full of vibrant colours, especially in the spring, with more than 100 varieties of azaleas and rhododendrons.

Open: by arrangement 16 April - 16 June, admission £6.00, children free. We would prefer visitors to email us.

Directions: On the A816 Oban to Lochgilphead road. Opposite Kames Bay and the fish farm. Two-and-a-half miles south of Kilmelford and two-and-a-half miles north of Arduaine.

Opening for: Netherlorn (Church of Scotland): Kilmelford Church New Annexe

Argyll & Lochaber

 21 KILDALLOIG
Campbeltown PA28 6RE
Mr and Mrs Joe Turner
T: 07979 855930 E: kildalloig@gmail.com

Coastal garden with some interesting and unusual shrubs including Australasian shrubs and trees, climbing roses, and herbaceous perennials. There is a woodland walk and a pond garden with aquatic and bog plants.

Open: by arrangement 1 May - 31 October, admission £5.00, children free. Group visits must be pre-booked.

Directions: Take the A83 to Campbeltown, then three miles south-east of the town past Davaar Island.

Opening for: Marie Curie & Macmillan Cancer Support

22 KINLOCHLAICH WALLED GARDEN
Appin PA38 4BD
Miss F M M Hutchison
T: 07881 525754 E: fionakinlochlaich@gmail.com
W: www.kinlochlaichgardencentre.co.uk

Octagonal walled garden incorporating a large Nursery Garden Centre with a huge variety of plants growing and for sale. Bluebell woodland walk and spring garden. Many rhododendrons, azaleas, trees, shrubs and herbaceous plants, including many unusual ones such as embothrium, davidia, stewartia, magnolia, eucryphia and tropaeolum. A quarter of the interior of the walled garden is borders packed with many unusual and interesting plants, espaliered fruit trees, and with an ancient yew in the centre, and another quarter is vegetable growing.

Open: 3 March - 31 October, 10am - 4pm, admission by donation. Winter by appointment – we are generally about. Accommodation also available, please see www.kinlochlaichgardenselfcatering.co.uk/

Directions: On the A828 in Appin between Oban, 18 miles to the south, and Fort William, 27 miles to the north. The entrance is next to the police station. Infrequent bus Oban to Fort William – request stop.

Opening for: The Appin Village Hall & Down's Syndrome Scotland: West of Scotland Branch

Inverary Castle Gardens © Nick McCann

Argyll & Lochaber

23 KNOCK NEWHOUSE

Lochgair PA31 8RZ
Mrs Hew Service
T: 01546 886628 E: corranmorhouse@aol.com

Like all good gardens, it has evolved over time. The garden is centred on a 250 foot lochan, a small waterfall and lily pond. The first trees and rhododendrons were planted in the 60s, with major additions in the 90s. A variety of cut leaf and flowering trees were added after the storms of 2011/12. As a result, the garden now has a wide range of specimen trees, camellias, hoheria, eucryphia, stewartia to name a few in addition to the azaleas and rhododendrons. January flowering is followed with spring flowers and bluebells and then into the autumn with spectacular colours.

Open: Saturday/Sunday, 11/12 May & Sunday 2 June, 1pm - 5pm, admission £6.00, children free. Plants for sale. Please pre-book group visits. I am delighted to welcome visitors at any time, please let me know when you would like to visit.

Directions: On the A83. The house is not visible from the road. From Lochgilphead, a ½ mile south of Lochgair Hotel and on the left-hand side of the road, and from Inveraray on the right-hand side of the road a ½ mile after the Lochgair Hotel; the drive opening is marked and enters the woods. Bus Route – Inveraray to Lochgilphead

Opening for: Cancer Research UK & The Lochgair Association (SCIO): Village Hall Fund

24 ORMSARY GARDENS

Ormsary, Lochgilphead, Argyll PA31 8PE
Lady Lithgow
T: 01880 770738 E: mclithgow@ormsary.co.uk

Ormsary is on the shore of Loch Caolisport looking across to Islay and Jura. The house policies are resplendent in spring with bluebells and daffodils under fine oak trees. There are woodland gardens with azaleas, rhododendrons and a collection of trees and shrubs. The walled garden, which has evolved over a couple of centuries, is on two levels. The top half is a kitchen garden producing plants, fruit and vegetables for the house; a winter garden and 'Muscat of Alexandria' vinery have been heated by hydroelectric power for 100 years. A magnificent *Polylepis australis* beckons to the lower Secret Garden with its lawn, roses, magnolias and long mixed border. It opens onto the banks of Ormsary Water. There are also woodland walks accessed via the upper woodland garden with specimens of Wollemi Pine, Gingko and Turkish Oak.

Open: by arrangement 1 June - 30 September, admission £6.00, children free.

Directions: Take the A83 road from Lochgilphead towards Campbeltown for four miles, then take the B8024 signposted to *Kilberry*, travel ten miles and follow signs to the *Estate Office* for directions to the garden.

Opening for: Mary's Meals

Argyll & Lochaber

 25 STRACHUR FLOWER & WOODLAND GARDENS
Strachur PA27 8BX
Sir Charles and Lady Maclean

The flower garden is sheltered by magnificent beeches, limes, ancient yews and Japanese maples. There are herbaceous borders, a burnside rhododendron and azalea walk, rockery, tulips and spring bulbs. Enjoy the old woodland of Strachur Park, laid out in 1782, and the wildlife rich lochan.

Open: Sunday 12 May & Sunday 19 May, 1pm - 5pm, admission £5.00, children free.

Directions: Turn off the A815 at Strachur House Farm entrance. Park in farm square. Bus Dunoon – Inveraray. From Edinburgh/Glasgow take the ferry from Gourock to Dunoon.

Opening for: British Red Cross

 26 THE SECRET GARDEN
Isle of Lismore, Oban, Argyll PA34 5UL
Eva Tombs
T: 01631 760128 E: eva.tombs@gmail.com

A unique garden at the centre of a biodynamic farm on the Island of Lismore in the Inner Hebrides. The garden created from a field has a strong geometric layout that reflects the ecclesiastical history of the island. It has a vegetable garden, a tree nursery, a physic garden, an orchard and a polytunnel. The garden is a haven for wildflowers, birds, bees and butterflies. Standing stones, meadows, new woodlands, mountains and the sea encompass the whole. There is also a herd of rare breed Shetland cattle, chickens, ducks and friendly cats.

Open: by arrangement 1 January – 1 December, admission £6.00, children free. Plants, seeds, fruit and vegetables, flowers, meat and eggs for sale. No dogs please, there are lots of animals around. Refreshments by arrangement.

Directions: Please telephone for directions. Approximately two miles from Port Appin ferry.

Opening for: All proceeds to SGS Beneficiaries

Kames Bay   Ormsary Gardens

Ayrshire & Arran

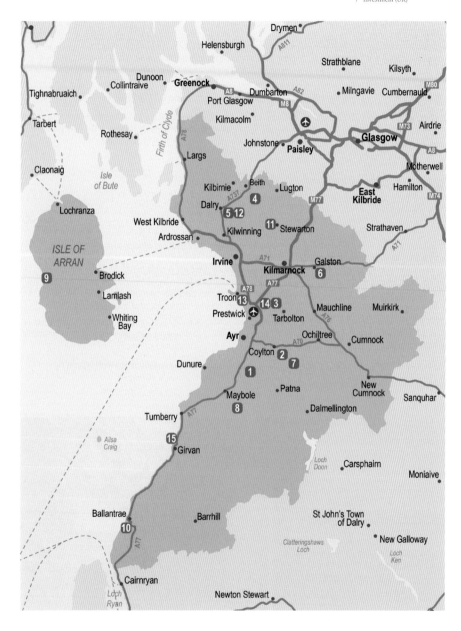

Ayrshire & Arran

OUR VOLUNTEER ORGANISERS

District Organisers:	Rose-Ann Cuninghame	45 Towerhill Avenue, Kilmaurs KA3 2TS racuninghame@gmail.com T: 07748 280036
	Lavinia Gibbs	Dougarie, Isle of Arran KA27 8EB info@scotlandsgardens.org
District Administrator:	Tony Rowley	trowleyx@gmail.com
Area Organisers:	Pattie Kewney Kirsten McClelland-Brooks Marjorie Quinn Wendy Sandiford Jane Tait Sue Veitch	
District Photographers:	David Blatchford Rob Davis	
Treasurers:	Lizzie Adam Carol Freireich	Bayview, Pirnmill, Isle of Arran KA27 8HP 18 Netherblane, Blanefield, Glasgow G63 9JW

GARDENS OPEN ON A SPECIFIC DATE

Blair Castle & Estate, Dalry, Ayrshire	Sunday, 5 May
Underwood Lodge, Craigie, Kilmarnock, South Ayrshire	Saturday, 11 May
Burnhouse, Cemetery Road, Galston	Sunday, 12 May
Barnweil Garden, Craigie, near Kilmarnock	Sunday, 26 May
Barrmill Community Garden, Barrmill Park and Gardens	Saturday, 15 June
Dalhowan Farm, Crosshill, Maybole	Sunday, 30 June
Dougarie, Isle of Arran	Tuesday, 2 July
Whitewin House, Golf Course Road, Girvan	Saturday/Sunday, 13/14 July
Whitewin House, Golf Course Road, Girvan	Saturday/Sunday, 20/21 July
Whitewin House, Golf Course Road, Girvan	Saturday/Sunday, 27/28 July
Whitewin House, Golf Course Road, Girvan	Saturday/Sunday, 3/4 August
Whitewin House, Golf Course Road, Girvan	Saturday/Sunday, 10/11 August
Whitewin House, Golf Course Road, Girvan	Saturday/Sunday, 17/18 August
Whitewin House, Golf Course Road, Girvan	Saturday/Sunday, 24/25 August

GARDENS OPEN REGULARLY

Glenapp Castle, Ballantrae, Girvan	1 January - 31 December

Ayrshire & Arran

GARDENS OPEN BY ARRANGEMENT

The Carriage House, Blair Estate, Dalry	29 March - 31 October
Kirkmuir Cottage, Stewarton	1 April - 30 August
Burnside, Littlemill Road, Drongan	1 April - 30 September
Auldbyres Farm Garden, Coylton	13 April - 2 September
The Pines, Southwood Road, Troon	1 May - 31 July
Barnweil Garden, Craigie, near Kilmarnock	21 May - 21 July
Dougarie, Isle of Arran	22 May - 30 August
1 Burnton Road, Dalrymple	1 June - 31 August
Whitewin House, Golf Course Road, Girvan	1 July - 31 August
Barnweil Garden, Craigie, near Kilmarnock	14 September - 20 October

The Pines © David Blatchford

Burnhouse

Ayrshire & Arran

1 BURNTON ROAD

Dalrymple KA6 6DY
David and Margaret Blatchford
T: 01292 561988 E: d.blatchford273@btinternet.com

A tiny slice of jungle nestled within a small triangular plot. To the front of the house are two beds planted with nectar-secreting plants and seasonal colour. To the rear, an anonymous door leads to a small patio, home to some bonsai, a collection of potted terrestrial ferns and stone troughs hold tender and hardy succulents. A serpentine path meanders through dense planting of palms, brugmansia, bananas and tree ferns. Of particular note is the use of hardy and tender bromeliads and a collection of aroids such as *Arisaemia, Alocasia, Colocasia* and Giant *Zantedeschia*. Flower highlights are provided by lilies (species and cultivars) and later in the season, Cannas, and hardy gingers such as *Hedychium* and *Roscoea*. Nestling amongst the foliage is the giant leafed *Tetrapanax* together with the rare terrestrial fern *Lophosoria*.

Open: by arrangement 1 June - 31 August, admission £5.00, children free.

Directions: From the north take the A77 Ayr to Stranraer. At the Bankton roundabout, turn left onto the A713 and follow the road past the hospital to the junction with B742, turn right into the village and park in the White Horse car park at the T junction. The garden is on the corner of Burnton and Barbieston Roads. From the south take the A77 towards Ayr, turn right onto the B7034. Follow into the village, at Kirkton Inn junction turn left onto Barbieston Road. Bus 52 from Ayr. The 52 leaves Ayr bus Station at 20 minutes to the hour and will drop you at the White Horse.

Opening for: Dalrymple, Skeldon and Hollybush Project

AULDBYRES FARM GARDEN

Coylton KA6 6HG
Marshall and Sue Veitch
E: su.pavet@btinternet.com

Surrounded by a working farm, this compact, established garden has mature shrubs, wildlife pond, bog garden and stream, borrowing stunning countryside views towards Ayr and Arran. Well-behaved spring borders give way to a riot of summer perennial favourites. Many 'found objects' of agricultural interest. Extensive containers brighten the farmyard with seasonal displays.

Open: by arrangement 13 April - 2 September, admission £5.00, children free. Personal tour on request. Ideal for couples and small groups. Extend your visit by walking the adjacent community nature trail.

Directions: In Coylton take the road signposted *B742*, past Coylton Arms Pub in Low Coylton, *Auldbyres* is signposted on the left after ½ mile.

Opening for: Beatson West of Scotland Cancer Centre

Ayrshire & Arran

 3 ## BARNWEIL GARDEN
Craigie, near Kilmarnock KA1 5NE
Mr and Mrs Ronald W Alexander
E: ronaldwalexander@btinternet.com

An earlier opening date than usual highlights the late spring woodland garden, that surrounds the more formal borders and lawns next to the 19th-century house. The woodland features azaleas, species and hybrid rhododendrons, as well as acers and magnolias with primulas, meconopsis, smilacina and a wide variety of hostas, ferns and other foliage focused plants especially lining Oscar's ditch. Another woodland feature is the Golden Glade where golden leaved trees, shrubs and under-planting should be at its most potent. The golden philadelphus should be in full flower and the arching sprays of white-stemmed golden bramble (rubus) are particularly graceful. Herbaceous and rose borders nearer the house will have an early summer display of perennial geraniums, alliums, astrantia and many others whilst the species and old roses will be flowering. During June and July visitors can still see the wide selection of David Austin and other roses while herbaceous borders will be at their peak. During September and October you can see the autumn leaf colours of Parrotia, Liquidambar and American oaks with displays of sedums, dahlias and anemones.

Open: Sunday 26 May, 2pm - 5pm. Also open by arrangement 21 May - 21 July and 14 September - 20 October. Admission £6.00, children free.

Directions: From the south take the A719 off the A77 at Sandyford roundabout continue on the A719 for 2.5 miles before turning left onto the B730. Take the first left signposted *Barnweil Monument*, and the garden is on the right. From the north on the A77 take the left at the B730 Tarbolton (past Hayes). Go two miles on the right, signposted *Barnweil Monument* and the garden is on the right.

Opening for: Tarbolton Parish Church of Scotland & The Ridley Foundation

 4 ## BARRMILL COMMUNITY GARDEN
Barrmill Park and Gardens KA15 1HW
The Barrmill Conservation Group
E: jean42gilbert@gmail.com
W: https://www.facebook.com/BarrmillCG

This large woodland garden is carved from a 19th-century whinstone quarry and situated within a 1890s parkland, once known for the quoiting green provided for the village thread mill and ironstone pit workers of that time. Enhancement of the gardens began in 2010 by volunteers, with assistance from *Beechgrove* in 2012. Features include enchanted woodland walks, a fairy trail, a nature trail, the Vale Burn, views of the Dusk Water, a restored 19th-century cholera pit aka 'The Deid Man's Plantin', a new Celtic tree circle and guided walks. The woodland backdrop is complemented by an understorey of natural planting throughout.

Open: Saturday 15 June, 2pm - 5pm, admission £6.00, children free.

Directions: From Stewarton take the A735 to Dunlop, go left down Main Street B706 to Burnhouse, over at crossroads to Barrmill B706. From Lugton south on the A736, take the right at Burnhouse, B706 to Barrmill. From Glasgow on the M8 take J28a signposted *Irvine*, on Beith bypass take the left at B706 to Barrmill.

Opening for: Barrmill and District Community Association

Ayrshire & Arran

5 BLAIR CASTLE & ESTATE

Dalry, Ayrshire KA24 4ER
Siobhan Nanson, Head of Business Development and Events
T: 01294 833100 E: Siobhan@blairestate.co.uk

Blair Castle private gardens will be open for visitors to enjoy the beautiful, landscaped gardens which include a collection of trees dating back to the 18th century. The gardens have undergone a major restoration project, with new beds created including a collection of rhododendrons, magnolias and azaleas. This is also the perfect time to see the bluebells on the estate.

Open: Sunday 5 May, noon - 4:30pm, admission £6.00, children free. Refreshments, soup, teas/coffees and cakes will be available to purchase. We will also be selling plants. Cash only. Sorry dogs are not allowed.

Directions: Exit the A737 at the Highfield roundabout. Take the first exit towards Stewarton on the B707. Follow this road for 0.8 mile and then turn right onto Blair Road. Turn left to enter the estate at the north gates. We will be operating a one-way system on the day for visitors.

Opening for: Dalry Community Development Hub

6 BURNHOUSE

Cemetery Road, Galston KA4 8LL
Kevin and Marjorie Quinn
T: 07927 907853 E: mbquinn2018@gmail.com

The garden surrounds the house which dates from the 17th century. Mature beech and lime trees shelter an abundance of rhododendrons and azaleas. Newer plantings of trees and shrubs add year-round colour and interest with underplantings of perennials and bulbs. Tubs of cheery spring flowers add colour around the garden. Raised beds have recently been added for vegetables, fruit trees and herbs. A colourful maple grove, a den for the youngsters and a rockery with alpines and small rhododendrons beside the burn all add interest. Cross the bridge to the main lawn which is framed with trees and shrubs chosen for different seasons. There are various seats in sheltered spots to enjoy, wildflowers and fruit trees.

Open: Sunday 12 May, 11am - 4pm, admission £6.00, children free. Sorry no dogs.

Directions: At the roundabout near Tesco take the B7037 into Galston. Go over the bridge and straight ahead at the traffic lights. After 100 metres turn left following the sign to *Sorn* (B7037). At the outskirts of the village turn sharp right into Cemetery Road and Burnhouse is immediately on the left.

Opening for: Ayrshire Cancer Support

7 BURNSIDE

Littlemill Road, Drongan KA6 7EN
Sue Simpson and George Watt
T: 01292 592445 E: suesimpson33@btinternet.com

This maturing and constantly changing six-and-a-half acre garden began in 2006. There is a wide range of plants from trees to alpines, giving colour and variability all year. Next to the road flows the Drumbowie Burn, parallel to which is a woodland border with erythroniums, hellebores, trilliums, rhododendrons and acers. Near the house are a raised bed and large collection of troughs, with an interesting range of alpines. The garden boasts herbaceous beds, ericaceous garden, screes, three alpine glasshouses with award-winning plants, an

Ayrshire & Arran

extensive Streptocarpus collection, polytunnel, pond and arboretum - underplanted with daffodils, camassia, fritillaries and crocus. With a view towards matrimonial harmony, there are two sheds which may be of interest. The garden is only 15 minutes from Dumfries House.

Open: by arrangement 1 April - 30 September, admission £6.00, children free. Sue and George are happy to receive single visitors and groups, large or small. If we don't answer, simply send an email - we check regularly. Hot drinks and biscuits available on request for £3.50. Visit the Scotland's Gardens Scheme website for additional openings.

Directions: From the A77 Ayr bypass take the A70 Cumnock for 5¼ miles, at Coalhall, turn onto the B730 Drongan (south) for 2½ miles. Burnside entrance is immediately adjacent to a black/ white parapeted bridge. Ordnance survey grid ref: NS455162.

Opening for: Alzheimer's Research UK

 ### 8 DALHOWAN FARM
Crosshill, Maybole KA19 7RN
Fiona and Robbie Baird
T: 07850 282130 E: crosshill.fionabaird@tiscali.co.uk

Situated on the edge of the village, the garden of this working dairy farm has clear views towards the Heads of Ayr. Central to the garden is the lawn, around which are a wide range of mixed perennial borders. In spring these are highly colourful with a variety of daffodils. A raised pond complements some of the external walls and border edges, constructed from recycled sandstone. A long hosta border stretches the length of the farmhouse, where it benefits from shade. Mature trees and shrubs help to protect the garden from the prevailing winds. Two greenhouses protect tender plants over winter, from which a large number of cuttings are taken to fill numerous containers around the farmyard.

Open: Sunday 30 June, 1pm - 5pm, admission £6.00, children free. Additional opening date with daffodils in April, check website for information. Sorry no dogs.

Directions: Follow the A77 south from Ayr to Maybole, take the B7023 towards the village of Crosshill, continue to the end of the village. Parking is available in the field at the end of the village, with a short walk along the road to enter the garden.

Opening for: The Ayrshire Hospice

 ### 9 DOUGARIE
Isle of Arran KA27 8EB
Mrs S C Gibbs
E: laviniawgibbs@gmail.com

Most interesting terraced garden in a castellated folly built in 1905 to celebrate the marriage of the 12th Duke of Hamilton's only child to the Duke of Montrose. Good selection of tender and rare shrubs and herbaceous border. Small woodland area with trees including azara, abutilon, eucryphia, hoheria and nothofagus.

Open: Tuesday 2 July, 2pm - 5pm. Also open by arrangement 22 May - 30 August. Admission £5.00, children free. Cream teas will be served in the 19th century boat house. Cash payments only. There is free parking.

Directions: Five miles from Blackwaterfoot. Regular ferry sailing from Ardrossan and Claonaig (Argyll). Information from Caledonian MacBrayne, Gourock, T: 01475 650100. Parking is free.

Opening for: Pirnmill Village Association

Ayrshire & Arran

10 GLENAPP CASTLE

Ballantrae, Girvan KA26 0NZ
Mr Paul Szkiler
T: 01465 831212 E: info@glenappcastle.com
W: www.glenappcastle.com

The 36-acre grounds at Glenapp Castle are secluded and private. Many rare and unusual plants and shrubs can be found, including magnificent specimen rhododendrons. Paths meander round the azalea pond, through established woodland leading to the wonderful walled garden with a 150-foot Victorian glasshouse. Fresh herbs and fruit from the garden are used every day in the castle kitchen. Much of the gardens were designed by Gertrude Jekyll (1843-1932), the world-famous garden designer, applying the principles of the Arts and Crafts Movement, who worked in collaboration with Edwin Lutyens. A new walk has been created opening up the Glen, where Glenapp's Champion Trees will be found.
Champion Trees: *Abies cilicica, Cercidiphyllum japonicum* and *Picea likiangensis*.

Open: 1 January - 31 December, dawn - dusk, admission by donation.

Directions: From the north take the A77 south. Pass through Ballantrae, crossing the River Stinchar as you leave. Take the first turning on the right, 100 yards beyond the river (not signposted). From the south take the A77 north, turn left 100 yards before the bridge over Stinchar at Ballantrae. The Castle gates are one mile along this road.

Opening for: Donation to SGS Beneficiaries

11 KIRKMUIR COTTAGE

Stewarton KA3 3DZ
Mr and Mrs Brian Macpherson
E: dhmmacp@gmail.com

This garden was created in 1997 from a small field and includes a large pond which was originally a small quarry. It covers approximately one-and-a-half-acres of mature garden and, using hedging and shrubbery, the garden is split into garden 'rooms' including woodland, formal borders, laburnum arch, herbaceous borders, rhododendrons and azaleas. Large lawn area and wildlife pond. The garden also features many interesting and unusual artefacts and sculptures.

Open: by arrangement 1 April - 30 August, admission £6.00, children free. All garden visitors, societies and walking groups are welcome. Dogs on leads please.

Directions: From the M77 take the B778 to Stewarton. At the traffic lights, turn left and continue to the mini-roundabout. Turn in right towards the B778 Kilwinning. Continue for 100 yards under the railway bridge, take an immediate left at the war memorial and continue along Kilwinning, head until you reach the countryside. Kirkmuir is the first farm road on the right hand side. The cottage and garden is on the left at the end of the farm road. Please follow these directions not SatNav.

Opening for: Capability Scotland

Ayrshire & Arran

THE CARRIAGE HOUSE
12
Blair Estate, Dalry KA24 4ER
Mr and Mrs Luke Borwick
T: 07831 301294 E: lina@blairtrust.co.uk

Set within the glorious historic Blair Polices dating back to the 1500s, at the Carriage House, the Borwicks have planted a beautiful new Arboretum. This continues to build on the vision of past generations of Blairs of creating a sanctuary of rare species trees. Over the past three years a collection of over 160 trees and shrubs has transformed a 10-acre field into a peaceful refuge with year-round variety and colour. Mown paths wend their way around providing different vistas and points of interest including the mermaids rescuing a girl carved by a local artist from the stump of a Portuguese Laurel. Look out for the 24-year old Wellingtonia (*Sequoiadendron giganteum)* grown from seed here at Blair, an avenue of eight different lime trees which earned a *Queen's Green Canopy Award*, a *Metasequoia glyptostroboides* 'Golden Dawn' and many other rare trees. To sit on one of the benches created from our own wood and enjoy the energies of the Arboretum is a special experience. The Carriage House garden, created from a field over the past 20 years and planted with many varieties of roses and mature shrubs, is also available for a wander. You are welcome to bring a picnic and we welcome garden societies and walking groups.

Open: by arrangement 29 March - 31 October, admission £6.00, children free. Email us or text 07831 301294 using 'Garden Visit' as the subject. Please leave your contact name and number. Dogs very strictly on short leads due to sheep in the field.

Directions: A737 from Beith. At the roundabout before Dalry take the first left signposted *Stewarton*. Then go straight on, signposted *Bike Route Irvine*. Keep going for approximately two miles and keep the estate wall on the right until you come to South Lodge (white building). Turn right down the drive for Blair Estate - The Carriage House is on the right. Public transport to Dalry. Follow SatNav KA24 4ER and enter Blair Estate through the South Lodge.

Opening for: The National Trust for Scotland

THE PINES
13
Southwood Road, Troon KA10 7EL
Cheryll and Alasdair Cameron
E: cheryllcameron2@gmail.com

In nine years our one-acre plot has been transformed from a barren children's playground with only mature pine trees and rhododendrons, to a colourful seaside garden. Our exposed coastal situation causes windburn in many supposedly hardy plants, so we have formed a windbreak for the borders with mixed shrubs including griselinia, hawthorn and photinia. Billowing grasses sit alongside perennials including helenium, euphorbia and agapanthus, all interspersed with tulips, lilies and alliums. The coastal theme is accentuated by cordyline, phormium, *Fatsia japonica* and eucalyptus. We have bark woodland paths and our garden is a haven for birds, bees and butterflies.

Open: by arrangement 1 May - 31 July, admission £6.00, children free.

Directions: From the A77 at Dutch House Roundabout, follow the A78 and then the A79, then immediately right to Troon on the B749. Southwood Road is first left and The Pines is the last property. Stagecoach X14 passes the property.

Opening for: The Ayrshire Hospice

Ayrshire & Arran

 14 UNDERWOOD LODGE
Craigie, Kilmarnock, South Ayrshire KA1 5NG
Marilyn Badman
T: 01563 830439 E: mbadman1@sky.com

Underwood Lodge's secluded garden is set in surrounding farmland and woodland. The main structure of the garden has been in place for over 20 years with mature trees, shrubs, herbaceous and wall-grown plants. Recent changes to the garden include the development of a woodland, scree garden and installation of a summer house, pergola and glasshouse. Deer and rabbit fencing was added in autumn 2023 to give greater protection. We continue to enhance the planting in all areas.

Open: Saturday 11 May, 11am - 5pm, admission £6.00, children free. There is limited parking on site so it is preferable to book a timed slot for the visit to secure a parking space. Other off-site parking is available for non-booked visits.

Directions: Southbound on the A77, pass Hansel Village and take the next left signposted *Underwood/Ladykirk*. Northbound on the A77 take the exit to Symington, then first right, to join the southbound carriageway. Take the Underwood/Ladykirk turning. At the stone bridge, turn left and Underwood Lodge is the first house on the left.

Opening for: *Annbank Parish Church Of Scotland*

 15 WHITEWIN HOUSE
Golf Course Road, Girvan KA26 9HW
Linda Finnie and Graeme Finnie
T: 01465 712358 M: 07855 269247 E: lafinnie@hotmail.com

Whitewin House was built for Baronet Henry Tate of Tate and Lyle. The house stands in one acre of formal Victorian Garden, redesigned over a five year period in the form of an English Manor House Garden which, of course, comes with its challenges, because of its coastal location. The rockeries, beautiful scalloped lawns and the plethora of statuary all complement the use of authentic Victorian bedding plants, trees and shrubs, ideally mirroring the ambience and grandeur of the house interior. In 2022, two water features were added to the garden. Home to celebrated international mezzo-soprano Linda Finnie, Whitewin House is fortunate in having a prime position in Golf Course Road, having been the first house built there, standing majestically overlooking the Firth of Clyde, Ailsa Craig, Arran and the Kintyre Peninsula. Whitewin House was encouraged to apply for Garden of the Year in May 2022, following an invitation by a representative from *More4 television.*

Open: Saturday/Sunday, 13 July - 25 August, 2pm - 5pm. And open by arrangement 1 July - 31 August. Admission £6.00, children free. Teas and coffees will be served in the conservatories and the garden.

Directions: Approaching Girvan from the north on the A77, the turning to Golf Course Road is on the right-hand-side of the road before the town centre following signs for the *Golf Course.* From the south on the A77 come through Girvan, turn left at the lights, then first left and follow signs for the *Golf Course.* Entrance to the property will be signposted.

Opening for: *All proceeds to SGS Beneficiaries*

Berwickshire

Sponsored by

RATHBONES

Incorporating
Investec Wealth &
Investment (UK)

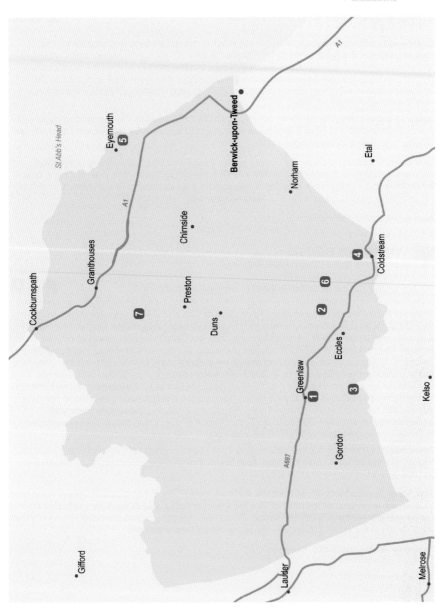

Berwickshire

GARDENS OPEN ON A SPECIFIC DATE

Bughtrig, near Leitholm, Coldstream	Friday, 29 March - Monday, 1 April
Harlaw Farmhouse, Eccles near Kelso, Roxburghshire	Sunday, 14 April
The Moorhouse, Duns	Sunday, 23 June
Ruthven House, Coldstream	Sunday, 30 June

GARDENS OPEN REGULARLY

Bughtrig, near Leitholm, Coldstream	1 May - 30 September

GARDENS OPEN BY ARRANGEMENT

Ruthven House, Coldstream	1 January - 13 September
Broomhill Villa, 4 Edinburgh Road, Greenlaw	2 April - 1 July
Netherbyres, Eyemouth	1 May - 31 August
Lennel Bank, Coldstream	1 May - 31 October

Would you like to get involved?

We're always looking for new gardens and people to help out with our garden opening programme.

If you're interested and would like to find out more, please visit scotlandsgardens.org/join-in/ or call the office on **0131 226 3714** for a friendly chat.

Berwickshire

1 BROOMHILL VILLA
4 Edinburgh Road, Greenlaw TD10 6XF
Tatyana Aplin
T: 07957 288557 E: aplin848@btinternet.com

Broomhill garden is on the northern side of Greenlaw comprising half-an-acre of spring colour nestled between village and farmland. The garden is maintained by a passionate plant collector featuring narcissus, tulips, meconopses and hundreds of other flowers. The collection has been developed along informal lines with treats at every turn. A radiant display of blooms that changes through the year is intended not only for the visual pleasure of the garden but also for the house with cut flower arrangements as well as produce for the table and larder.

Open: by arrangement 2 April - 1 July, admission £5.00, children free. Small groups are welcome.

Directions: On the A697 at the northern end of Greenlaw Village.

Opening for: Cancer Research UK

2 BUGHTRIG
near Leitholm, Coldstream TD12 4JP
Mr and Mrs William Ramsay
E: ramsay@bughtrig.co.uk

A traditional, hedged, Scottish family garden with an interesting combination of sculpture, herbaceous plants, shrubs, annuals and fruit. It is surrounded by fine specimen trees, which provide remarkable shelter. In the grounds of Bughtrig Gardens is the recently opened Admiral Ramsay Museum, which has been created in memory of all who served at D-Day, Dunkirk and during World War II.

Open: Friday 29 March - Monday 1 April, 9am - 4.30pm. Also open 1 May - 30 September, 9am - 4.30pm. Admission £5.00, children free. The museum's opening times are the same.

Directions: ¼ mile east of Leitholm on the B6461.

Opening for: Donation to SGS Beneficiaries

Lennel Bank © Jannie Bos

Berwickshire

3 HARLAW FARMHOUSE
Eccles near Kelso, Roxburghshire TD5 7RA
Jean Wood
T: 07883422519 E: jean.greenfingers@gmail.com

Harlaw is set in a one-acre garden surrounding a typical Berwickshire farmhouse, in a truly rural setting with lovely Border views. The owner has spent many years building up a collection of over 65 varieties of named daffodils and narcissus, naturalised throughout the garden. It has a mature nuttery with several highly productive walnut, hazel and gingko biloba trees and an orchard with apple, pear and plum trees. In the summer there is a large cutting garden and vegetable patch. There are two greenhouses with a large cactus collection. The gardener is a keen plantswoman, propagating most of her own stock.

Open: Sunday 14 April, 2pm - 5pm, admission £5.00, children free.

Directions: From the east drive through Eccles village then take the first turning on the right signposted *Loan Knowe*. Continue to the *cycle route* sign, turn left and the house is one mile on the left. From Ednam, go through the village, take the left turn to Hume, go to the T-junction, turn right and continue to the white cottage, take the right fork *cycle route* and Harlaw is ½ mile on the right.

Opening for: Border Womens Aid

4 LENNEL BANK
Coldstream TD12 4EX
Mrs Honor Brown
T: 01890 882297 E: honor.b.brown@gmail.com

Lennel Bank is a terraced garden overlooking the River Tweed, consisting of wide borders packed with shrubs and perennial planting, some unusual. The water garden, built in 2008, is surrounded by a rockery and utilises the slope, ending in a pond. There is a small kitchen garden with raised beds in unusual shapes. Different growing conditions throughout the garden from dry, wet, shady and sunny, lend themselves to a variety of plants and enhance interest in the garden.

Open: by arrangement 1 May - 31 October, admission £5.00, children free. Refreshments can be provided for visiting groups, with advance notice.

Directions: On the A6112 Coldstream to Duns road, one mile from Coldstream.

Opening for: Donation to SGS Beneficiaries

5 NETHERBYRES
Eyemouth TD14 5SE
Col S J Furness
T: 01890 750337

An unusual, elliptical walled garden, dating from 1740, with a mixture of flowers, fruit and vegetables. A very old pear tree, possibly dating from the 18th century, and the largest rose in Berwickshire, *Rosa filipes* 'Kiftsgate'. A wide variety of roses and herbaceous borders.

Open: by arrangement 1 May - 31 August, admission £5.00, children free. Only open for parties of four or more.

Directions: ½ mile south of Eyemouth on the A1107 to Berwick.

Opening for: All proceeds to SGS Beneficiaries

Berwickshire

6 RUTHVEN HOUSE
Coldstream TD12 4JU
Keith and Karen Fountain
T: 01890 840680 E: ruthvenhouse@btconnect.com

The three acres of Ruthven's garden have lovely views towards the Cheviots. The garden's central feature is two ponds joined by a winding stream. The garden is composed of various differing areas - herbaceous borders, woodland areas, a gravel garden, a knot garden, rockeries, an orchard laid to meadow, a kitchen garden, a nuttery, a small lavender field, a shade bed to the back of the house and, adjacent to the house, a formal rose garden. Much of the work to create the garden from the original few small beds around the house has only been undertaken in the last few years, so the garden has not yet reached complete maturity. The small fold of Highland cattle, hopefully including a young calf, in the adjacent field complete the scene.

Open: Sunday 30 June, noon - 5pm. Also open by arrangement 1 January - 13 September. Admission £6.00, children free. Groups and individuals are welcome.

Directions: Four miles north of Coldstream on the old Duns road.

Opening for: *Borders General Hospital, Margaret Kerr Unit: and Macmillan Centre (Sunday 30 June) & Scottish Association For Mental Health (1 January - 13 September)*

Ruthven House

Berwickshire

7 THE MOORHOUSE
Duns TD11 3RY
Mike and Bridget Bevan
T: 07848 803776 E: bordersecoflowers@gmail.com

The **Borders Eco Flowers** garden at The Moorhouse is designed to produce organic cut flowers and foliage throughout the year. Whilst most cut flowers sold in Scotland are imported, our flowers are grown here, not flown here! All are grown in an environmentally friendly manner without the use of chemical fertilisers and pesticides. Not only are we eco-friendly gardeners, we are eco-friendly florists too! We harvest the flowers at their peak and create posies, bouquets and all kinds of unique floral creations.

Open: Sunday 23 June, 1pm - 5pm, admission £5.00, children free. Dogs must remain on leads, as we have free range hens and ducks. We will also have posies and bouquets available for sale and will provide a couple of bouquet-making displays during the afternoon.

Directions: Ignore your SatNav once you have left the A6112. **From Duns,** take the A6112 towards Grantshouse. Ignore the left-hand turn (B6355) signposted *Abbey St Bathans.* Proceed through the village of Preston and 3 miles further on, turn left signposted *Edin's Hall Broch.* Continue up the hill for 1½ miles and you will see *The Moorhouse* (painted yellow) on the right. **From the A1,** turn off at Grantshouse onto the A6112, signposted Duns. After 3½ miles, turn right signposted *Edin's Hall Broch.* Continue up the hill for 1½ miles and you will see *The Moorhouse* (painted yellow) on the right.

Opening for: Borders Pet Rescue

The Moorhouse

Caithness & Sutherland

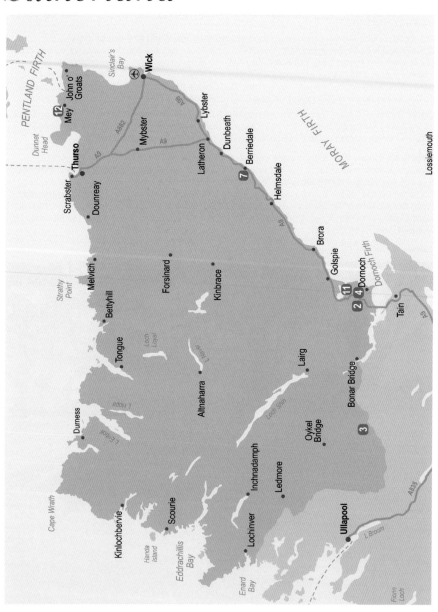

Caithness, Sutherland, Orkney & Shetland

Shetland

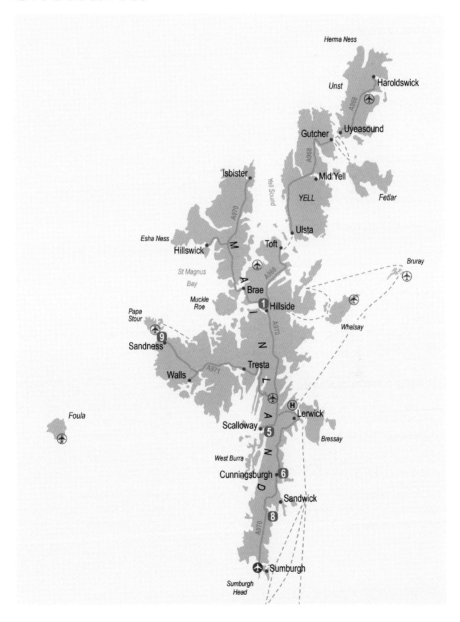

Caithness, Sutherland, Orkney & Shetland

OUR VOLUNTEER ORGANISERS

District Organisers:	Miranda Jones	Rowanlea, Main Street, Lairg IV27 4DD
	Sara Shaw	Amat, Ardgay, Sutherland IV24 3BS
		info@scotlandsgardens.org
Area Organisers:	Caroline Critchlow	Old Granary Quoy, Orphir, Orkney KW17 2RD
	Lisa Croft	Orkney
	Mary Leask	VisitScotland, Market Cross, Shetland ZE1 0LU
	Steve Mathieson	VisitScotland, Market Cross, Shetland ZE1 0LU
District Photographer:	Colin Gregory	Iona, Reay, Caithness, KW14 7RG
Treasurer:	Nicola Vestey	

GARDENS OPEN ON A SPECIFIC DATE

16 Mulla, Voe, Shetland	Saturday/Sunday, 27/28 April
Old Granary Quoy and The Quoy of Houton, Orphir, Orkney	Sunday, 2 June
Amat, Amat Lodge, Ardgay	Saturday/Sunday, 6/7 July
Auchlea, Balnapolaig Muir, Dornoch	Saturday, 20 July
16 Mulla, Voe, Shetland	Saturday/Sunday, 20/21 July
42 Astle, Dornoch	Saturday/Sunday, 27/28 July
Skelbo House, Skelbo, Dornoch	Saturday/Sunday, 27/28 July
Langwell, Berriedale	Sunday, 28 July

GARDENS OPEN REGULARLY

Norby, Burnside, Sandness, Shetland	1 April - 31 December
The Castle and Gardens of Mey, Mey	1 May - 30 September
Nonavaar, Levenwick, Shetland	1 June - 30 September

GARDENS OPEN BY ARRANGEMENT

16 Mulla, Voe, Shetland	1 April - 30 September
Highlands Garden, East Voe, Scalloway, Shetland	1 May - 31 October
Keldaberg, Cunningsburgh, Shetland	1 June - 30 September

Caithness, Sutherland, Orkney & Shetland

1 **16 MULLA**
Voe, Shetland ZE2 9XQ
Linda Richardson
T: 07765 037516 E: linda@lindarichardson.co.uk

A garden on the Clubb of Mulla, a hillside overlooking Olnafirth with views of the sea and Lower Voe. Started in October 2016, the steep overgrown plot looked like a continuation of the moor at the back of the house. This garden shows what can be achieved in a very windy and exposed situation, battling against the extremes of the Shetland weather. Gardening with wildlife in mind, trees were planted in the spring of 2017, now providing shelter for birds. Six years on, there are herbaceous borders, rockery, a vegetable bed, 3.6 x 2.4 metre greenhouse, mini wildflower meadow strips and a natural water feature which is a long drainage ditch planted up with willows and water-loving plants. Always a work in progress, more trees will be added this year. The owner is an artist-printmaker with an open studio that folk are welcome to look round too.

Open: Two plant sale weekends with tea and cake – Saturday/Sunday, 27/28 April, 10:30am - 4:30pm. Also open Saturday/Sunday, 20/21 July, 10:30am - 4:30pm. And open by arrangement 1 April - 30 September. Look for the open sign for 16 Mulla on the main road. If the sign is out, the garden and studio are open or you can telephone us to arrange a visit. Admission by donation.

Directions: Eighteen miles north of Lerwick on the A970 is Voe. Pass the *North Isles junction* and *Tagon Stores* on your right. Turn right into Mulla and number 16 is up the hill on your left. Bus no. 21 (Hillswick) and 23 (Toft) stop on the main road at the bottom of Mulla.

Opening for: Shetland UHI: Shetland Community Wildlife Group

16 Mulla

Caithness, Sutherland, Orkney & Shetland

2 **42 ASTLE**
Dornoch IV25 3NH
Fay Wilkinson

Organic wildlife garden at the edge of boggy moorland. Mature trees and shrubs are mixed with herbaceous perennials, vegetables and flowers for cutting. Changes are continually being made to focus on providing food and homes for pollinating insects.

Open: Saturday/Sunday, 27/28 July, 11am - 4pm, admission £4.00, children free.

Directions: A9 from the south: pass the turn off to Dornoch, take the first left after the Tall Pines Restaurant, signposted *Astle*. After 1 ½ miles take the left fork, cross the river and no. 42 is the second house on the left. A9 from the north: turn right 100 yards before the Tall Pines Restaurant, then follow directions above.

Opening for: *Bumblebee Conservation Trust*

42 Astle © Colin Gregory

3 **AMAT**
Amat Lodge, Ardgay IV24 3BS
Jonny and Sara Shaw
T: 07712 266500 E: sara.amat@aol.co.uk

Over the last few years there have been big changes in the garden and there is now much more interest during the summer months. There is a new mini stumpery and many changes to original borders. The river Carron flows around the edge of the garden and the old Amat Caledonian Forest is close by. Large specimen trees surround the house, plus many new ones planted in the policies in the last few years. There are several herbaceous borders, rhododendrons, trees and shrubs, all set in a large lawn. It is possible to go on a short woodland and river walk and you may see red squirrels which were reintroduced some years ago and are often in and around the garden.
Champion Trees: Abies Procera, Noble Fir.

Open: By arrangement 1-31 May, also Saturday/Sunday, 6/7 July, 2pm - 5pm, admission £5.00, children free.

Directions: Take the road from Ardgay to Croick, nine miles. Turn left at the red phone box and the garden is 500 yards on the left.

Opening for: *Marie Curie & Horatio's Garden*

Caithness, Sutherland, Orkney & Shetland

 AUCHLEA
Balnapolaig Muir, Dornoch IV25 3HY
John and Fiona Garvie

The creation of Auchlea garden from its natural state as a wetland of rushes and whins began in 1998 with the drainage and sowing of a lawn on introduced topsoil. The planting of trees, mostly around its periphery was also begun then. Extensive herbaceous borders with a wide variety of colour and species have been gradually developed. There is also a sheltered vegetable garden, made more productive using raised beds, alongside a recently replanted bog garden. The habitual, accumulated use of garden and household compost has progressively improved stony ground around the boundary, where a mixed hedge has made good progress.

Open: Late cancellation

Directions: Situated on the B9168. This B road is on the right driving up the A9. Take the B road and Auchlea is the first house on the right.

Opening for: Blythswood Care

 HIGHLANDS GARDEN
East Voe, Scalloway, Shetland ZE1 0UR
Sarah Kay
T: 01595 880526/ 07818 845385 E: info@easterhoull.co.uk
W: www.selfcatering-shetland.co.uk/the-garden/

The garden is in two parts. The upper garden is mostly a rockery, with a large selection of plants, shallow pond, seating area, polycrub and greenhouse with fruit and vegetables. The lower garden is on a steep slope with a spectacular sea view over the village of Scalloway. There is a path to lead visitors around and the garden features a large collection of plants, vegetable patch, deep pond and pergola. It was awarded a *Shetland Environmental Award* in 2014 for its strong theme of recycling. The owner also has an art studio which you are most welcome to visit when you view the garden.

Open: by arrangement 1 May - 31 October, admission £4.00, children free. Dogs are not allowed in the garden.

Directions: Follow the A970 main road towards the village of Scalloway. Near the top of the hill heading towards Scalloway take a sharp turn to the left, signposted *Easterhoull Chalets*. Follow the road to chalets (painted blue with red roofs) and you will see the yellow *SGS* sign for the garden. Bus 4 from Lerwick/Scalloway.

Opening for: Macmillan Cancer Support

Caithness, Sutherland, Orkney & Shetland

Highlands Garden

6 **KELDABERG**
Cunningsburgh, Shetland ZE2 9HG
Mrs L Johnston
T: 01950 477331/07774539693 E: linda@cunningsburghhall.com

A 'secret garden' divided into four areas. A beach garden of grasses, flowers and driftwood. The main area is a sloping perennial border leading down to a greenhouse and vegetable plot and up to a decked area with containers and exotic plants including agaves, pineapple lilies, cannas and gunneras. The new area has trees, raised vegetable beds, a rockery, retaining walls and an arbour in which to rest. There is a pond with goldfish and aquatic plants and now a polycrub to grow vegetables, fruit trees and a grapevine.

Open: by arrangement 1 June - 30 September, admission £4.00, children free.

Directions: On the A970 south of Lerwick is Cunningsburgh, take the Gord junction on the left after passing the village hall. Continue along the road to the second house past the *Kenwood* sign.

Opening for: RNLI

Caithness, Sutherland, Orkney & Shetland

7 LANGWELL

Berriedale KW7 6HD
Welbeck Estates
T: 01593 751278 / 751237 E: caithness@welbeck.co.uk

A beautiful and spectacular old walled garden with outstanding borders situated in the secluded Langwell Strath. Charming wooded access drive with a chance to see deer.

Open: Sunday 28 July, noon - 4pm, admission £5.00, children free.

Directions: Turn off the A9 at Berriedale Braes, up the private (tarred) drive signposted *Private – Langwell House.* It is about 1¼ miles from the A9.

Opening for: RNLI

8 NONAVAAR

Levenwick, Shetland ZE2 9HX
James B Thomason
T: 01950 422447

This is a delightful country garden, sloping within drystone walls and overlooking magnificent coastal views. It contains ponds, terraces, trees, bushes, varied perennials, annuals, vegetable garden and greenhouse.

Open: 1 June - 30 September, 2pm - 5pm, admission £5.00, children free.

Directions: Head south from Lerwick. Turn left at the *Levenwick* sign soon after Bigton turnoff. Follow the road to the third house on the left after the Midway stores. Park where there is a *Garden Open* sign. Bus 6 from Lerwick - Sumburgh.

Opening for: Cancer Research UK

9 NORBY

Burnside, Sandness, Shetland ZE2 9PL
Mrs Gundel Grolimund
T: 01595 870246 E: gundel.g5@btinternet.com

A small but perfectly formed garden and a prime example of what can be achieved in a very exposed situation. Blue painted wooden pallets provide internal wind breaks and form a background for shrubs, climbers and herbaceous plants, while willows provide a perfect wildlife habitat. There are treasured plants such as *Chionochloa rubra*, pieris, Chinese tree peonies, a selection of old-fashioned shrub roses, lilies, hellebores and grasses from New Zealand. There is also a lovely selection of interesting art and textiles in the house.

Open: 1 April - 31 December, dawn – dusk, admission £4.00, children free.

Directions: Head north on the A970 from Lerwick then west on the A971 at Tingwall. At Sandness, follow the road to Norby, turn right at the Methodist Church, Burnside is at the end of the road. Bus 10 Sandness - Walls.

Opening for: Survival International

Caithness, Sutherland, Orkney & Shetland

10 **OLD GRANARY QUOY AND THE QUOY OF HOUTON**
The Quoy of Houton, Orphir, Orkney KW17 2RD
Caroline Critchlow and Colleen Batey
T: 01856 811355

Old Granary Quoy The Quoy of Houton, Orphir, Orkney KW17 2RD (Caroline Critchlow): A newly-planted and designed garden, adjacent to The Quoy of Houton. Fabulous views over Scapa Flow, ponds and a water garden. The home of Orkney perennial geraniums and an extensive range of plants suitable for this exposed coastal location. The lantern greenhouse is a new acquisition featuring an indoor fig tree. Caroline Critchlow has designed award winning gardens and is the resident gardening guru on *BBC Radio Orkney*.
The Quoy of Houton Orphir, Orkney KW17 2RD (Dr Colleen Batey): An unusual historic walled panoramic garden with 60-foot rill which leads the eye to the spectacular coastal views of Scapa Flow. Carefully planted to withstand winds in excess of 60 mph, with floral interest from March to September. Winner of *Gardeners' World* Britain's best challenging garden 2017 and listed in the top ten *UK coastal gardens*. Featured on *Beechgrove* and in the book *Island Gardens*.

Open: Sunday 2 June, 10am - 4pm. Admission £8.00, or £4.00 per garden, children free. Teas in the lantern greenhouse, bookable in advance, £10.00 per person. T: 01856 811355.

Directions: From Orphir take the turning to Houton Ferry at the first junction signed *Quoy of Houton*, turn right by the car park. Park here and walk 10 minutes along the coastal road around the bay to the gardens. Disabled access please ring to arrange as parking is very limited. The gardens are a 10-minute walk from the bus stop.

Opening for: FOTNW

11 **SKELBO HOUSE**
Skelbo, Dornoch IV25 3QG
Alison Bartlett
E: SkelboHouseGarden@gmail.com

Extensive woodland garden with spectacular views over Loch Fleet. Mixed herbaceous borders, rose garden and shrubberies surround the house. Lawns slope down to a small lochan and river walkway. Mature trees throughout. Large kitchen garden.

Open: Saturday/Sunday, 27/28 July, 11am - 4pm, admission £5.00, children free.

Directions: from the south, on the A9 take the small turning opposite the Trentham Hotel (just past the Dornoch turn-offs). At the side of Loch Fleet turn left, then at the ruined castle take the second farm road which is fairly rough, and follow round to your right. If coming from the north take the Loch Fleet road signposted to *Embo* from the A9.

Opening for: Mary's Meals

Caithness, Sutherland, Orkney & Shetland

12 THE CASTLE AND GARDENS OF MEY

Mey KW14 8XH
The Queen Elizabeth Castle of Mey Trust
T: 01847 851473 E: enquiries@castleofmey.org.uk
W: www.castleofmey.org.uk

Her Majesty Queen Elizabeth the Queen Mother, bought what was then Barrogill Castle in 1952 before renovating and restoring the z-plan castle and creating the beautiful gardens you see today; renaming it The Castle and Gardens of Mey. This romantic and unique garden is a reminder that, however daunting the weather, it is often possible with a little vision and energy to create and maintain a garden in the most unlikely of locations. The castle now includes an animal centre, gift shop and tearoom serving delicious locally sourced food and drinks, often using produce from the castle's very own gardens.

Open: 1 May - 30 September, 10:30am - 4pm, admission details can be found on the garden's website. Card and contactless payments only. The gardens are closed in late July and early August, please check the website for specific dates.

Directions: On the A836 between Thurso and John O'Groats.

Opening for: Donation to SGS Beneficiaries

The Castle & Gardens of Mey © Colin Gregory

Dumfriesshire

Sponsored by

RATHBONES

Incorporating
Investec Wealth &
Investment (UK)

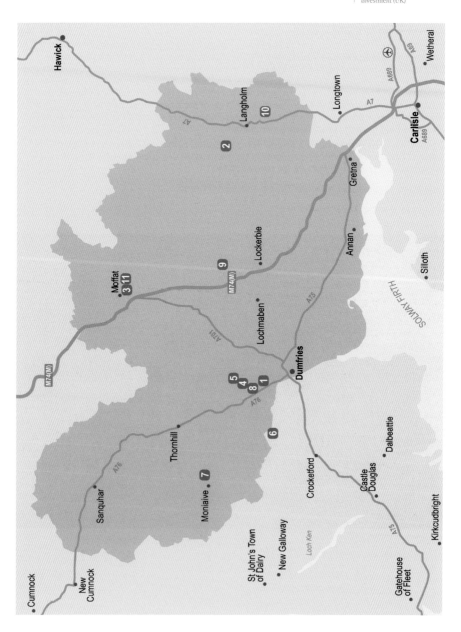

Dumfriesshire

OUR VOLUNTEER ORGANISERS

District Organiser:	Sarah Landale	Dalswinton House, Dalswinton, Auldgirth, Dumfries DG2 0XZ info@scotlandsgardens,org
Area Organisers:	Fiona Bell-Irving Pamela Crosbie Liz Mitchell	Bankside, Kettleholm, Lockerbie DG11 1BY Dalswinton Mill, Dalswinton, Dumfries DG2 0XY Drumpark, Irongray DG2 9TX
District Photographer:	Stuart Littlewood	stu@f8.eclipse.co.uk
Treasurer:	Leslie Jack	Gledenholm House, Ae, Dumfries DG1 1RF

GARDENS OPEN ON A SPECIFIC DATE

Tinnisburn Plants, Upper Millsteads, Canonbie	Saturday/Sunday, 17/18 February
Craig, Langholm	Sunday, 18 February
Tinnisburn Plants, Upper Millsteads, Canonbie	Saturday/Sunday, 23/24 March
Tinnisburn Plants, Upper Millsteads, Canonbie	Saturday/Sunday, 20/21 April
Portrack, The Garden of Cosmic Speculation, Holywood	Saturday/Sunday, 4/5 May
Dalswinton House, Dalswinton	Sunday, 12 May
Tinnisburn Plants, Upper Millsteads, Canonbie	Saturday/Sunday, 18/19 May
Cowhill Tower, Holywood	Sunday, 2 June
Waterside Garden, Moffat	Sunday, 2 June
Tinnisburn Plants, Upper Millsteads, Canonbie	Saturday/Sunday, 15/16 June
The Hewke, Lockerbie, Dumfries	Sunday, 23 June
Dalswinton Mill, Dalswinton	Sunday, 4 August
Peilton, Moniaive	Date to be confirmed

GARDENS OPEN REGULARLY

Craigieburn House, by Moffat	31 March - 31 October (not Monday)
Tinnisburn Plants, Upper Millsteads, Canonbie	1 April - 31 August (Friday, Saturday & Sunday)

GARDENS OPEN BY ARRANGEMENT

Drumpark, Irongray	1 May - 30 August
Waterside Garden, Moffat	1 May - 30 August

Dumfriesshire

1 COWHILL TOWER
Holywood DG2 0RL
Mr and Mrs P Weatherall
T: 01387 720304 E: clara@cowhill.co.uk

This is an interesting walled garden. There are topiary animals, birds and figures and beautiful woodland and river walks. Splendid views can be seen from the lawn right down the Nith Valley. There is also a variety of statues, including several from the Far East.

Open: Sunday 2 June, 2pm - 5pm, admission by donation.

Directions: Holywood is one-and-a-half miles off the A76, five miles north of Dumfries.

Opening for: Maggie's

2 CRAIG
Langholm DG13 0NZ
Mr and Mrs Neil Ewart
T: 013873 70230 E: nmlewart@googlemail.com

Craig snowdrops have evolved over the last 40 or so years. Round the house and policies, a large variety has been planted with a varied flowering season stretching from the start of January until April and peaking mid-February. Large drifts of *Leucojum vernum* (winter snowflake) have started to naturalise here and along the riverbank, a variety of snowdrops swept down by the river have naturalised in the adjacent woodland, known as the Snowdrop Walk.

Open: Sunday 18 February, noon - 4pm for Snowdrops and Winter Walks, admission £5.00, children free. Teas will be available at Bentpath Village Hall. Bentpath is one mile further on towards Eskdalemuir. Snowdrops for sale.

Directions: Craig is three miles from Langholm on the B709 towards Eskdalemuir.

Opening for: Kirkandrews Kirk Trust: The Friends of Kirkandrews Church

3 CRAIGIEBURN HOUSE
by Moffat DG10 9LF
Janet and Peter McGowan
T: 07557 928648 E: bideshi@aol.com

A beautiful and varied six-acre, plant-lovers' garden in a natural location in scenic Moffat Dale. Meconopsis, trilliums, rhododendrons, magnolias, arisaemas, bamboos, hoherias and many more types of plants flourish in the shelter of mature woodland. A Himalayan glen has been recreated with plants from the region where the Craigie Burn tumbles down a gorge with a series of waterfalls. Downstream is a fern garden with over 70 varieties. Candelabra primulas, rodgersias, cardiocrinum, orchids and other rare plants thrive in the bog garden and woodland glades. Double herbaceous borders come into their own later in the summer and keep the display going throughout the season. Other garden areas include a rose garden, formal pond and autumn garden. A nursery sells hardy plants propagated on site, many of them rare or unusual. The garden has been created over the past 30 years by Janet and Peter, with Dawa Sherpa, building on its old setting, and continues to evolve. Its links to Robert Burns – including his song 'Craigieburn Wood' – provide another layer of history.

Open: The garden is open to visitors from Easter, Sunday 31 March to 31 October, 10.30am - 6pm (every day except Mondays, but open on Bank Holidays). Many of the special plants in the garden may be purchased at the nursery area.

Dumfriesshire

Directions: Three miles from the A74(M) junction 15, two miles east of Moffat on the A708 Selkirk Road. Coming from Moffat, there are traffic lights straight ahead at the end of the bend. You can't miss the lodge and prayer flags.

Opening for: All proceeds to SGS Beneficiaries

 ### 4 DALSWINTON HOUSE
Dalswinton DG2 0XZ
Mr and Mrs Peter Landale
T: 01387 740220 E: sarahlandale@gmail.com

Late 18th-century house sits on top of a hill surrounded by herbaceous beds and well-established shrubs, including rhododendrons and azaleas, overlooking the loch. Attractive walks through woods and around the loch. It was here that the first steamboat in Britain made its maiden voyage in 1788 and there is a life-size model beside the water to commemorate this. Over the past years, there has been much clearing and development work around the loch, which has opened up the views considerably.

Open: Sunday 12 May, 12noon - 5pm, admission £5.00, children free. Homemade teas will be available from 2 - 5pm. Picnics are allowed in the Walled Garden, around the loch and on the lawns up by the House.

Directions: Take the A76 north from Dumfries to Thornhill. After seven miles, turn right to Dalswinton. Drive through Dalswinton village, past the red church on the right and follow estate wall on the right. Entrance is by either the single lodge or double lodge entrance set in the wall.

Opening for: Kirkmahoe Parish Church of Scotland

Dalswinton House © Stuart Littlewood

Dumfriesshire

5 DALSWINTON MILL

Dalswinton DG2 0XY
Colin and Pamela Crosbie
T: 01387 740070 E: colincrosbiehort@btinternet.com

A newly-created, plantsman's garden set around an 18th-century watermill with the Pennyland Burn running through it. The garden contains a wide range of perennials, trees and shrubs that favour the local climate and have been planted during the last few years. A variety of statuary can be found throughout the garden which sits in a hollow and can be only accessed by steps and there are slopes throughout the garden. Unfortunately, this makes the garden unsuitable for anyone with mobility requirements.

Open: Sunday 4 August, 2pm - 6pm, admission £5.00, children free.

Directions: Garden lies in Dalswinton, halfway between the A76 and the A701 on the Auldgirth to Kirkton Road. From Auldgirth take the first left after the Dalswinton Village Hall. The Mill is on the corner before the bridge. We are unable to offer disabled parking.

Opening for: IFDAS : River Garden Auchincruive

Dalswinton Mill

Dumfriesshire

6 DRUMPARK

Irongray DG2 9TX
Mr and Mrs Iain Mitchell
T: 01387 820323 or 07743 895351 E: iain.liz.mitchell@gmail.com

Well-contoured woodland garden and extensive policies nurture mature azaleas, rhododendrons and rare shrubs among impressive specimen trees. Water garden with primulas and meconopsis. Victorian walled garden with fruit trees and garden produce. There is also a beautiful herbaceous border. All planting is set in a natural bowl providing attractive vistas.

Champion Trees: *Abies cephalonica, Abies procera, Chamaecyparis lawsoniana, Cryptomeria japonica*.

Open: by arrangement 1 May - 30 August, admission by donation.

Directions: Dumfries bypass, head north on the A76 for a half mile, turn left at the signpost to *Lochside Industrial Estates* and immediately right onto Irongray Road; continue for five miles; gates in sandstone wall on left (half-mile after Routin' Brig).

Opening for: Loch Arthur

Drumpark © Stuart Littlewood

Dumfriesshire

 PEILTON
Moniaive DG3 4HE
Mrs A Graham
T: 01848 200363 E: amgatpeilton@gmail.com

This really very special and attractive woodland garden has a great variety of interesting rhododendrons, shrubs and flowering trees. It has been developed over many years and is of particular interest for the real plantsman.

Open: Please watch the SGS website for details of the opening dates. We are going to open when the garden is looking its best. This will be for a week in May or early June and teas will be available. Peilton is near the village of Moniaive with a number of good cafes and restaurants.

Directions: Off A702 between Kirkland of Glencairn and Moniaive.

Opening for: All proceeds to SGS Beneficiaries

 PORTRACK, THE GARDEN OF COSMIC SPECULATION
Holywood DG2 0RW
John Jencks

Forty major areas, gardens, bridges, landforms, sculpture, terraces, fences and architectural works. Covering 30 acres, The Garden of Cosmic Speculation, designed by the late Charles Jencks, uses nature to celebrate nature, both intellectually and through the senses, including the sense of humour.

Open: Saturday 4th and Sunday 5th May. Strictly by advance ticket only and tickets will go on sale via the Scotland's Gardens Scheme website in February 2024. Admission price and all details to be confirmed.

Directions: Portrack is one-and-a-half miles off the A76, five miles north of Dumfries.

Opening for: Maggie's

 THE HEWKE
Lockerbie, Dumfries DG11 2JY
Mr and Mrs Colin Endacott
T: 01576 610354 E: Diannepaula@hotmail.co.uk

A gently sloping garden with views across the Dryfe Valley. The approach is from the parking area through the Rock Garden towards a converted byre. The back wall features roses and a wisteria. A greenhouse is attached to the principal house, built in 1806. Continue past domestic ancillary accommodation (former coach house, stables and dovecote). You enter a courtyard abutting a former gig house to reach the walled garden which is split on two levels. The lower section features a vegetable garden and fruit bushes, whilst the upper section with bothy, displays roses and shrubs. This exits to a small woodland containing mature trees. Throughout the garden is a collection of copper beech trees and hedges, green beech hedges, rhododenrons, azaleas and fruit trees.
Champion Trees: Tulip and Walnut.

Open: Sunday 23 June, 2pm - 5pm, admission £5.00, children free.

Dumfriesshire

Directions: Take B7076 north from Lockerbie and after 2 miles, join B723 signposted to Boreland and Eskdalemuir. Continue past junction for Sibbaldbie and after 500 yards, just before road bears right, cross small stone bridge on the right.

Opening for: Epilepsy Scotland

---

 10 TINNISBURN PLANTS
Upper Millsteads, Canonbie DG14 0RY
Helen Knowles
T: 07544 373815 E: helen@tinnisburn.co.uk
W: tinnisburn.co.uk

Developed over the last 37 years, this one-acre plantsman's garden is home to an eclectic mix of truly hardy perennials, trees and shrubs. Planted for year-round colour and interest and to provide habitats for wildlife, there is something new to see each month. There is a woodland garden, rockery, bog garden, herbaceous borders and much more. Meconopsis grow well here and more are being planted out every year. In addition to the garden, there is a small orchard, wildlife ponds and mown paths through the wildflower meadows and, if you're lucky, you may spot red squirrels.
National Plant Collection: *Scilla (Chionodoxa)*.

Open: Saturday/Sunday, 17/18 February, 10am - 3pm for Snowdrops and Winter Walks. **(Advance booking essential for snowdrops.** Timeslots available each day: 10am to 12.30pm and 12.30pm to 3pm. **Please visit the SGS website to book).** Then open Saturday/Sunday, 23/24 March, 10am - 4pm for Scilla National Plant Collection. Open Saturday/Sunday, 20/21 April, 10am - 4pm for Daffodils. Open Saturday/Sunday, 18/19 May, 10am - 4pm for Meconopsis. Open Saturday/Sunday, 15/16 June, 10am - 4pm for Meconopsis and Primula. Open regularly 1 April - 31 August (Friday, Saturday & Sunday), 10am - 4pm. Admission £5.00, children free.

Directions: Take the B6357 north from Canonbie. At Harelaw turn left onto the B6318 and after 1 mile turn right onto our track. It is 1.5 miles long and is untarmacked but suitable for all vehicles. Just drive slowly and carefully.

Opening for: Macmillan Cancer Support & Fauna & Flora International

---

 11 WATERSIDE GARDEN
Moffat DG10 9LF
Ronnie Cann
T: 07714230235 E: rtdcann@gmail.com
W: holestone.net

Set in beautiful Moffatdale and bounded on one side by the Moffat Water, Waterside Garden is a plantsman's delight, home to woods, riverside walks and three acres of cultivated garden. There are many mature trees including oak, birch, beech and much more. Collections of species and hybrid rhododendrons and azaleas, bamboos and other flowering shrubs give year-round interest. There are herbaceous beds, giving colour in spring and summer, alpines, mixed plantings, spring bulbs, especially daffodils, and wildflower meadows.

Open: Sunday 2 June, 2pm - 5pm. Also open by arrangement 1 May - 30 August. Admission £5.00, children free. **Booking in advance essential for 2 June as parking is limited. Please visit the SGS website to book.**

Directions: Three miles north of Moffat on the A708 opposite Craigieburn Forest Car Park. From Selkirk the garden is about 14.5 miles south of St Mary's Loch.

Opening for: Moffat Water Hall

Dunbartonshire

Sponsored by

RATHBONES

Incorporating
Investec Wealth &
Investment (UK)

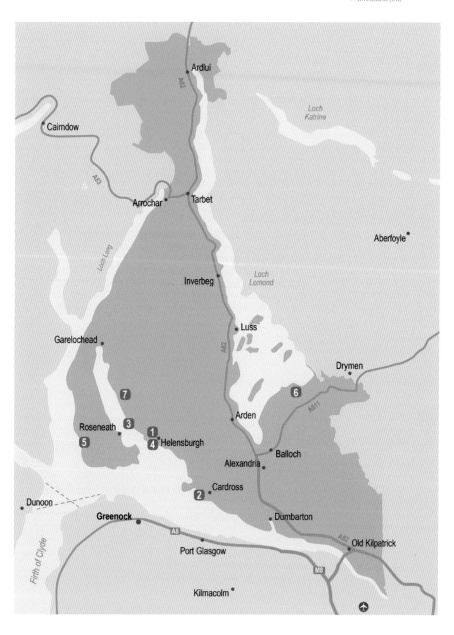

Dunbartonshire

OUR VOLUNTEER ORGANISERS

District Organiser:	Tricia Stewart	High Glenan, 24a Queen Street G84 9LG info@scotlandsgardens.org
Area Organisers:	Jim and Adrienne Kerr	Stonecroft, Ardenconnel Way, Rhu G84 8RZ
	Kathleen Murray	4 Cairndhu Gardens, Helensburgh G84 8PG
	Lesley and Norman Quirk	Glenard, Upper Torwoodhill Road, Rhu G84 8LE
Treasurer:	Claire Travis	54 Union Street, Alexandria G83 9AH

GARDENS OPEN ON A SPECIFIC DATE

Stuckenduff, Shore Road, Shandon	Sunday, 25 February
Ross Priory, Gartocharn	Sunday, 19 May
Geilston Garden, Main Road, Cardross	Sunday, 2 June
Brantwoode and High Glenan, 24a Queen Street, Helensburgh	Sunday, 23 June
James Street Community Garden Plant Sale, Helensburgh	Sunday, 1 September
Linn Botanic Gardens	Date to be confirmed

GARDENS OPEN REGULARLY

Glenarn, Glenarn Road, Rhu, Helensburgh	21 March - 21 September

Dunbartonshire

1

BRANTWOODE AND HIGH GLENAN
24a Queen Street, Helensburgh G84 9LG
Tricia and Tom Stewart, David W Henderson

Brantwoode (NEW) Munro Drive West, Helensburgh G84 9AA (David W Henderson): Brantwoode is a mix of informal and formal areas, chosen to complement the 1895 Arts & Crafts house. The south-facing front garden is beautifully terraced on three levels in red sandstone with a central lavender path dividing the main lawns. The top terrace is mainly perennials and small shrubs flanked by rambling roses. There is a shrubbery on the west side of the garden with rhododendrons, azaleas and acers while on the east side there is a woodland path with camellias, hydrangeas, magnolias and two large rhododendron trees. There are also several mature conifers. The lower terrace, sheltered by a beech hedge, has shrubs and many outstanding specimen trees, providing year-round interest. There is also a rockery with two small wildlife ponds. To the rear of the house is the formal rose garden with many scented and repeat-flowering roses backed by clematis and wisteria on the high sandstone wall. There is also a working area and small fruit garden.

High Glenan Helensburgh G84 9LG (Tom and Tricia Stewart): A secluded garden with burn and waterside plants, gravel garden, herb and herbaceous borders and kitchen garden with a selection of fruit and vegetables. Extensive programme of hard landscaping has been undertaken over the last ten years.

Open: Sunday 23 June, 2pm - 5pm, admission £6.00, children free.

Directions: Brantwoode is the middle house behind Helensburgh Upper Station. Parking either in W. Lennox Drive or Rossdhu Drive. **High Glenan** is approximately ½ mile along Queen Street from its junction with Sinclair Street on the right hand side.

Opening for: Rhu and Shandon Parish Church of Scotland: Tower Appeal & The Woodland Trust Scotland

2

GEILSTON GARDEN
Main Road, Cardross G82 5HD
The National Trust for Scotland
T: 01389 849187 E: geilstongarden@nts.org.uk
W: www.nts.org.uk/visit/places/Geilston-Garden/

Geilston Garden has many attractive features including the walled garden with herbaceous border providing summer colour, tranquil woodland walks and a large working kitchen garden. This is the ideal season for viewing the Siberian iris in flower along the Geilston Burn and the Japanese azaleas.

Open: Sunday 2 June, 2pm - 5pm. Normal NTS garden admission rates apply, see NTS website for details. Last entry to the garden is at 4pm. Garden open until 5pm. Plant sale and homemade teas will be served.

Directions: On the A814, one mile from Cardross towards Helensburgh.

Opening for: Donation to SGS Beneficiaries

Dunbartonshire

Geilston © NTS

3 GLENARN

Glenarn Road, Rhu, Helensburgh G84 8LL
Michael and Sue Thornley
T: 01436 820493 E: masthome@btinternet.com
W: www.glenarn.com

Glenarn survives as a complete example of a ten-acre garden which spans from 1850 to the present day. There are winding paths through miniature glens under a canopy of oaks and limes, sunlit open spaces, a vegetable garden with beehives, and a rock garden full of surprise and season-long colour. The famous collections of rare and tender rhododendrons and magnolias give way in midsummer to roses rambling through the trees and climbing hydrangeas, followed by the starry white flowers of hoherias and eucryphias to the end of the season. There is a Silent Space at the top of the garden with views over the Gareloch. Champion Trees: Notably *Magnolia rostrata*.

Open: 21 March - 21 September, dawn - dusk, admission £6.00, children under 16 free. Season Ticket £20. There may be local plants for sale.

Directions: On the A814, two miles north of Helensburgh, up Pier Road. Cars to be left at the gate unless passengers have limited mobility.

Opening for: Rhu and Shandon Parish Church of Scotland: Tower Appeal

Dunbartonshire

4 JAMES STREET COMMUNITY GARDEN PLANT SALE

James Street, Helensburgh G84 8XD

The Gardeners of James Street

Developed from a derelict children's playground, the Community Garden is a relaxed area for contemplation with mixed herbaceous beds, maze and young trees. The plant sale will include a wide selection of perennials and locally grown trees, shrubs, herbaceous, alpine and house plants.

Open: Sunday 1 September, noon - 3pm, admission by donation.

Directions: Travel west along Princes Street from Sinclair Street through Colquhoun Square, turn right up James Street and the Community Garden is on the left. Park on the street.

Opening for: James Street Community Garden

5 LINN BOTANIC GARDENS

Cove, By Helensburgh G84 0NR

Matthew Young

The Linn Botanic Gardens used to be one of the only privately owned gardens to be accredited as a botanical garden, under the stewardship of its creators, Jim and Jamie Taggart. Sadly Jamie died on a plant-hunting expedition to Vietnam in 2013, and Jim's failing health and old age limited the care he could take of the place from that point onwards. He himself then passed away in 2019, at which point the garden was closed and was not maintained at all until 2021 when it was purchased by the current owners.

Since then extensive work has been taking place to renovate and reopen the gardens, and to rebuild the disintegrating villa at their heart. It is still very much a work in progress, but large parts of the old plant collection remain intact. You are invited to explore what has been restored and to discuss the plans to complete the repair work and then further develop the garden in the future, but please do bear in mind that it is a long way from being the finished article just yet.

Open: Dates to be confirmed. **Booking essential.** Please visit the SGS website for details.

Directions: From Helensburgh, head North to Garelochhead. Go through Garelochhead and turn left on the B833, towards Rosneath and Kilcreggan. Drive around the whole peninsula, through both those villages until you reach Cove. Past Cove Country Store and Cove Burgh Hall you will see Cove picnic area by the shore on your left, which is the only public parking facility. From there, walk up the wee lane along the burn, between the two garden walls and we are 20 metres along on the left. Alternative you can take the 316 bus to Coulport from Colquhoun Square in Helensburgh and ask the driver to let you off at Cove picnic area.

Opening for: Scottish Refugee Council

Dunbartonshire

Linn Botanic Gardens

 6 ## ROSS PRIORY
Gartocharn G83 8NL
University of Strathclyde

Mansion house with glorious views over Loch Lomond with adjoining garden. Wonderful rhododendrons and azaleas are the principal plants in the garden, with a varied selection of trees and shrubs throughout. Spectacular spring bulbs, border plantings of herbaceous perennials, shrubs and trees. Extensive walled garden with glasshouses, pergola and ornamental plantings. Children's play area and putting green beside the house.

Open: Sunday 19 May, 2pm - 5pm, admission £5.00, children free.

Directions: Ross Priory is one and a half miles off the A811 at Gartocharn. Bus from Balloch to Gartocharn.

Opening for: Friends Of Loch Lomond & The Trossachs & Loch Lomond Rescue Boat

 7 ## STUCKENDUFF
Shore Road, Shandon G84 8NW
Colin & Louise Burnet

Stuckenduff is a three-and-a-half acre garden overlooking the Gareloch with mature trees, rhododendrons, azaleas, mixed borders and a magical carpet of bluebells in May. The garden was partially re-landscaped in 2001 when a tennis court was laid alongside the original old walls. The annual snowdrop display spreads from January to March and is a treat to behold for any galanthophile.

Open: Sunday 25 February, 2pm - 5pm for Snowdrops and Winter Walks, admission £5.00, children free. Live music will be performed during the afternoon.

Directions: Stuckenduff is on Shore Road, off the A814, take the Kings Point/Queens Point exit then turn sharply left onto the slip road. Entrance is opposite the post box.

Opening for: Muscular Dystrophy UK: Georgie's Genes & Ellen MacArthur Cancer Trust

East Lothian

Sponsored by

RATHBONES

Incorporating
Investec Wealth &
Investment (UK)

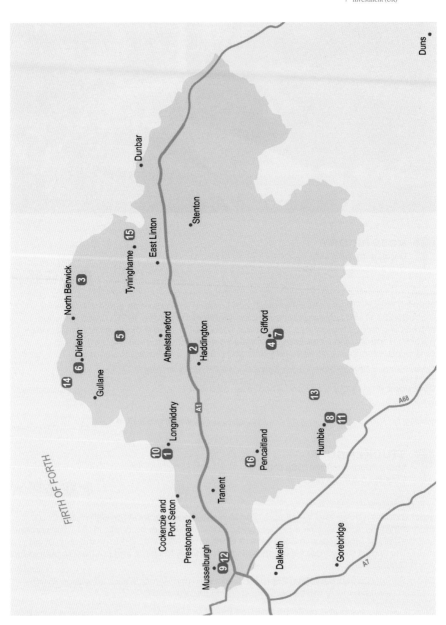

East Lothian

OUR VOLUNTEER ORGANISERS

District Organiser: Joan Johnson   eastlothian@scotlandsgardens.org

Area Organisers: Jane Craiglee
                      Frank Kirwan
                      Claire Turnbull

District Photographers: Delia Ridley-Thomas
                         Malcolm Ross

Treasurer: Colin Wilson

GARDENS OPEN ON A SPECIFIC DATE

Shepherd House, Inveresk, Musselburgh	Sunday 18 February
Humbie Dean, Humbie	Wednesday, 20 March
A Blackbird Sings, 20 Kings Park, Longniddry	Saturday, 13 April
Winton Castle, Pencaitland	Sunday, 14 April
Humbie Dean, Humbie	Wednesday, 17 April
Tyninghame House and The Walled Garden, Dunbar	Sunday, 12 May
Humbie Dean, Humbie	Wednesday, 15 May
Longwood, Humbie	Wednesday, 15 May
A Blackbird Sings, 20 Kings Park, Longniddry	Saturday, 18 May
Broadwoodside, Gifford	Sunday, 19 May
Shepherd House, Inveresk, Musselburgh	Sunday, 19 May
Blackdykes Garden, Blackdykes Farmhouse, North Berwick	Friday/Saturday, 7/8 June
Dirleton Village, Dirleton	Saturday/Sunday, 8/9 June
Humbie Dean, Humbie	Wednesday, 12 June
Inveresk Village, Inveresk, Musselburgh	Saturday/Sunday, 15/16 June
Blackdykes Garden, Blackdykes Farmhouse, North Berwick	Thursday/Friday, 20/21 June
Congalton House, North Berwick	Friday, 21 June
Longniddry Gardens, Longniddry	Sunday, 23 June
Tyninghame House and The Walled Garden, Dunbar	Sunday, 23 June
Gifford Bank, Gifford	Saturday/Sunday, 29/30 June
A Blackbird Sings, 20 Kings Park, Longniddry	Saturday, 13 July
Humbie Dean, Humbie	Wednesday, 17 July
The Gardens at Archerfield Walled Garden, Dirleton	Sunday, 11 August
Humbie Dean, Humbie	Wednesday, 14 August
Longwood, Humbie	Wednesday, 14 August
A Blackbird Sings, 20 Kings Park, Longniddry	Saturday, 17 August
Amisfield Walled Garden, Haddington	Saturday/Sunday, 24/25 August
Humbie Dean, Humbie	Wednesday, 2 October

East Lothian

GARDENS OPEN REGULARLY

Shepherd House, Inveresk, Musselburgh

6 - 29 February (Tues & Thurs) &
16 April - 25 July (Tues & Thurs)

Stobshiel House, Humbie

3 April - 25 September (Wed only)

GARDENS OPEN BY ARRANGEMENT

Stobshiel House, Humbie (Groups only)

3 April - 25 September

A Blackbird Sings, 20 Kings Park, Longniddry (Groups only)

15 April - 17 September

Inveresk Village Eco House

East Lothian

 A BLACKBIRD SINGS
20 Kings Park, Longniddry EH32 0QL
Graham and Maxine Pettigrew
T: 01875 853003

Situated in the Glassel Park Estate, the planting of this long garden reflects East Lothian habitats including heather moorland, grassland and woodland as well as areas of related plant types such as rockery, roses, ferns and peonies. Together they form a pattern of gardens within a garden. A large water lily pond houses newts and a second pond within a rockery is fed by a waterfall. A cold conservatory contains cacti and insectivorous plants. Vertical structure is provided by a large number of specimen small trees such as cornus, maples, magnolias, contorted robinia, Chinese rowan and honey locust. Animal and bird carvings in wood reflect the local fauna.

Open: Saturday 13 April, Saturday 18 May, Saturday 13 July & Saturday 17 August, 1pm - 5pm. Also open with Longniddry Gardens on Sunday 23rd June 1-5pm. Also open to groups by arrangement from 15 April to 17 September. Please call 01875 853003.

Directions: By car: enter Dean Road from A198, right at Kings Avenue, right at Kings Park. By bus (124): Old Dean Road stop, down Old Dean Road, right at Kings Avenue, right at Kings Park.

Opening for: Scottish Wildlife Trust Ltd & Leuchie

 AMISFIELD WALLED GARDEN
Haddington EH41 3TE
Amisfield Preservation Trust
W: www.amisfield.org.uk

A large 18th-century walled garden, abandoned for many years until around 15 years ago and since transformed. The garden, which has an area of approximately eight acres, is completely enclosed by 16 foot high walls of dressed stone. Each corner features an elegant stone pavilion. Over the years, herbaceous borders, vegetable plots and fruit trees have been planted and new paths laid. A hornbeam walk, maze, sensory gardens and potager have been added. Apple trees were planted on the diagonal pathways and small orchards have been introduced. Willow beds surround the Winter Garden. A wildflower meadow and pond have been introduced as a further step in our biodiversity plan. A garden of interest and joy all year round.

Open: Saturday/Sunday, 24/25 August, 11am - 3pm, admission £6.00, children free. Teas, flowers, garden produce, history talks, nature-based children's activities.

Directions: Take the A199 from Haddington; turn south one mile east of Haddington at Stevenson/Hailes Castle junction – brown *Amisfield Walled* garden sign. Turn right just after bridge over River Tyne. Parking available.

Opening for: Amisfield Preservation Trust

East Lothian

3 **BLACKDYKES GARDEN**
Blackdykes Farmhouse, North Berwick, East Lothian EH39 5PQ
Sir How & Lady Dalrymple

Blackdykes Garden was created 30 years ago from open fields. The three-acre site has extensive views southwards towards the Lammermuirs. The formal heart of the garden consists of a series of rooms hemmed in by stone walls and clipped hedges of yew, beech and hornbeam. These are planted with roses, irises, climbers and perennials. Surrounding the formal garden is a network of mown grass paths and avenues, fringed with species roses, ornamental trees, shrubs and topiary. There is also a vegetable garden with sweet pea trellises and soft fruit.

Open: Friday/Saturday, 7/8 June & Thursday/Friday, 20/21 June, 10am - 5pm, admission £6.00, children free.

Directions: Leave North Berwick on the A198 towards Dunbar. Half a mile after Tesco, turn right at Rhodes Holdings. After one mile you will arrive at Blackdykes.

Opening for: Leuchie

Blackdykes garden © Huw Dalrymple

4 **BROADWOODSIDE**
Gifford EH41 4JQ
Anna and Robert Dalrymple
W: www.broadwoodside.com

'Broadwoodside is a remarkable achievement. It is a country house that is both memorable and noteworthy, without ever falling into the trap of architectural pretension. That is perhaps because the humble origins of the steading still shine through the transformation to lend texture and interest to the buildings. No less remarkable is the way that the house graduates into the garden and the garden into the landscape. This is a house that feels not merely at home in its setting, but born from it. Finally, there is the delight of the place, enlivened with colour, inscriptions and beautiful things. If Arcadia possessed a country house, surely this would be it.' *Country Life, 2023.*

Open: Sunday 19 May, 11am - 5pm, admission £7.00, children free. Supporting Leuchie House National Respite Centre.

Directions: On the B6355 going out of Gifford towards Pencaitland, at the Golf Course junction.

Opening for: Leuchie

East Lothian

5 CONGALTON HOUSE
North Berwick EH39 5JL
Clare and John Carson

. . . .

The garden, which surrounds a stone-built Victorian house, is an attractive family garden with a wide variety of plants and good colour throughout the summer months. It has a number of mature trees and herbaceous borders, most of which have been planted over the last 20 years (this is since we have had a full-time, trained gardener, Bruce Rankine). Other attractions include rose beds and peonies, usually at their best in June, a sunken garden and a rockery. The woodland garden, which was planted about 15 years ago, is now beginning to mature.

Open: Friday 21 June, 11am - 5pm, admission £6.00, children free.

Directions: On the B1347 between Haddington and North Berwick.

Opening for: Camphill (Blair Drummond) Trust Limited

6 DIRLETON VILLAGE
Dirleton EH39 5EH
The Gardeners of Dirleton & Historic Scotland

. . . .

Dirleton is widely recognised as one of Scotland's prettiest conservation villages. Its traditional houses are clustered around the extensive village green, medieval castle dating from the 13th century, and the 400-year-old parish church. Expect the village to be a blaze of colour on the opening weekend, when up to 15 of its gardens will be open to the public for charity. These are scattered throughout the village, each within a short walking distance of the village green, where ample free parking is available. The gardens can all be visited on a single ticket. They are very different in size and style and you will find that their owners love to share their knowledge and answer questions. Compact gardens around the village centre contrast with larger ones on Chapelhill, which provide extensive views south over the surrounding countryside. Your ticket will also admit you to the castle gardens. These contain an impressive formal parterre and a herbaceous border extending to over 200 yards in length, claimed to be one of the longest such borders in the world. Dirleton Village Association is a conservation charity.

Open: Saturday/Sunday, 8/9 June, 2pm - 5:30pm, admission £7.00, children free. Parking, tickets and village map are available at the Green. Delicious teas will be served in the church hall by RNLI supporters and church helpers.

Directions: By car – two miles west of North Berwick off the A198. By public transport – East Coast buses X5 and 124 from Edinburgh.

Opening for: Dirleton Village Association & RNLI

East Lothian

7 GIFFORD BANK
Gifford EH41 4JE
Mr and Mrs Austin

Gifford Bank is a Georgian house set in four acres on the edge of the village. Lawns to the front and side of the house are edged by woodland whilst a walled garden provides a more formal area. The four quadrants of the walled garden include a circular lawn area, raised beds for soft fruit, a herb and rose garden and an orchard. There are large herbaceous borders on all four sides. Beautiful scented roses grow over six arches that connect the gravel path. The garden to the rear of the house includes water features and a large fire bowl planter. This year we are supporting Gifford Village Hall (known as Gifford Community Association).

Open: Saturday/Sunday, 29/30 June, 1pm - 5pm, admission £7.00, children free.

Directions: When leaving Gifford on the B6355 Edinburgh Road, Gifford Bank is the last property on the right before the de-restriction signs. Regular Gifford Circle bus service from Haddington.

Opening for: Gifford Community Association

Gifford Bank   Inveresk village

East Lothian

8 HUMBIE DEAN
Humbie EH36 5PW
Frank Kirwan
E: frank.kirwan@gmail.com

A two-acre ornamental and wooded garden on a variety of levels, sandwiched between two burns at 600 feet, planted for interest throughout the season. A limited palette of plants with hosta, hellebores, perennial geraniums, primula, meconopsis, martagon lilies, clematis, spring bulbs, ground cover, herbaceous and shrub planting, bluebell meadow, mature and recent azalea and rhododendron planting. The lower sections of the garden are only accessible by a series of steps.

Open: Wednesday 20 March, Wednesday 17 April, Wednesday 15 May, Wednesday 12 June, Wednesday 17 July, Wednesday 14 August & Wednesday 2 October, 10:30am - 4pm, admission £6.00, children free.

Directions: Enter Humbie from the A68, pass the school and the village hall on the left then immediately turn right just before the Humbie Hub. Take the second left and Humbie Dean is on the left between two small bridges. Limited parking. Find using what3words: shorthand. frog.limbs

Opening for: Mamie Martin Fund

9 INVERESK VILLAGE
Inveresk, Musselburgh EH21 7TE
The Gardeners of Inveresk

This year we will present a new garden, a neat garden attached to the redeveloped 1862 Inveresk Combination Poorhouse and a much-visited garden in the past which has re-joined the Open event. These are in addition to previously opened gardens which include a television star, one complementing an eco house, one large tiered garden and one garden surrounding the house of the previous area coal mine manager. The National Trust for Scotland property, Inveresk Lodge Garden, has great potential for children with pond dipping an ever-popular pursuit at this venue. Musselburgh's highly-rated allotments will also be open within the circular trail which passes a very interesting topiary hedge outside a cottage in Double Dykes. The mix of large and small gardens, some of which are wrapped round by high stone walls and others more exposed to the wind and relatively dry climate, will offer visitors many ideas to think over when they return home. The Romans recognised the quality of the soil in this area when they settled here during the Antonine era between 140 and 165 AD and some of the land may well have been in continuous cultivation since then.

Open: Saturday/Sunday, 15/16 June, 2pm - 5pm, admission £8.00, children free. **Tickets sold at Inveresk Lodge Garden.** Inveresk Village invites keen gardeners everywhere to enjoy the beauty of domestic gardens, allotments and a National Trust Property. To tempt you further there will be hot and cold refreshments, baked goods, and ice cream from Luca's. Alex Thompson will play relaxing keyboard music on both afternoons. The village gardens are open over two days for the second time. Enthusiasts can visit on both days if they retain their village map and a sticky badge.

Directions: Southside of Musselburgh on the A6124. The 140 bus stops in the village. Spreading visits over two days has been integral in preventing dangerous parking congestion. It is essential that able-bodied people who arrive by car **do not park on the main A6124** road running through the village as this impedes smooth emergency vehicle movements.

Opening for: St.Columba's Hospice Care

East Lothian

10 LONGNIDDRY GARDENS
Longniddry EH32 OLF
The Gardeners of Longniddry

Longniddry is an attractive village with extensive green spaces, popular beaches and outstanding sea views. Our gardens are tended by enthusiastic gardeners some of whom are old hands and some recent converts to gardening – all will be delighted to discuss their gardens with visitors. The gardens exhibit a variety of size, layout and planting, ensuring something for everyone. One of the smaller gardens is modern and shows what can be achieved with attractive and innovative hard landscaping. Another small addition is a very young 'urban woodland' garden designed over the past few years with most plants either freebies or sale bargains. Larger gardens include new and mature trees and herbaceous planting ranging from self-seeding cottage style to the more formal, with some now influenced by the modern concept of rewilding. There are veggie plots, potagers, containers of all sorts and ponds. Outbuildings range from working greenhouses to summer houses and gazebos. There's lots to see and enjoy so please join us!

Open: Sunday 23 June, 1pm - 5pm, admission £8.00, children free. **Cash only for admission £8.00. Teas and plants – all paid separately.** Tickets and maps will be available at the three gardens nearest the entrances to Longniddry. These gardens will be well signposted.

Directions: On the A198 from North Berwick (east) or Edinburgh (west). Access also from the B1348 (the coast road from Port Seton/Cockenzie) and the B1377 (from Drem). Longniddry is also on the North Berwick train line from Edinburgh Waverley and bus route 124 from Princes Street, Edinburgh.

Opening for: Parkinsons UK & Blood Bikes Scotland

11 LONGWOOD
Humbie EH36 5PN
Linda Flockhart and Sandra Gentle

An extensive, long-established country garden at 800 feet, undergoing renewal. There are ducks and hens, stream and ponds as well as areas of wild garden and borders including roses, vegetables, lawns and woodlands. Stunning views over the Forth.

Open: Wednesdays 15 May and 14 August, 10.30am - 4pm. Admission £5.00, children free.

Directions: From the B6368 (Humbie to Haddington road) about one mile east of Humbie take the direction south to *Blegbie Farm* (signposted). Follow the road for circa two miles, passing Humbie Mains Farm as you go. You will find Blegbie Farm at a hard right-hand bend. The drive for Longwood will be straight in front of you, right beside Blegbie. Go straight up the drive and park at the bottom of the cottages. Do not turn right or left.

Opening for: Médecins Sans Frontières

East Lothian

 12 **SHEPHERD HOUSE**
Inveresk, Musselburgh EH21 7TH
Sir Charles and Lady Fraser
T: 0131 665 2570 E: ann.shepherdhouse@gmail.com
W: www.shepherdhousegarden.co.uk

A constantly evolving artist's garden that never stands still, with lots of surprises including a shell house built in 2014, rose parterres, a rill and fountains. At its heart are the plants filling every border, spilling over arches and lining paths, which are the inspiration for Ann's paintings. The season starts with the snowdrop collection of over 70 cultivars, moves on through hellebores, tulips, irises and roses. One of the garden's features is a mirror steel diamond sculpture to commemorate the Frasers' diamond wedding anniversary and 60 years in this garden.

Open: Tuesdays and Thursdays, 2 – 4pm from 6 - 29 February, and Sunday 18 February, 11am - 4pm for Snowdrops. Then open on Tuesdays and Thursdays, 2 – 4pm from 16 April - 25 July, and Sunday 19 May, 11am - 4pm. Admission £6.00, children free.

Directions: The garden is near Musselburgh. From the A1 take the A6094 exit signposted *Wallyford and Dalkeith* and follow signs to *Inveresk*.

Opening for: Trees For Life

 13 **STOBSHIEL HOUSE**
Humbie EH36 5PD
Mr Maxwell and Lady Sarah Ward
T: 01875 833646 E: stobshiel@gmail.com

The garden at Stobshiel House is effectively split into four main parts viz., the walled garden, the shrubbery, the pond and lawns and the woodland areas. Each area is laid out and planted to provide the visitor with all year round interest from swathes of aconites, snowdrops, narcissi in spring to a vast array of perennials, roses, clematis and annuals throughout summer and autumn. The extensive collection of shrubs and mature trees offer a fantastic backdrop during all seasons.

Open: 3 April - 25 September (Wednesdays only), 9:30am - 3pm. **Groups by arrangement: stobshiel@gmail.com**. Admission £6.00, children free. Teas, coffee, lunch and home baking are available at the Humbie Hub.

Directions: On the B6368 Haddington/Humbie road; sign to *Stobshiel* one mile. Find using what3words: jumbo.hides.blogs

Opening for: Fostering Compassion, SCIO

East Lothian

14   ## THE GARDENS AT ARCHERFIELD WALLED GARDEN
Archerfield Estate, Dirleton, EH39 5HQ
Kerry Lyall, Head Gardener
W: www.archerfieldwalledgarden.com

Our walled gardens, developed over the last eight years, comprise a series of themed spaces designed to provide year-round interest. Explore our perennial meadow with swaying grasses and fruit trees; our two cutting gardens of fresh blooms and grasses and seed heads for drying. See our artist-in-residence's beautiful botanical casts. We have incredible edibles in the potager; a productive polytunnel full of tender crops; light and dark borders with plants selected for their foliage, colour and textural qualities and a wildlife area with willow tunnels, a stumpery and lily pond. Do come and wander, sit, observe and enjoy. There is so much to see!

Open: Sunday 11 August, 10am - 5pm, admission £5.00, children free. Children's activities from 10am to 12pm: Mini-beast trail (free) and Fairy Garden workshop (drop-in £3). Garden tours at 1.45pm and 3pm. Homemade teas and garden produce stall all using produce from the garden. Botanical casting exhibition.

Directions: By bus East Coast Buses no 124 from Edinburgh. Bus stops (2nd stop) after Gullane, at entrance to Archerfield Estate then a 10 min walk to Archerfield Walled Garden.
By car via the A198 East Lothian coast road, turn in to Archerfield Estate, one minute drive to car park at Archerfield Walled Garden. Or refer to our website.

Opening for: Stepping Out Project

The Gardens at Archerfield Walled Garden © Delia Ridley-Thomas

East Lothian

 15 ## TYNINGHAME HOUSE AND THE WALLED GARDEN
Tyninghame House, Dunbar EH42 1XW
Mrs C Gwyn, Tyninghame Gardens Ltd

The formal walled garden combines the lawn, sculpture and yew hedges, an Apple Walk, extensive herbaceous planting including roses and peonies with an informal arboretum. Splendid 17th century sandstone Scottish baronial house, remodelled in 1829 by William Burn. The gardens include herbaceous border, formal rose garden, Lady Haddington's Secret Garden with old-fashioned roses and an extensive Wilderness spring garden with rhododendrons, azaleas, flowering trees and bulbs. Grounds include a one mile beech avenue to the sea. The Romanesque ruin of St Baldred's Church commands views across the Tyne Estuary and Lammermuir Hills. Tyninghame has been awarded 'Outstanding' for every category in the Inventory of Gardens and Designed Landscapes of Scotland.

Open: Sunday 12 May, 1pm - 5pm. Also open Sunday 23 June, 1pm - 5pm. Admission £6.00, children free.

Directions: Gates on the A198 at Tyninghame Village. Bus 120.

Opening for: Lynton Day Centre (Sunday 12 May) & Tyninghame Village Hall and Community SCIO (Sunday 23 June)

 16 ## WINTON CASTLE
Pencaitland EH34 5AT
Sir Francis Ogilvy, Winton Trust
T: 01875 340222
W: www.wintoncastle.co.uk

An historic Renaissance and neo-Gothic Castle estate in East Lothian, just 30 minutes from Edinburgh. Set in mature and colourful grounds. A glorious spring display of daffodils and cherry blossom surrounds the castle, whilst extensive mixed borders and a wisteria walkway provide interest in the Walled Garden. Take a walk around Sir David's Loch, the natural woodland area at The Dell and enjoy the beautiful borders of the castle terraces, accessed by gravelled sloping pathways and stone steps.

Open: Sunday 14 April, noon - 4:30pm, admission £6.00, children free. Guided Castle and Garden Tours, teas, home baking and light refreshments available at Cafe Winton. Dogs are welcome within grounds.

Directions: Entrance off the B6355 Trent/Pencaitland Road.

Opening for: East Lothian Foodbank

Edinburgh, Midlothian & West Lothian

Sponsored by

RATHBONES

Incorporating
Investec Wealth &
Investment (UK)

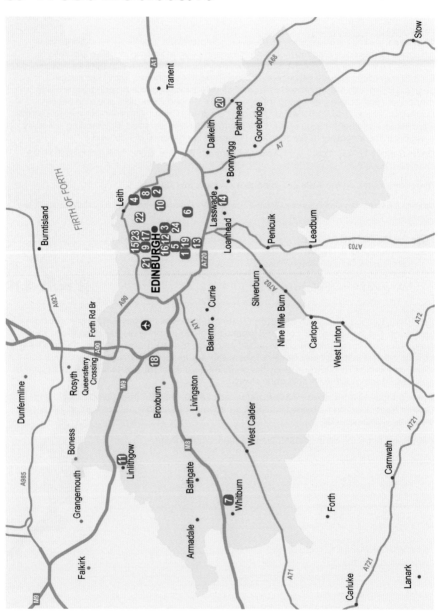

Edinburgh, Midlothian & West Lothian

OUR VOLUNTEER ORGANISERS

District Organisers: Jerry & Christine Gregson   101 Greenbank Crescent, Edinburgh EH10 5TA
info@scotlandsgardens.org

Area Organisers: Kate Fearnley   23 Lasswade Road, Eskbank EH22 3EE
Annette Henderson   5 Melville Terrace, Eskbank EH22 3AR
Caroline & Michael Pearson   42 Pentland Avenue, Edinburgh EH13 0HY
Gillian Polley   3 Swanston Road, Edinburgh EH10 7BB

Media Volunteer: Fiona Taylor

Treasurers: Kevin Maginnis   69 Ferryfield, Edinburgh EH5 2PS

GARDENS OPEN ON A SPECIFIC DATE

Preston Hall Walled Garden, Pathhead	Saturday/Sunday, 17/18 February
101 Greenbank Crescent, Edinburgh	Sunday, 28 April
Dr Neil's Garden, Duddingston Village	Saturday/Sunday, 4/5 May
Greentree, 18 Green Hill Park, Edinburgh	Sunday, 5 May
Regent, Royal and Carlton Terrace Gardens, Edinburgh	Saturday, 11 May
Redcroft, 23 Murrayfield Road, Edinburgh	Saturday/Sunday, 11/12 May
Hunter's Tryst, 95 Oxgangs Road, Edinburgh	Sunday, 12 May
Moray Place and Bank Gardens, Edinburgh	Sunday, 19 May
20 Blackford Road, Edinburgh	Sunday, 2 June
Dean Gardens, Edinburgh	Sunday, 9 June
Maggie's Edinburgh, Western General Hospital, Crewe Road, Edinburgh	Sunday, 9 June
14 East Brighton Crescent, Portobello, Edinburgh	Sunday, 16 June
Claremont, Redmill	Sunday, 16 June
Stockbridge Gardens, Edinburgh	Sunday, 23 June
Merchiston Cottage, 16 Colinton Road, Edinburgh	Sunday, 23 June
Whitehouse & Grange Bowling Club, 18a Hope Terrace, Edinburgh	Sunday, 30 June
Fountainbank, 5 Back Station Road, Linlithgow, West Lothian	Saturday/Sunday, 6/7 July
Pentland Crescent Gardens, 2 Pentland Crescent, Edinburgh	Sunday, 7 July
Claremont, Redmill	Sunday, 14 July
Craigentinny Telferton Allotments, Telferton Road, Edinburgh	Sunday, 21 July
39 Nantwich Drive, Edinburgh	Saturday, 3 August
77 Kirk Brae, Edinburgh	Sunday, 4 August
Claremont, Redmill	Sunday, 4 August

Edinburgh, Midlothian & West Lothian

GARDENS OPEN REGULARLY

Newliston, Kirkliston	1 May - 2 June

GARDENS OPEN BY ARRANGEMENT

Kevock Garden, 16 Kevock Road, Lasswade	1 January - 29 December
Hunter's Tryst, 95 Oxgangs Road, Edinburgh	1 April - 30 September
101 Greenbank Crescent, Edinburgh	1 May - 31 July
5 Greenbank Crescent, Edinburgh	1 May - 30 September

20 Blackford Road

Edinburgh, Midlothian & West Lothian

1 **101 GREENBANK CRESCENT**
Edinburgh EH10 5TA
Jerry and Christine Gregson
T: 0131 447 6492 E: jerry_gregson@yahoo.co.uk

After some changes to make maintenance easier, we are back to holding an open day. While the house is on a busy bus route, it hides a fascinating garden on a sloping site. There are views over Braidburn Valley Park to the Pentland Hills. Paths wind down from the oval lawn, past a handsome magnolia tree, to a terrace which overlooks a water feature and flowering shrubs. Further steps lead past a scree bed of azalea and rhododendron to a productive area of vegetable beds, fruit trees and a neatly-concealed composting area. We aim to have colour, contrast and interest all year round.

Open: Sunday 28 April, 2pm - 5pm. Also open by arrangement for groups of eight or more 1 May - 31 July. Admission £5.00, children free. Please note the garden is not suitable for anyone with limited mobility.

Directions: From the city centre take the A702 through Morningside. Continue uphill and turn right at Greenbank Church on to Greenbank Crescent. Buses 5 and 16; the stop is for Greenbank Row.

Opening for: St.Columba's Hospice Care

2 **14 EAST BRIGHTON CRESCENT**
Portobello, Edinburgh EH15 1LR
Jim and Sue Hurford
E: sue.hurford@gmail.com

Roughly two thirds of an acre suburban garden, developed over 40 years. People have said the following about it: 'A little bit of countryside in the town', 'Booming with green', 'A bosky bower' and 'There is such a wide range of plant material and every little corner holds a new gem'.

Open: Sunday 16 June, 2pm - 5pm, admission £5.00, children free.

Directions: Buses 21, 12 and 49 to Brighton Place, and 15, 26, 40 and 45 to Portobello High Street. Brighton Place intersects Portobello High Street just east of the bus stops.

Opening for: The Trussell Trust

3 **20 BLACKFORD ROAD**
Edinburgh EH9 2DS
John and Tricia Wood

Victorian walled garden of a quarter of an acre. Large collection of trees, shrubs and herbaceous perennials established over some four decades giving colour and interest all year round. Tulips in pots are followed by many rhododendrons and camellias, then hostas and euphorbias. The bulb season starts with daffodils, crocuses, bluebells then lilies in pots and finally cyclamen in autumn.

Open: Sunday 2 June, 2pm - 5pm, admission £6.00, children free. Plant sale and band, 'The Busking Sharks'.

Directions: Buses 9, 24 and 5.

Opening for: Parkinsons UK

Edinburgh, Midlothian & West Lothian

4 39 NANTWICH DRIVE
Edinburgh EH7 6RA
Michael and Susan Burns

Large wildlife-friendly garden run on organic principles. Includes mini orchard, pond, mixed borders, greenhouse and a secret garden. There are mini woodland walks and an allotment for vegetables, plus a compost area, worm bin and rotary bin.

Open: Saturday 3 August, 2pm - 5pm, admission £6.00, children free.

Directions: Bus 19 to Craigentinny Road or bus 26 to Kekewich Drive.

Opening for: The Henry Doubleday Research Association

5 5 GREENBANK CRESCENT
Edinburgh EH10 5TE
Sandy Corlett
T: 0131 4471119 E: sandycorlett@hotmail.co.uk

South-facing, newly designed, sloping terraced garden with views over Braidburn Valley Park to the Pentlands. Colourful chaos of herbaceous plants, shrubs, roses and small trees. Hard features include a gazebo, pergola, greenhouse and water feature.

Open: by arrangement 1 May - 30 September, admission £5.00.

Directions: From the city centre take the A702 through Morningside, continue uphill on Comiston Road, turn right at Greenbank Church on to Greenbank Crescent. Buses 5, 16, 11.

Opening for: NASS: (Spinal Arthritis)

6 77 KIRK BRAE
Edinburgh EH16 6JN
Michael Brown and Angela Casey
E: mvbrown55@gmail.com

A south Edinburgh garden of roughly 1200 square metres surrounded by a stone wall. Featuring a mix of mature and younger trees, herbaceous beds and borders, a vegetable patch, lawn, a 19th century cast iron vinery, an old monkey puzzle, pond and a patio. Since 2002 the garden has evolved from the traditional and formal to an informal, wildlife-friendly garden with a wide variety of plants, trees and shrubs. The planting aims for year-round colour and variety, with a growing emphasis on fruit and vegetables and on small design elements. Still on its journey and very much a work in progress, the newest initiative is to turn some of the lawn into a small wildflower meadow. All inputs are peat-free and as organic as possible.

Open: Sunday 4 August, noon - 5pm, admission £5.00, children free.

Directions: 77 Kirk Brae is towards the top of the hill on the left hand side, the number 77 is clearly marked on the main and side gates. Parking is on Kirk Brae or in the quieter Wolrige Road nearby. The 31 bus stops close to the property in each direction at the *Kirk Park* stop.

Opening for: SupportED or The Community Eating Disorders Charity

Edinburgh, Midlothian & West Lothian

7 CLAREMONT
Redmill EH47 OJY
Trevor and Faye Yerbury
E: info@yerburystudio.com

'Claremont' is situated only two minutes from J4 of the M8 and yet it's an idyllic oasis. It is an eclectic garden created over 18 years and before we moved in, it was just grass with a few rhododendrons. The garden has three areas; to the front are various herbaceous borders, to the side we have our hosta collection, containing over 150 hostas and to the rear there are herbaceous borders, plus a stumpery/fernery which was created in 2022. We have three ponds, one very large, a rockery, a dovecot, newly-created rose garden and interesting trees including a grand monkey puzzle. New for 2024 we have created a brand-new herbaceous border, the stumpery has been expanded over the winter and a new greenhouse has been installed.

Open: Sunday 16 June, Sunday 14 July and Sunday 4 August, 2pm - 5pm. Admission £5.00, children free.

Directions: Take the M8 and leave at J4 heading for Whitburn. At the first set of traffic lights turn right for Whitburn. After 100 metres turn first right at the bollards and come straight down.

Opening for: Alzheimer Scotland & Breast Cancer Campaign Scotland

8 CRAIGENTINNY TELFERTON ALLOTMENTS
Telferton Road, off Portobello Road, Edinburgh EH7 6XG
The Gardeners of Craigentinny and Telferton
E: ctallotments@gmail.com

Established in 1923, this independent allotment site is a tranquil and charming space, hidden away in a built-up area, where the local community benefit from growing their own vegetables and fruit. Come and enjoy tea, home baking and a chat with our friendly plot-holders.

Open: Sunday 21 July, 2pm - 5pm, admission £4.00, children free.

Directions: Park on Telferton Road. Buses 15, 26, 45.

Opening for: Craigentinny Telferton Allotments

9 DEAN GARDENS
Edinburgh EH4 1QE
Dean Gardens Management Committee

Nine acres of semi-woodland garden with spring bulbs on the steep banks of the Water of Leith in central Edinburgh. Founded in the 1860s by local residents, the Dean Gardens contain part of the great structure of the Dean Bridge, a Thomas Telford masterpiece of 1835. Lawns, paths, trees and shrubs with lovely views to the weir in the Dean Village and to St Bernard's Well. There is also a children's play area.

Open: Sunday 9 June, 2pm - 5pm, admission £5.00, children free.

Directions: Entrance at Ann Street or Eton Terrace.

Opening for: Macmillan Cancer Support

Edinburgh, Midlothian & West Lothian

 DR NEIL'S GARDEN
Duddingston Village EH15 3PX
Dr Neil's Garden Trust
E: info@drneilsgarden.co.uk
W: www.drneilsgarden.co.uk

A wonderful, secluded landscaped garden on the lower slopes of Arthur's Seat including conifers, heathers, alpines, a physic garden, herbaceous borders and ponds.

Open: Saturday/Sunday, 4/5 May, 2pm - 5pm, admission £5.00, children free.

Directions: Park at the kirk car park on Duddingston Road West and then follow signposts through the manse garden.

Opening for: Dr Neils Garden Trust

 FOUNTAINBANK
5 Back Station Road, Linlithgow, West Lothian EH49 6AF
Mrs Tracey Smith
T: 01506 843506

Fountainbank is a new, developing garden with disabled access. A varied garden with a mix of herbaceous plants, shrubs and trees with features including a pond, alpines and raised vegetable beds plus a few pieces of art. A nature-friendly environment designed for disabled access and relaxation.

Open: Saturday/Sunday, 6/7 July, 10am - 4pm, admission £5.00, children free.

Directions: Linlithgow Station is next to the house. Alternatively, any bus stop at the east end of the High Street is a short walk from the garden. If driving, leave the High Street at the B9080 and turn sharp right after the railway bridge. Disabled parking only at the house.

Opening for: Multiple Sclerosis Society

GREENTREE
18 Green Hill Park, Edinburgh EH10 4DW
Alison Glen

A rare opportunity to appreciate a mature garden which, with the exception of one magnificent old copper beech tree, is completely planted and created by its owner Alison Glen. Designed with an artist's appreciation of form, this woodland garden shelters a large collection of rhododendrons. There are many beautiful specimen trees and shrubs including *Hoheria glabrata, Halesia carolina* and several magnolia species. The garden is fully wheelchair accessible and there are several ways to move through it; from the Japanese-inspired stream garden presided over by a mature *Pinus wallichiana* at one end, to the newly developed borders at the other.

Open: Sunday 5 May, 10am - 5pm, admission £5.00, children free.

Directions: Buses 11, 16, 15, 23, 5. By car: from the east - Chamberlain Road, Strathearn Road, from the north - Morningside Road, from the west - Colinton Road.

Opening for: Alzheimer Scotland

Edinburgh, Midlothian & West Lothian

13 HUNTER'S TRYST
95 Oxgangs Road, Edinburgh EH10 7BA
Jean Knox
T: 07708 653584 E: jean.knox@blueyonder.co.uk

Well-stocked and beautifully designed, mature, medium-sized town garden comprising herbaceous and shrub beds, lawn, fruit and some vegetables, water features, seating areas, trees and an example of cloud pruning. This is a wildlife-friendly garden that has been transformed from a wilderness 40 years ago and continues to evolve. In 2017 two raised beds were added to the front garden. This hidden treasure of a garden was featured on *Beechgrove* in June 2015 and on *The Instant Gardener* in June 2016.

Open: Sunday 12 May, 2pm - 5pm. Also open by arrangement 1 April - 30 September. Admission £6.00, children free.

Directions: From Fairmilehead crossroads head down Oxgangs Road to Hunter's Tryst roundabout and it's the last house on the left. Buses 4, 5, 27, 400. The bus stop is at Hunter's Tryst and the garden is opposite.

Opening for: St.Columba's Hospice Care & Lothian Cat Rescue

14 KEVOCK GARDEN
16 Kevock Road, Lasswade EH18 1HT
David and Stella Rankin
E: stella@kevockgarden.co.uk
W: www.kevockgarden.co.uk

This wonderful hillside garden has magnificent views over the North Esk Valley. Its steep slope creates a range of different habitats with a wide diversity of plants, ranging from those that love hot, sunny conditions to those that prefer the cool, damp places near the pond and woodland glades. Mature specimen trees, rhododendrons, azaleas and unusual shrubs are underplanted with many rare woodland plants. Lawns have been relaid, surrounding borders have been planted, and there is a new rock garden. Kevock Garden has featured in many magazine articles and gardening programmes.

Open: by arrangement 1 January - 29 December, admission £5.00, children free. Individuals and couples are welcome as well as groups. Please email to arrange.

Directions: Kevock Road lies to the south of the A678 Loanhead/Lasswade Road. Five minutes from the city bypass Lasswade Junction and on the 31 Lothian Bus route to Polton/Bonnyrigg Road.

Opening for: Fischy Music

Edinburgh, Midlothian & West Lothian

15 MAGGIE'S EDINBURGH

Western General Hospital, Crewe Road, Edinburgh EH4 2XU
Maggie's Centre
W: www.maggies.org

At Maggie's we believe that gardens can have an amazing, positive effect on health and well-being. Each of our centres has a beautiful garden designed alongside the building to ensure a strong connection between the outside and inside. The garden was designed by Emma Keswick and has been adapted to grow and flourish alongside two new extensions. The walled garden and statue gardens create a connection with nature and the ever-changing seasons. Emma's planting design ensures the garden has year-round colour and creates a calming transition away from the hospital. The garden is fully accessible for all with enclosed spaces cleverly interspersed with more open areas with longer views.

Open: Sunday 9 June, 2pm - 5pm, admission £5.00, children free. Homemade teas and plants for sale. There will also be guided tours of the Maggie's Centre available.

Directions: Maggie's is located behind Ward 1 at the Western General Hospital. Enter the hospital at the Crewe Road entrance (Hospital Main drive), follow the path under the road bridge and take the first left into Maggie's. Lothian Buses: 19, 19A, 28, 28B, 29, 37, 37A, 38; First Bus: 129. For vehicle access enter the hospital via the Telford Road entrance, parking is free, follow parking signs on the day.

Opening for: Maggie's

16 MERCHISTON COTTAGE

16 Colinton Road, Edinburgh EH10 5EL
Esther Mendelssohn

Previously open for nearly twenty years we are happy to open again after a six year gap. Come and enjoy our romantic walled garden within a mile of the city centre providing a haven for wildlife based on a tapestry of habitats including numerous water features. It has been gardened on organic principles for nearly 40 years with productive fruit trees, apples, pears, plums, quince, medlar and black mulberry. Soft fruit including gooseberries, raspberries, blueberries and red, white and blackcurrants all benefit from the pollinating bees kept in hives in the garden which also give us the added bonus of honey. A roof garden devoted to growing fruit and vegetables has greatly enhanced the garden and provided new planting opportunities. Since Covid we have become involved with a new charity, Blood Bikes Scotland and are delighted to open our garden to help raise much needed funds for them.

Open: Sunday 23 June, 2pm - 5pm, admission £6.00, children free. There will be honey tasting and all being well a bee expert will be on hand.

Directions: Near Holy Corner, opposite George Watson's College School. Take Lothian Buses 11 or 16.

Opening for: Blood Bikes Scotland

Edinburgh, Midlothian & West Lothian

17 MORAY PLACE AND BANK GARDENS
Edinburgh EH3 6BX
The residents of the Moray Feu

Bank Gardens Edinburgh EH3 6BX (The Residents of Bank Gardens): Join us to celebrate the gardens of the Moray Feu in their spring and summer colours. Nearly six acres of secluded wild gardens with lawns, trees and shrubs with banks of bulbs down to the Water of Leith and stunning views towards Dean Bridge.
Moray Place Edinburgh EH3 6BX (The Residents of Moray Place): Private garden of three-and-a-half acres in the Georgian New Town is framed by the polygon of Moray Place, and is laid out with shrubs, trees and flower beds offering an atmosphere of tranquillity in the city centre.

Open: Sunday 19 May, 2pm - 5pm, admission £5.00, children free. There will be tea, coffee and home baking.

Directions: Bank Gardens enter by the gate at the top of Doune Terrace.

Moray Place enter by the north gate in Moray Place.

Opening for: Euan Macdonald Centre for Motor Neurone Disease Research

18 NEWLISTON
Kirkliston EH29 9EB
Mr and Mrs R C Maclachlan
T: 0131 333 3231 E: newliston@gmail.com

A well preserved 18th-century parkland/designed landscape rather than a garden as such. Full of mature rhododendrons and azaleas, fine vistas and allées of trees. The walk around the woods and lake is a carpet of wild garlic and bluebells in the spring. The wood to the east of the house is in the pattern of the Union Jack, best appreciated by standing in the centre where all the radiating paths meet. The house, designed by Robert Adam, is also open.

Open: 1 May - 2 June, 2pm - 6pm, admission £5.00, children free.

Directions: Four miles south of the Forth Road Bridge, entrance off the B800.

Opening for: CHAS

19 PENTLAND CRESCENT GARDENS
2 Pentland Crescent, Edinburgh EH10 6NP
Jan Polley

Neighbouring gardens all laid out very differently, offering a wide range of ideas for visitors. The gardens include colourful herbaceous borders, a range of fruit and vegetables and a woodland garden which shows what can be done with a sloping site. There are ideas for planting in the sun and shade, rockeries, a garden pond, and various patios and seating areas.

Open: Sunday 7 July, 2pm - 5pm, admission £7.00, children free.

Directions: From the city centre take the A702 through Morningside, continue uphill and turn right at Comiston Springs Avenue. Pentland Crescent is first left. Buses 11 or 15 and get off at the Comiston Springs Avenue stop.

Opening for: Marie Curie

Edinburgh, Midlothian & West Lothian

20 PRESTON HALL WALLED GARDEN

Pathhead EH37 5UG
William and Henrietta Callander
T: 07971 028697 E: henrietta@prestonhall.co.uk
W: www.prestonhall.co.uk

Preston Hall is a 3.5 acre walled garden based in Pathhead. Restoration of the 18th century walled garden started in 2011, and today Head Gardener Kate Danesh oversees the ever-evolving transformation. February will see the first glimpse of life again in the garden with the appearance of snowdrops. The Walled Garden and surrounding parkland are carpeted in the beautiful white flowers.

Open: Saturday/Sunday, 17/18 February, 10am - 4pm, admission £5.00, children free.

Directions: Twelve miles south of Edinburgh off the A68, one mile east of Pathhead Village.

Opening for: MY Name'5 Doddie Foundation

21 REDCROFT

23 Murrayfield Road, Edinburgh EH12 6EP
James and Anna Buxton
T: 0131 337 1747 E: annabuxtonb@aol.com

Redcroft is a mature walled garden surrounding an attractive Arts and Crafts house. It is a hidden haven off a busy road with a variety of different features and habitats: old shrubberies, an orchard, a rockery, a pond, and a large lawn with contrasting longer grass. It is well maintained with clipped shrubs - some of them quite unusual - and some cloud pruning. May is very colourful with rhododendrons and many other flowering shrubs and wall plants, and the greenhouse is full of tender plants. There will be tulips in pots and many other spring bulbs. Children and buggies are very welcome and there will be plenty of activities. We hope older children will enjoy our treehouse. Dogs on leads welcome.

Open: Saturday/Sunday, 11/12 May, 2pm - 5pm, admission £6.00, children free. There will be a **Bumper SGS Plant Sale.** Delicious tea with home baking. Music in the garden: No Strings Attached Wind Band will play on Saturday afternoon, apple pressing on both days. Mostly wheelchair accessible.

Directions: Murrayfield Road runs north from Corstorphine Road to Ravelston Dykes. There is easy free parking available. Buses 12, 26, 31, get off at Murrayfield Stadium. Bus 38 goes up Murrayfield Road.

Opening for: Little Sparta Trust

22 REGENT, ROYAL AND CARLTON TERRACE GARDENS

17a Royal Terrace Mews, Carlton Terrace Lane Entrance, Edinburgh EH7 5BZ
RRCT Gardens Association

The largest of Edinburgh's New Town gardens still in private ownership, it remains largely unchanged since its formation in 1830. The design consists of an upland lawn of seven acres planted with specimen trees. The flanking woodlands of five acres are planted with spring bulbs giving a carpet of colour. Sitting on the lower slope of Calton Hill, the garden has beautiful views of Edinburgh and the surrounding countryside.

Edinburgh, Midlothian & West Lothian

Open: Saturday 11 May, noon - 4pm, admission £7.50, children free. Dogs welcome but they must be on short leads.

Directions: Trams: To Picardy Place then walk along Blenheim Place and Royal Terrace turning right onto Carlton Terrace Lane, where the green garden gate is straight ahead.
Buses: to Elm Row or London Road and directions above.

Opening for: Firefly

 23 ### STOCKBRIDGE GARDENS
Garden trail runs between Logie Green Gardens EH7 4HE and
Royal Circus Gardens North EH3 6TN
Gardeners of Stockbridge
E: JW.homeoffice@gmail.com

Visit some of the surprising horticultural delights behind the discrete terraces of Stockbridge/ New Town and relax in a classic Georgian pleasure garden. Bringing fresh air and wildlife into the heart of the city, the collection provides lots of creative solutions to urban gardening with year-round interest through a mix of seasonal planting and structural evergreens which the gardeners will be on hand to talk about.

Open: Sunday 23 June, noon - 4:30pm, admission £8.50, children free. Tickets and route maps available at both trail ends. Plants for sale at Logie Green Gardens. See Scotland's Gardens Scheme website for up-to-date details.

Directions: Buses 23 and 27 to Dundas Street and Canonmills, 8 to Rodney Street and Canonmills, 36 to Hamilton Place and Broughton Road, 29 to Royal Circus.

Opening for: Shelter Scotland & Médecins Sans Frontières

 24 ### WHITEHOUSE & GRANGE BOWLING CLUB
18a Hope Terrace, Edinburgh EH9 2AR
Whitehouse & Grange Bowling Club
E: wandgbc@icloud.com
W: www.wandgbc.com

The walled garden provides a backcloth for those bowling on the green or just sitting on the sidelines. The main feature is the rose garden, replanted in 2020, in part responding to Covid lockdowns when the clubhouse was off limits. Trees mark the coronations of George VI and Charles III. In 2022, children from Sciennes Primary assisted in planting trees to mark Queen Elizabeth II's Jubilee and the Club's 150th anniversary.

Open: Sunday 30 June, 2pm - 5pm, admission £5.00, children free. Teas, coffees, scones & cakes, Luca's ice cream, licensed bar.

Directions: Heading south on Marchmont Road, cross over Strathearn Road onto Kilgraston Road, past the church on the left side and take the first turning on the right. Buses: 5, 9 and 24 to Beaufort Road stops.

Opening for: Eric Liddell Community & St.Columba's Hospice Care

Fife

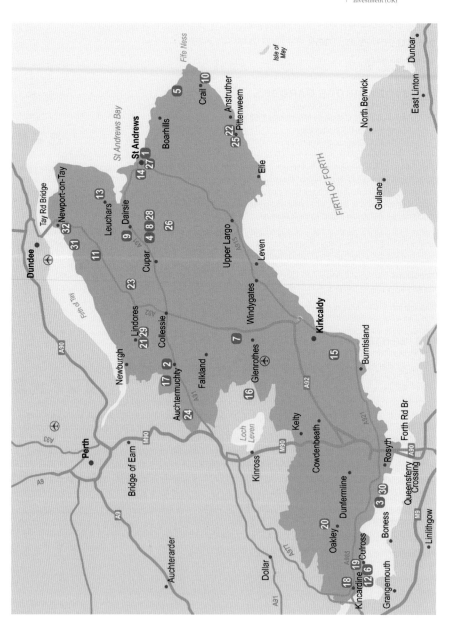

Fife

OUR VOLUNTEER ORGANISERS

District Organisers:	David Buchanan-Cook	Helensbank, 56 Toll Road, Kincardine FK10 4QZ
	Julia Young	South Flisk, Blebo Craigs KY15 5UQ
		info@scotlandsgardens.org
Area Organisers:	Alison Aiton	Craigview Cottage, Blebo Craigs KY15 5UQ
	Clare Ansell	Coul House, Maree Way, Glenrothes KY7 6NW
	Pauline Borthwick	96 Hepburn Gardens, St Andrews KY16 9LP
	Catherine Erskine	Cambo Farmhouse, Kingsbarns KY16 8QD
	Anna Morton	
	Fay Smith	37 Ninian Fields, Pittenweem KY10 2QU
Treasurer:	David Buchanan-Cook	Helensbank, 56 Toll Road, Kincardine FK10 4QZ

GARDENS OPEN ON A SPECIFIC DATE

Dunimarle Castle, Balgownie West, Culross	Saturday/Sunday, 10/11 February
Lindores House, by Newburgh	Saturday, 24 February
South Flisk, Blebo Craigs, Cupar	Sunday, 5 May
Craig Cottage, Blebo Craigs	Sunday, 5 May
Edenhill, Kennedy Gardens, St Andrews	Thursday 9 May
Edenhill, Kennedy Gardens, St Andrews	Thursday 16 May
The Garden with the Dragon, 2, Upper Wellheads, Limekilns	Saturday, 18 May
Edenhill, Kennedy Gardens, St Andrews	Thursday 23 May
The Garden with the Dragon, 2, Upper Wellheads, Limekilns	Saturday, 25 May
Pitlochie House, Gateside	Sunday, 26 May
Kirklands, Saline	Sunday, 26 May
Earlshall Castle, Leuchars	Sunday, 26 May
Lindores House, by Newburgh	Sunday, 2 June
Swallows Rest, Lindores	Sunday, 2 June
Auchtermuchty Open Gardens, Fife	Saturday/Sunday, 15/16 June
Pitlochie House, Gateside	Saturday/Sunday, 15/16 June
Pittenweem: Gardens in the Burgh, Pittenweem	Sunday, 16 June
Kirkbrae House, Culross	Saturday/Sunday, 22/23 June
Earlshall Castle, Leuchars	Sunday, 23 June
Blanerne, West Road, Charlestown	Saturday/Sunday, 29/30 June
Blebo Craigs Village Gardens, Blebo Craigs, Cupar	Sunday, 30 June
Moonzie House, By Cupar	Sunday, 30 June
Craigfoodie, Dairsie	Sunday, 30 June
Crail: Gardens in the Burgh, Crail	Saturday/Sunday, 6/7 July
Kirkbrae House, Culross	Saturday/Sunday, 20/21 July
Pitlochie House, Gateside	Sunday, 28 July
Blanerne, West Road, Charlestown	Saturday, 17 August
Kirkbrae House, Culross	Sunday, 18 August
Pitlochie House, Gateside	Sunday, 1 September

Fife

Greenhead Farmhouse, Greenhead of Arnot, Leslie	Sunday, 15 September
SGS Autumn Plant Sale at St Andrews Botanic Garden, St Andrews	Sunday, 6 October
Carol Concert at Dunimarle Castle, Balgownie West, Culross	Date to be confirmed
Coul House, Maree Way, Glenrothes	Date to be confirmed

GARDENS OPEN REGULARLY

Cambo Gardens, Kingsbarns	1 January - 31 December
Glassmount House, by Kirkcaldy	1 April - 30 September
Dunimarle Castle, Balgownie West, Culross	1 May - 31 May (not Monday & Tuesday)
Willowhill, Forgan, Newport-on-Tay	27 - 29 April (Sat - Mon), 1 & 3 June and 1 July - 31 August (Sat & Mon)

GARDENS OPEN BY ARRANGEMENT

Harthill, Reediehill Farm, Auchtermuchty	2 January - 31 October
Dawson's Garden, The Old Post Office, Kilmany	6 January - 22 December
Madeira, Grangemuir, Pittenweem	1 February - 30 September (Tuesday, Thursday & Friday)
Kirklands, Saline	1 April - 30 September
South Flisk, Blebo Craigs, Cupar	1 April - 30 June
The Tower, 1 Northview Terrace, Wormit	1 April - 1 October
Rosewells, Baldinnie, Ceres	1 April - 30 September
46 South Street, St Andrews	1 April - 31 July
Willowhill, Forgan, Newport-on-Tay	27 April - 31 August
Helensbank House, Kincardine	1 June - 31 August
Blanerne, West Road, Charlestown	1 June - 31 August

Fife

1 46 SOUTH STREET
St Andrews KY16 9JT
Mrs June Baxter
T: 01334 474995 E: ejbaxter986@gmail.com

Renowned town garden in medieval long rig, with orchard underplanted with wildflowers and bulbs, and many unusual flowering shrubs. Roses and other climbers clothe the surrounding high walls. Shrub roses planted in a delightful central parterre fill the air with scent. An historic and unique feature in St Andrews, but also a wonderfully planted space where different styles of planting complement the range of plants used. Historic doocot.

Open: by arrangement 1 April - 31 July, admission £5.00, children free.

Directions: Access and parking information on request.

Opening for: Friends of Craigtoun

2 AUCHTERMUCHTY OPEN GARDENS
Fife KY14 7AP
The Gardeners of Auchtermuchty

A wide variety of gardens, many hidden and behind walls. The diversity of gardens makes this village well worth a visit. One garden has a forest orchard set in woodland with many mature trees and an emphasis on encouraging into the garden wildlife in all its forms. Another garden – started in 2012 but already looking well established – contains a range of plants, trees, shrubs, roses and an amazing border of meconopsis. Other gardens show an extensive range of formal herbaceous and informal borders, shrubs and trees – including a fine old specimen Redwood.

Open: Saturday/Sunday, 15/16 June, noon - 5pm, admission £6.00, children free. Tickets will be available at a number of the gardens – for exact details please check the website nearer the time. Please wear appropriate footwear, as some gardens have rough areas. Disabled access to some gardens may be limited. Dogs are not allowed.

Directions: On the A91 from Cupar and Kinross. B936 from Falkland and Newburgh. Stagecoach buses 36 or 94A. Moffat & Williamson buses 64, 64A and 66.

Opening for: Auchtermuchty Community Centre

3 BLANERNE
West Road, Charlestown KY11 3EW
Lesley and Geoff Fenlon
E: lesleyabloomer@gmail.com

South-facing hidden village garden with lots of paths to follow and many places to sit, both sunny and shaded. The centrepiece of the garden is a large oval pond with wildlife-friendly planting. Surrounding the pond are several mini-gardens including a rose courtyard garden with catmint, salvias, beech, false indigo and featuring a bubble fountain. There is also a vegetable patch, woodland, a shady courtyard and a summerhouse garden enclosed by a young purple beech/wild rose hedge.

Open: Saturday/Sunday, 29/30 June, 11am - 4pm. Also open Saturday 17 August, 11am - 4pm. And open by arrangement 1 June - 31 August. Admission £6.00, children free.

Fife

Directions: Driving: follow signs from the A985 into Charlestown. Follow the road until you see the village shop, The Sutlery, which is available for takeaway all day Saturday and Sunday mornings – these can be eaten in the garden. Parking is behind the Charlestown Workshop which is next to the shop. **Cycling:** National Route76 passes c20m from the house. **Public transport:** bus 6/6A from Dunfermline or bus 88A from Kincardine or Inverkeithing. Get off at The Green in Charlestown and walk towards the shop. From the village shop, walk west about 20m along West Road. Turn left down the tarmac driveway opposite 10 West Road, and the garden is on the right hand side at the end.

Opening for: Mary's Meals

 4 BLEBO CRAIGS VILLAGE GARDENS
Blebo Craigs, Cupar KY15 5UG
Gardeners of Blebo Craigs

A selection of cottage gardens in this charming rural village, situated between Cupar and St Andrews; most gardens have stunning views over the surrounding countryside. The gardens are all different, many with beautiful herbaceous borders and unusual trees and there are also ponds, orchards and a living roof. Because the village is on a hill, please be aware that some of the gardens will involve steps.

Open: Sunday 30 June, 11am - 4pm, admission £6.00, children free. The plant sale will take place in the parking area. Homemade soup, teas, coffees and cake available in the Village Hall from 11am onwards.

Directions: From St Andrews: B939 for 5 miles, village sign on your left at the bus stop pointing right and taking you straight to the village. **From Cupar:** B940 to Pitscottie, turn left onto the B939 and, after a couple of miles, turn left into the village. Turn left at the phone box for the Village Hall and signs to the parking area.

Opening for: Blebo Craigs Village Hall 2000 Trust

 5 CAMBO GARDENS
Kingsbarns KY16 8QD
Trustees of Cambo Heritage Trust
T: 01333 451040 E: hello@cambogardens.org.uk
W: https://www.cambogardens.org.uk/

Best known for snowdrops (mail order February), but exciting throughout the year, this Victorian walled garden features constantly evolving, magnificent herbaceous borders featuring rare and unusual plants, many of which are propagated for sale at Cambo. The garden is renowned too for its tulips and a stunning rose collection. Outside the main garden an inspiring Winter Garden and North American Prairie continue to be developed. Woodland walks to the sea.
National Plant Collection: *Galanthus.*
Champion Trees: Bundle Beech.

Open: Open year round, admission details can be found on the garden's website. Cafe, gift shop and plants for sale throughout the year. Check our website for events throughout the year.

Directions: A917 between Crail and St Andrews.

Opening for: Donation to SGS Beneficiaries

Fife

6 · CAROL CONCERT AT DUNIMARLE CASTLE
56 Toll Road KY12 8JN
Mr David Buchanan-Cook for tickets
E: Helensbank@aol.com
W: www.helensbank.com

The annual SGS Christmas Carol concerts will take place on two separate Saturday afternoons in Advent. The dates will be listed on both the SGS and Dunimarle websites from November. Set in the beautiful candle-lit private chapel of Dunimarle Castle, just outside Culross, this is the perfect way to celebrate the season. A wide selection of traditional and modern carols performed by Bel Canto, interspersed with seasonal, humorous, festive readings. 'A truly magical experience.'

Open: December date to be confirmed Tickets including refreshments (children free) must be booked in advance as numbers are restricted. The event quickly sold out in 2022 so do book early to avoid disappointment.

Directions: Situated on the B9037 to the west of Culross, approximately 500 yards from the village. Parking is available in the village's west car park. From there, follow the coastal path west to the Rose Arch.

Opening for: to be confirmed

7 · COUL HOUSE
Coul House, Maree Way, Glenrothes KY7 6NW
Dean & Clare Ansell
T: 07525 791277 E: Clareansell5@gmail.com

A hidden gem, Coul garden lies within the grounds of Coul House, an imposing B-listed Victorian farmhouse which dates back to circa 1875. A mix of hydrangeas, roses, rhododendron and wisteria are contained in this ever-evolving amateur garden. The garden has more recently been redesigned with hard landscaping and includes a small pond. Come and take a walk around and enjoy a cup of tea and home baking.

Open: Date to be confirmed – please check the SGS website.

Directions: From the A92, follow signs for Pitcairn

Opening for: Juvenile Diabetes Research Foundation Limited & Glenrothes & District Foodbank

Greenhead Farmhouse

Fife

8 CRAIG COTTAGE
Blebo Craigs KY15 5UQ
David & Elizabeth Wallace

Situated a few hundred yards from South Flisk is the charming Craig Cottage – a total contrast to South Flisk but the two gardens complement each other perfectly. Most of the garden has been planted since the owners moved here in 2014, although the small area of shrubs close to the cottage is original. Half of the lawn is now 'meadow' with a recent planting of fritillaries. The rest of the garden has borders containing a range of interesting plants, a rose screen, rhododendrons, azaleas, and specimen and fruit trees. Below that there is a productive vegetable plot. In addition, a recently extended rockery leads to an area of paths between thymes, camomile and other ground cover plants broken up by hedges and trees to provide windbreaks. The garden has fine examples of dry stone walling, most of which is the restoration/rebuilding of the original.

Open: Sunday 5 May, 2pm - 5pm, admission £6.00, children free. Opening in conjunction with South Flisk at which parking is available for visiting both gardens. Separate admission charges apply for each garden.

Directions: A short walk from South Flisk – see separate listing.

Opening for: The Prince's Trust: supporting young people in Scotland

9 CRAIGFOODIE
Dairsie KY15 4RU
Mr and Mrs James Murray
T: 01334 870291

Unusually, Craigfoodie House sits within its walled garden and the garden itself is on a sloping site, with the view from the upper terraces stretching beyond the garden into the valley below. The walled garden is quartered with its clock lawn, malus lawn, parterre and extensive vegetable garden. There are many individual features – the large herbaceous border, dry rill, mixed borders, espalier fruit, pleached lime hedge and much else. Enjoy the Mediterranean-style terraces, informal woodland garden, the grass tennis court and planting of young trees and shrubs (a current development area) and a stroll round the Knoll to its magnificent viewpoint. Craigfoodie has featured on *The Beechgrove Garden* and in articles in several national magazines.

Open: Sunday 30 June, 2pm - 5pm, admission £6.00, children free.

Directions: On A91 from Cupar to St Andrews turn left at Dairsie School then follow signs.

Opening for: The Pitcairn Trust

10 CRAIL: GARDENS IN THE BURGH
Crail KY10 3TT
Gardeners of Crail

Take an enjoyable stroll around this quintessential East Neuk village and explore its many beautiful gardens. These include gardens in varied styles and planting schemes – cottage, historic, plantsman's and bedding. The stunning coastal location presents some challenges for planting but also allows for a great range of more tender species to flourish.

Fife

Open: Saturday/Sunday, 6/7 July, 2pm - 5pm, admission £6.00, children free. Tickets and maps are available on the day from Crail Museum and participating gardens.

Directions: Approach the village from either St Andrews or Anstruther on the A917. Parking available in Marketgate.

Opening for: Crail Community Partnership

11 DAWSON'S GARDEN
The Old Post Office, Kilmany KY15 4PT
Liz Murray
T: 07531 571045 E: kilmanyartist@gmail.com

A small cottage garden, full of surprises. Developed from a bare rectangle of grass by the late artist Dawson Murray, it was designed to please the senses all year round with colour, form and scent. Stone paths edged with box meander out of sight past 13 apple trees and a plum tree; two varieties of fig; both a red and a green grape vine and roses chosen for scent. There are plenty of areas to sit and relax; by the pond, in a small grassy area through a rose and clematis arch, outside the studio facing the kitchen garden or up on the patio. All are accessible by wheelchair.
Champion Trees: Red Hazel.

Open: by arrangement 6 January - 22 December, admission £6.00, children free.

Directions: The Old Post Office is in the centre of the small hamlet of Kilmany, just off the A92, 8 miles from Dundee or 1.5 miles after Rathillet coming from the opposite direction. It can also be reached from Cupar via Foodieash.

Opening for: Overcoming MS

Craig Cottage

Kirklands

Fife

12 DUNIMARLE CASTLE
Balgownie West, Culross KY12 8JN
George Fleming
T: 07713 629040 E: castledunimarle@gmail.com
W: www.dunimarlecastle.co.uk

Dunimarle Castle sits on the outskirts of the historic village of Culross, surrounded by 52 acres of formal gardens, meadows and woodlands. Entering the grounds from the rose arch on the main road, you will find the imposing Victorian gothic-style chapel, beautifully framed by the striking tulip tree and rhododendrons. Follow the path up towards the castle to the Italianate yew-lined terrace with its south-facing wall, home to a growing collection of grapes and other fruiting plants. The Bastion Garden provides a perfect backdrop to the original Georgian part of the castle with its colourful borders and trees. A stroll up the once grand 'North Drive' takes you past specimen monkey puzzle trees sandwiched between dramatic redwoods and rhododendrons.
Champion Trees: Tulip Tree, Cedar, Monkey Puzzle, Redwood.

Open: Saturday/Sunday, 10/11 February, 10am - 4pm for Snowdrops and Winter Walks. Also open 1 May - 31 May (not Monday & Tuesday), 10am - 4pm. Admission by donation.

Directions: Situated on the B9037 to the west of Culross, approximately 500 yards from the village. Parking is available in the village's west car park. From there, follow the coastal path west to the Rose Arch.

Opening for: WFW

13 EARLSHALL CASTLE
Leuchars KY16 0DP
Paul & Josine Veenhuijzen
T: 01334 839205

Topiary gardens designed by Sir Robert Lorimer in the 1890s. The grounds also include a rose garden, croquet lawn, vegetable garden, orchard, park and wooded area.

Open: Sunday 26 May, 2pm - 5pm. Also open Sunday 23 June, 2pm - 5pm. Admission £6.50, children free.

Directions: On Earlshall Road, ¾ mile east of Leuchars Village (off A919).

Opening for: Leuchars St Athernase and Tayport Church of Scotland (Sunday 26 May) & The Royal Scots Dragoon Guards Charity (Sunday 23 June)

14 EDENHILL
Kennedy Gardens, St Andrews KY16 9DJ
Mr John Angus
T: 07710369747 E: 1edenhill@gmail.com

Behind the imposing exterior of a handsome Victorian house in St Andrews lies a true hidden gem of a garden, Edenhill. This is a mature garden designed and planted some years ago with the help of Michael Innes and lovingly nurtured and developed by the owner, John Angus. The garden is enclosed by handsome old walls clothed in clematis and honeysuckle and there are several mature trees, including a monkey puzzle. Beneath some rather special species rhododendrons there are carpets of colourful anemones, rare trilliums and some beautiful peonies. The sculptor, James Parker, has created some eye-catching sculptures for Edenhill and the most recent addition to this fascinating garden is a rill, the sound of which adds to the tranquillity of this very special garden.

Fife

Open: Thursday 9 May, Thursday 16 May & Thursday 23 May, 2pm - 5pm, admission £6.00, children free.

Directions: Kennedy Gardens is situated off Hepburn Gardens in residential St Andrews, only 5 minutes walk from St Andrews bus station (through Kinburn Park). The street sits above the University Science campus.

Opening for: Sightsavers

15 GLASSMOUNT HOUSE
by Kirkcaldy KY2 5UT
Peter, James and Irene Thomson
T: 01592 890214 E: mcmoonter@yahoo.co.uk

Densely planted walled garden with surrounding woodland. An A-listed sundial, Mackenzie & Moncur greenhouse and historical doocot are complemented by a number of newer structures. Daffodils are followed by a mass of candelabra and cowslip primula, meconopsis and *Cardiocrinum giganteum*. Hedges and topiary form backdrops for an abundance of bulbs, clematis, rambling roses and perennials, creating interest through the summer into September. The garden is now extending beyond the walls, with new areas of naturalistic planting blending the boundary between the surrounding fields and the woodland.

Open: 1 April - 30 September, 2pm - 5pm, admission £6.00, children free. Scottish finalist in Channel 4's *Garden of the Year* programme in 2022.

Directions: From Kirkcaldy, head west on the B9157. Turn left immediately after the railway bridge on the edge of town. Follow the single track road for 1½ miles and cross the crossroads. Glassmount House is the first turning on your right.

Opening for: Parkinsons UK

16 GREENHEAD FARMHOUSE
Greenhead of Arnot, Leslie KY6 3JQ
Malcolm and Maggie Strang Steel
T: 01592 840459

Greenhead is a medium-sized garden with beautiful borders which have a backbone of perennial shrubs among herbaceous planting, plus a scattering of annuals which provide on-going interest. September is one of the best months to visit this garden.

Open: Sunday 15 September, 2pm - 5pm, admission £6.00, children free.

Directions: A911 between Auchmuirbridge and Scotlandwell.

Opening for: Broke Not Broken : Kinross

Fife

17 HARTHILL
Reediehill Farm, Auchtermuchty KY14 7HS
Nichola and John Fletcher
T: 01337 828369 E: info@nicholafletcher.com
W: www.nicholafletcher.com

Harthill enjoys a tranquil setting in the Ochil hills just above Auchtermuchty with beautiful views and, if you are lucky, sightings of the herd of stunning pure white deer who also live there. The garden, of approximately one acre, offers a large flower garden, vegetables and fruit, two separate wild gardens planted with specimen trees, a lochan and a small woodland. Spring-time treats (late May to early June) are our meconopsis and primula beds with woodland plants at their best. Summer offers herbaceous interest including a pergola dripping with roses and a large mound with grasses, thalictrum and many very large plants. Autumn colours are in the trees and shrubs, with grasses and cyclamen through to early winter.

Open: by arrangement 2 January - 31 October, admission by donation. The garden will also be open under the Auchtermuchty Village opening – see separate listing.

Directions: Find 'Reediehill Deer Farm' on Google maps. Continue 50 metres up the drive then turn LEFT at HARTHILL sign. Continue over the cattle grid up the unsurfaced drive till you reach Harthilll house. Directions can be emailed.

Opening for: TST

18 HELENSBANK HOUSE
Kincardine FK10 4QZ
David Buchanan-Cook
T: 07739 312912 E: Helensbank@aol.com
W: www.helensbank.com

Hidden away from public view, this is an 18th-century walled garden, with main feature a Cedar of Lebanon, reputedly planted in 1750 by the sea captain who built the house. The tree is registered as a 'Notable Tree' and while it provides challenges for planting, in terms of shade and needle fall, the microclimate it provides has encouraged the owner's passion for pushing boundaries and growing unusual and exotic plants. Distinctive garden 'rooms' in part of the garden comprise a perennial blue and white cottage garden, a formal rose garden and an Italian double courtyard with citrus trees in pots. A 'hot' courtyard contains exotics including varieties of banana, acacia, iochroma, impatiens, melianthus and brugmansia. A shaded walk along the bottom of the garden leads to a Japanese themed area including a pagoda and dry river. A large glasshouse hosts various exotic and climbing plants. The garden has well over a hundred roses, including the National Collection of Portland roses. These are best viewed from mid June to early July.
National Plant Collection: Portland Roses.
Champion Trees: The garden has a 'notable' Cedar of Lebanon, the second largest in Fife.

Open: by arrangement 1 June - 31 August, admission £6.00, children free. There is an annual garden charity concert on the first Saturday of July when the roses will be looking their best. Tickets available in advance via email.

Directions: The garden is down a lane off the main Toll Road. *SGS* signs.

Opening for: Maggie's

Fife

19 KIRKBRAE HOUSE

Culross KY12 8JD
Sandra Bannister
E: Sandra.bannister18@gmail.com

An acre of walled garden sitting high in the village of Culross in the shadow of the Abbey. With meandering paths through perennial beds, bright annuals and shrubs and trees from as far as South America and Asia, the garden provides interest from late spring until autumn. The garden aims to provide an environment of joy, surprise and opportunity to sit and enjoy the spectacular garden views of the River Forth.

Open: Saturday/Sunday, 22/23 June, Saturday/Sunday, 20/21 July & Sunday 18 August, 11am - 4pm, admission £6.00, children free.

Directions: The garden is located on Kirk Street. On leaving the lower village start to climb up to the Abbey, the garden gates open directly onto Kirk Street. Car parking is either below the garden or near the Abbey. Buses come into the village from Dunfermline and Kincardine

Opening for: All proceeds to SGS Beneficiaries

20 KIRKLANDS

Saline KY12 9TS
Peter and Gill Hart
T: 07787 115477 E: peter@kirklandsgarden.co.uk
W: www.kirklandsgarden.co.uk

Kirklands, built in 1832, has been the Hart family home for 46 years. Over the years we have created a garden. The walled garden was reinstated from a paddock including terracing and raised beds. In 2023 we introduced two bee hives. Unfortunately, our box hedges in the walled garden and elsewhere are being removed due to box blight, but it gives us the opportunity to make some changes! The woodland garden starts in February with snowdrops then bluebells, hellebores, trilliums, fritillaries, rhododendrons, meconopsis and candelabra primulas. The rockery displays dwarf rhododendrons and azaleas. The herbaceous borders reach their peak in the summer. Down by the Saline Burn, the bog garden is home to a giant *Gunnera manicata*. Over the red or blue bridge there are 20 acres of naturally regenerating woodland with a pathway by the stream. To keep the grandchildren occupied, Peter built a tree house, climbing frame and rope swing, though we hope they will take an interest in gardening too!

Open: by arrangement 1 April - 30 September. Also open Sunday 26 May, 2pm - 5pm. Admission £6.00, children free.

Directions: Junction 4, M90, then B914. Parking in the centre of the village, then a short walk to the garden. Limited disabled parking at Kirklands.

Opening for: All proceeds to SGS Beneficiaries

Fife

21 LINDORES HOUSE
by Newburgh KY14 6JD
Robert and Elizabeth Turcan & John and Eugenia Turcan
T: 01337 840369

Situated between Lindores House and Lindores Loch, and with stunning views over the loch, the garden has been developed by the current owners over the last 45 years. It now includes extensive lochside and woodland walks with banks of snowdrops, leucojum, hostas, gunnera manicata, primula, astilbes, crocuses, fritillaria, spring and autumn cyclamen, hellebores and a notably impressive collection of trilliums. As well as the much older established trees – and in particular the splendid 17th Century yew (believed to be the largest in Fife which you can actually walk inside) there are more recent plantings of interesting specimen trees and shrubs. The herbaceous beds are mainly laid out formally around the old tennis court overlooking the loch. There is a one-acre walled garden, mainly used for growing fruit and vegetables, and a new garden in front of the recently converted stable building is under construction.

Open: Saturday 24 February, noon - 2pm for Snowdrops and Winter Walks. Also open Sunday 2 June, 2pm - 5pm. Admission £6.00, children free. Homemade bread and soup on Sunday 24 February.

Directions: Off A913 two miles east of Newburgh. Bus from Cupar.

Opening for: Siobhan's Trust (Saturday 24 February) & RC Diocese Of Dunkeld: St Columba's RC Church Cupar (Sunday 2 June)

22 MADEIRA
Grangemuir, Pittenweem KY10 2RB
Tara Macdonald
T: 07867 798746 E: tara@madeirainfife.com
W: www.madeirainfife.com

Madeira is a wonderful, ten-acre eco garden with a Victorian walled garden at its centre. We have an orchard and vegetable garden, pretty paths through woodland and plenty of bluebells and snowdrops. We don't use chemicals and fully support wildlife and the habitat they live in; the bee garden and our wilding areas are just two examples. The garden is a work in progress and we are continually creating spaces and fun things for kids to enjoy e.g. our dragon's den, Viking shelter, rope swings and more. We grow our own vegetables and love turning our fruit into juices, jellies, jams and ice-cream. We'd be delighted to show you round or let you wander and enjoy.

Open: by arrangement 1 February - 30 September (Tuesday, Thursday & Friday). Admission £6.00, children free. Open for Snowdrops & Winter Walks from 1 February to 11 March as part of the Scottish Snowdrop Festival.

Directions: Take the bus to Pittenweem and walk up Charles Street, past the recycling centre and we are 400 metres up on the left.

Opening for: All proceeds to SGS Beneficiaries

Fife

 23 MOONZIE HOUSE
By Cupar KY15 4NL
Katherine Watts
T: 07720 266298 E: Kathy@joe-cool.co.uk

Moonzie House was formerly the manse to historic Moonzie Kirk, which sits a few metres away at the top of the small hill. The modest walled garden has been developed over 35 years around a pre-existing central circular feature and echoes the circles and curves to create a garden that is traditional with some surprising features. As well as a wide variety of shrubs and perennials, the garden is home to a collection of over 60 different bamboo varieties which are subtly incorporated among more traditional plantings.

Open: Sunday 30 June, noon - 6pm, admission £6.00, children free.

Directions: From Cupar take the A913 (Newburgh, Perth Road). In approximately 3 miles, shortly after the large bends at Kilmaron, turn right to Moonzie. Take next left, signposted Moonzie Church and follow the single track road to the top. After the farmyard bear right following the track alongside the wall or follow parking instructions. **From Dundee** take the A92, after Rathillet, turn left where Moonzie signposted, then instructions as above. Similarly, from Edinburgh/Perth, from A92 at Parbroath crossroads take the A913 and then as above.

Opening for: Moonzie Kirk Preservation Trust

 24 PITLOCHIE HOUSE
Gateside KY14 7SQ
George & Fay Orr
T: 07730135953

This established garden has year-round interest. A restoration project with quirky features, characters and surprises! Comprising lots of different areas, the garden is carpeted in spring with snowdrops, daffodils, camassia and then bluebells. Following on there are over 140 varieties of hosta, plus heuchera, hellebores, roses, clematis, and lilies. There are formal herbaceous borders within two walled gardens, hedges, woodland, shaded planting, glass house, fruit trees, rhododendrons and azaleas. And pots of all description in every available corner.

Open: Sunday 26 May, 10am - 6pm. Also open Sunday 28 July, 10am - 6pm. And open Sunday 1 September, 10am - 6pm. Admission £6.00, children free. The garden will also be open with the Gardens of Auchtermuchty on Saturday and Sunday, 15 - 16 June, 12 - 5pm.

Directions: On the A912 Gateside to Perth. The garden is on the right hand side, 200 metres from the village main street

Opening for: Gateside And District Community Association

Fife

25 **PITTENWEEM: GARDENS IN THE BURGH**
Pittenweem KY10 2PG
Gardeners of Pittenweem
T: 07718 000802

An inspiring variety of gardens, many tucked away behind houses and garden walls, displaying a wide range of styles, from traditional to landscaped to richly productive and incorporating many interesting and unusual plants. This is a chance to visit old favourites and discover new projects.

Open: Sunday 16 June, noon - 5pm, admission £6.00, children free. Tickets and maps will be available from Art@47, 47 High Street, Pittenweem, KY10 2PG and from some of the gardens. Refreshments will be available in several venues as well as local coffee shops. Limited disabled access.

Directions: For tickets and maps follow postcode above to High Street. For parking, coming from the west follow signs to West Braes car park, from Ovenstone use car park next to football field/cemetery off Charles Street, and from the east turn right and park in Milton Road. Parking may also be available throughout the village.

Opening for: British Heart Foundation

26 **ROSEWELLS**
Baldinnie, Ceres KY15 5LE
Birgitta and Gordon MacDonald
E: g.macdonald54@hotmail.co.uk

Rosewells, designed by the garden owners, has developed over the last 25 years. It started as a one-and-a-half acre, overgrown paddock. The design is based on the texture and foliage of trees and shrubs to create year-round interest. In spring and summer, colour and scent become increasingly important. In spring, highlights are around 55 magnolias and rhododendrons, many of which are chosen for their foliage. Other highlights include flowering cornus, trillium, fritillaries, erythroniums, peonies, roses, ferns and acers. There have been a number of developments in recent years. More winding paths have been developed creating wildlife friendly areas. There is a new lavender walk which leads to a covered seating area at the bottom of the garden.

Open: by arrangement 1 April - 30 September, admission £6.00, children free.

Directions: B940 between Pitscottie and Peat Inn, one mile from Pitscottie. Rosewells is the ochre-coloured house.

Opening for: Save the Children UK

Fife

 27 **SGS AUTUMN PLANT SALE AT ST ANDREWS BOTANIC GARDEN**
St Andrews KY16 8RT
St Andrews Botanic Garden

The famous Fife Autumn Plant Sale returns to the St Andrews Botanic Garden. In addition to a fabulous selection of bare-root and potted plants, all grown locally within Fife, a number of selected Scottish specialist nurseries will be selling their wares. The plant sale starts promptly at 12 noon.

Open: Sunday 6 October, noon - 3pm, admission £3.00, children free. Plant donations - large and small - will be extremely welcome on the Friday and Saturday preceding the sale. For delivery details please contact Julia Young at *southfliskgarden@gmail.com* or David Buchanan-Cook at *helensbank@aol.com.*

Directions: The garden is located on Canongate, situated a 10/15 minute walk from the town centre. Follow the signs from the town down Viaduct Walk, which is a shared path for bikes and pedestrians. The 99C bus route goes past the garden and takes 5 minutes from the town centre. There is a free car park at the garden.

Opening for: St Andrews Botanic Garden Trust

 28 **SOUTH FLISK**
Blebo Craigs, Cupar KY15 5UQ
Mr and Mrs George Young
T: 01334 850859 E: southfliskgarden@gmail.com
W: www.standrewspottery.co.uk

The spectacular views to Perthshire and Angus, and the large flooded quarry full of fish (and occasional otter) and planted with impressive marginals, make this garden very special. Flights of old stone steps, cliffs, boulders, exotic ferns and mature trees form a backdrop for carpets of primroses, bluebells, spring bulbs and woodland plants like trilliums, camassia, meconopsis and colourful primulas, with rhododendrons in flower from March until July. In front of the house is a charming, mature walled garden with traditional cottage-garden planting. Next to the house is the St Andrews Pottery where George will be demonstrating his pottery skills for those who need a break from the garden! A new water garden with a stream running through it was created in 2023.

Open: Sunday 5 May, 11am - 5pm. Also open by arrangement 1 April - 30 June. Admission £6.00, children free. On 5 May, South Flisk is opening with Craig Cottage, just down the road.

Directions: Six miles west of St Andrews off B939 between Strathkinness and Pitscottie. There is a small stone bus shelter opposite the road into the village and sign saying *Blebo Craigs.* See map on our website. Bus to Blebo Craigs.

Opening for: Médecins Sans Frontières

Fife

29 SWALLOWS REST
Lindores KY14 6JD
Stuart & Elaine Ingram
T: 07703 435055 E: Elaine.ingram@icloud.com

The current owners moved in at the beginning of 2011 to a garden of grass and weeds. Since then, beds have been hand-dug, a slope filled with dwarf conifers and heathers, a pond and small stream made, and step-over fruit trees planted. The garden also hosts many perennials, shrubs, trees and acid-loving plants. Over 50 varieties of narcissus prolong spring interest, along with many hellebores and rhododendrons.

Open: Sunday 2 June, 2pm - 5pm, admission £6.00, children free.

Directions: Two miles east of Newburgh on the A913 past Den of Lindores, on the left, house with a white door with a stained glass panel of a swallow scene. The garden is opening on 2 June in conjunction with Lindores House - see above listing. As there is limited parking at Swallows Rest, visitors are advised to park at, and walk from, Lindores House.

Opening for: All proceeds to SGS Beneficiaries

30 THE GARDEN WITH THE DRAGON
2, Upper Wellheads, Limekilns KY11 3JQ
Mr and Mrs Duncan Philp
T: 01383 872047 E: df.philp@btinternet.com

A quirky coastal garden hidden behind a walled plot. Scatterings of California poppies, bluebells and a varied mix of annuals and perennials with a small clear pond. Different themes blend in the garden, all overseen by a majestic dragon sculpture perched on a tree.

Open: Saturday 18 May, 1pm - 4pm. Also open Saturday 25 May, 1pm - 4pm. Admission £6.00, children free.

Directions: Take the A985 from Rosyth or Kincardine and follow directions for Limekilns and Charlestown. The No.6 bus from Dunfermline bus station on the hour.

Opening for: The Five Sisters Zoo Rescue and Conservation SCIO

South Flisk © Carolyn Bell

Fife

31 **THE TOWER**
1 Northview Terrace, Wormit DD6 8PP
Peter and Angela Davey
T: 01382 541635 M: 07768 406946 E: adavey541@btinternet.com

Situated four miles south of Dundee, this one-acre Edwardian landscaped garden has panoramic views over the River Tay. Set on a hill, a series of paths meander around ponds and a small stream, rockeries featuring hellebores and low-level planting, a curved lawn and larger borders. Original woodland paths lead to a granite grotto with a waterfall pool. At the rear of the house the vegetable garden features raised beds made from granite sets. The garden is colourful throughout the summer, with many architectural plants accentuating the clever hard landscape design.

Open: by arrangement 1 April - 1 October, admission £6.00, children free.

Directions: From B946 park on Naughton Road outside Spar shop and walk up path on left following signs.

Opening for: Brain Tumour Research

32 **WILLOWHILL**
Forgan, Newport-on-Tay DD6 8RA
Eric Wright and Sally Lorimore
T: 01382 542890 E: e.g.wright@dundee.ac.uk
W: www.willowhillgarden.weebly.com

An evolving three-acre garden. The house is surrounded by a series of mixed borders designed with different vibrant colour combinations for effect in all seasons. Spectacular mix of roses, herbaceous perennials and annuals planted through the wide borders are a highlight in mid to late summer. A new 'no dig' 160-foot border in shades of white, blue, purple and pale yellow was created in 2019/2020. Come and see! April and May for late spring bulbs and flowers; June and July for roses and high summer colour; August for late summer colour.

The plant stall includes a lovely selection from the garden. Visitors are welcome to bring their own refreshments and picnic in the garden. A season ticket for all these dates, and by arrangement, is £20 plus p&p and admits the ticket holder plus guest. It comes with a limited edition of the Willowhill Garden Guide: 35 pages of beautiful photographs with descriptions of key garden features and plantings. A **season ticket** with booklet is a perfect gift for garden lovers for a birthday or at Christmas and do treat yourself too! Season tickets are available online at **tinyurl.com/4srm6rux** or by post (cheque for £23 payable to Scotland's Garden Scheme) from S. Lorimore, Willowhill, Forgan, Newport-on-Tay, Fife DD6 8RA.

Open: by arrangement from 27 April to 31 August. And open Saturday, Sunday and Monday, 27/28/29 April. Then open Saturday 1 June and Monday 3 June. Then Mondays and Saturdays from 1 July to 31 August. The garden will be open from 1 - 5pm on all dates.

Directions: 1½ miles south of Tay Road Bridge. Take the B995 to Newport off the Forgan roundabout. Willowhill is the first house on the left-hand side next to West Friarton Farm Strawberry Shed.

Opening for: Rio Community Centre: Newport-on-Tay

Glasgow & District

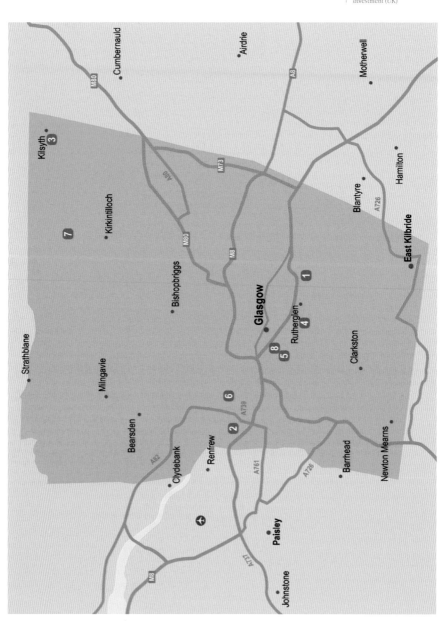

Glasgow & District

OUR VOLUNTEER ORGANISERS

District Organiser:	Heidi Stone	info@scotlandsgardens.org
Area Organisers:	Caroline Anderson	
	Ian Angus	
	Hilda Kelly	
	Anne Murray	
	Jim Murray	
District Photographer:	Alison Cummings	
Treasurer:	Vivien Pritchard	

GARDENS OPEN ON A SPECIFIC DATE

Kilsyth Gardens, Allanfauld Road	Sunday, 26 May
The Gardens of Milton of Campsie, Milton of Campsie	Sunday, 23 June
King's Park Walled Garden, 325 Carmunnock Road, Glasgow	Saturday, 6 July
SWG3 Community Garden, 100 Eastvale Place, Glasgow	Sunday, 21 July
Strathbungo Garden, March Street, Glasgow	Sunday, 28 July
Horatio's Garden, National Spinal Unit, Queen Elizabeth University Hospital, Govan Road, Glasgow	Sunday, 1 September
12 Chatelherault Avenue (A Soiree in September), Cambuslang	Saturday, 14 September

GARDENS OPEN REGULARLY

The Hidden Gardens, 25a Albert Drive, Glasgow	Year round - see website

GARDENS OPEN BY ARRANGEMENT

Kilsyth Gardens, Allanfauld Road	1 April - 31 August

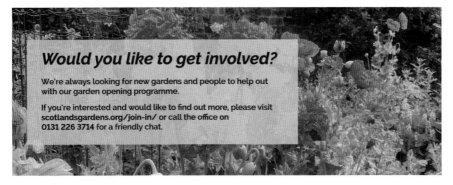

Would you like to get involved?

We're always looking for new gardens and people to help out with our garden opening programme.

If you're interested and would like to find out more, please visit scotlandsgardens.org/join-in/ or call the office on 0131 226 3714 for a friendly chat.

Glasgow & District

1 | 12 CHATELHERAULT AVENUE (A SOIREE IN SEPTEMBER)
Cambuslang, Glasgow G72 8BJ
Paul and Sheona Brightey

Come and join us for a delightful evening soiree in September with wine and music, which will be held in the garden. The front is split into a gravel garden and a white, scented woodland garden. Go through the gate to the back and you will find a garden where the aim of the owners is to grow as many different edibles as possible: herbs, soft fruit, vegetable beds, fruit arches and edible hedging. Lots of research has revealed more unusual edibles, such as fuchsia berries, cannas and hosta. There is also a greenhouse, which, in addition to a very productive grapevine, helps Paul indulge his passion for growing chillies. Seven fluffy hens live here too. There are two ponds, one of which has a healthy population of frogs, and the other is a little pond in a Victorian sink (for closer wildlife inspections). There are herbaceous perennials and a cut-flower bed, a pizza oven and BBQ and around the corner is a food smoker. Lots of lovely places to sit, in a garden that aims to be as much a living and socialising space as a productive garden.

Open: Saturday 14 September 7pm, admission by donation.

Directions: At Junction 2 of the M74 Glasgow to Cambuslang, exit onto Cambuslang Road/A724 towards Rutherglen, stay on Cambuslang Road/A724. Turn right onto Buchanan Drive then right onto Richmond Drive which become Chatelherault Avenue. Follow yellow *SGS* signs.

Opening for: Simon Community Scotland & Scottish Autism

2 | HORATIO'S GARDEN
National Spinal Unit, Queen Elizabeth University Hospital, Govan Road, Glasgow G51 4TF
Horatio's Garden
E: chelsea.lowe@horatiosgarden.org.uk
W: Horatiosgarden.org.uk

Carefully created by acclaimed garden designer and RHS Judge, James Alexander-Sinclair, Horatio's Garden Scotland opened in 2016 and supports patients affected by spinal cord injury from across the whole of Scotland, their loved ones and NHS staff. The gardens provide peaceful, yet vibrant, horticultural havens. Horatio's Garden Scotland features a woodland garden awash with striking seasonal blooms and framed by a beautiful collection of Betula pendula trees, as well as artfully planted borders, courtyard garden, gorgeous garden room, fruitful glasshouse and much more. There's plenty to explore in this thoughtful, therapeutic garden; one which rarely opens to the public and is unusually nestled right in the heart of a Greater Glasgow & Clyde NHS hospital.

Open: Sunday 1 September, 2pm - 5pm, admission £7.00, children free.

Directions: From the east or west of the city: on the M8 motorway to Junction 25, follow signs for the *Clyde Tunnel* (A739) for three-quarters of a mile, then follow signs for the *Queen Elizabeth Hospital*. Turn left into Govan Road and the hospital is on the left. From north of the River Clyde: go through the Clyde Tunnel (A739) and follow signs for the hospital. Please look at our website for the hospital estate map for directions to the garden and available parking.

Opening for: Horatio's Garden

Glasgow & District

3 KILSYTH GARDENS
Allanfauld Road G65 9DE
Mr George Murdoch, Mr and Mrs Alan Patrick
T: 07743 110908 E: alan.patrick3@googlemail.com

Aeolia Allanfauld Road, Kilsyth G65 9DE (Mr George Murdoch): A third-of-an-acre woodland garden developed since 1960 and designed to have something in flower every month of the year. The garden contains a large variety of mature specimen trees and shrubs, maples, primulas, hardy geraniums and herbaceous plants. Spring bulbs provide early colour and lilies and dahlias provide late season interest. There are a couple of small ponds for wildlife, two greenhouses and a fruit production area. The owner is a member of the *Scottish Rhododendron Society* and has a collection of over 100 specimens, some grown from seed. Areas of the garden are often under development to provide something new to see and provide material for the extensive plant sale, which is all home grown.

Blackmill Allanfauld Road, Kilsyth G65 9DE (Mr and Mrs A Patrick): Across the road from Aeolia is Blackmill through which the Garrel Burn flows. The garden includes the magnificent seven-metre waterfall with its ever-changing moods throughout the year. On one side of the property, on the site of an old water-powered sickle mill, is an acre of mature specimen trees, rhododendrons and shrubs with an ornamental pond and a rock pool built into the remains of the mill building. Across the burn there is a further two acres of woodland glen with paths along the waterside offering glimpses of the many cascading waterfalls. A large area of wildflowers has been newly introduced alongside the burn. A micro-hydro scheme is on view, along with many different examples of dry stone walls. Visitors remark on the sense of tranquillity and peace they experience in the garden and appreciate the works of art created from repurposed stone and salvaged material.

Open: Sunday 26 May, 2pm - 5pm. Also open by arrangement 1 April - 31 August. Admission £6.00, children free. Tea, coffee and box of home-baked cakes £4.00, children £1.00. By arrangement openings for parties of six or more. WC available but not suitable for disabled.

Directions: Turn off the A803 into Parkburn Road up to the crossroads (parking attendant will advise on parking). The 89 bus Glasgow - Kilsyth has a stop at the crossroads a couple of minutes walk to the gardens. The nearest station is Croy, then take the bus 147 or 344 to Kilsyth.

Opening for: Strathcarron Hospice

Kilsyth Gardens

Glasgow & District

4 KING'S PARK WALLED GARDEN

King's Park, 325 Carmunnock Road, Glasgow G44 5HL
Friends of King's Park
E: contactus@friendsofkingsparkglasgow.co.uk
W: friendsofkingsparkglasgow.co.uk

The C-listed walled garden within King's Park would have served as a kitchen garden for the original James Hamilton estate in the 18th century, with colourful beds and borders and fruit trees. In recent years, Friends of King's Park have adopted the garden from Glasgow City Council with the aim of reinstating it to its former glory. The garden is split into quarters, two of which FOKP planted with trees, shrubs, perennials and spring bulbs between 2022 and 2023. The east-facing bed has been planted with weeping cherry trees, underplanted with a selection of bulbs and a variety of perennials. The north-facing bed has a row of beautiful cherry trees. The south-facing wall will showcase cordons of a range of fruiting trees, which FOKP extended over winter 2023. We aim to further enrich the experience of visiting this garden and as a charitable organisation, will continue to raise funds to fully restore the walled garden. There will be a number of activities, stalls and displays available on the day. The garden is also open daylight hours all year round for anyone to enjoy (times may vary!). Another point of interest is the sensory garden (located behind the mansion house).
Champion Trees: Yew trees (in main King's Park).

Open: Saturday 6 July, 2pm - 5pm, admission £5.00 or donation, children free. Children's activities please refer to the scotlandsgardens.org website.

Directions: Free on-street parking is available in all streets surrounding the park. King's Park is accessible by public transport: buses 5 and 31 for the Carmunnock Road entrances, 34 and 75 for the Menock Road entrance. King's Park train station is a two-minute walk from the Menock Road entrance.

Opening for: FARE Scotland Ltd

King's Park Walled Garden

Glasgow & District

 5 STRATHBUNGO GARDEN
March Street, Glasgow G41 2PX
Frank Burns
W: facebook.com/strathbungogarden

Nestled behind Glasgow's busy main road artery to the Southside, you will happen upon a hidden walled terrace garden which marks the historical boundary to Strathbungo. It's an unexpected cottage-style city garden, showing how a piece of ground can be turned into a lovely colourful space for all the occupants of the terrace to enjoy. Inventive container planting is a key feature of this distinct urban retreat, which holds year-round interest. There is a range of fruit trees, some of which are trained as minarettes and stepovers. Why not visit Strathbungo Garden on Facebook and see what's been happening in the garden over the past months?

Open: Sunday 28 July, 2pm - 5pm, admission £4.00, children free.

Directions: From the south take the M74 to Junction 1A Polmadie. Turn left onto Polmadie Road, then turn right at the next traffic lights onto Calder Street. Proceed to Nithsdale Drive, then turn left into March Street where ample parking can be found. From the north take the M8 and join the M74, turn right into Polmadie Road at Junction 1A.

Opening for: ALVO Rural South Lanarkshire

 6 SWG3 COMMUNITY GARDEN
100 Eastvale Place, Glasgow G3 8QG
Jeremy Needham, Head Gardener

Situated behind the main SWG3 warehouse building, it's a surprise to walk up the steps leading to this space and be delighted by the sight of trees, grasses, shrubs and perennials making a beautiful garden where there was once only derelict land between two railway lines. The garden has wide paths curving through the beds and the various indigenous trees subtly define the shape of the garden. Apart from the interesting planting, this garden, which was designed by the horticulturist and garden designer Jeremy Needham, has beehives and two different heights of raised beds which are used by the local community as allotments. Many of the plants were donated to SWG3 by *The New York Times*, who had their offices for COP26 in their buildings.

Open: Sunday 21 July, 2pm - 5pm, admission £5.00, children free.

Directions: The nearest station to SWG3 in Glasgow is Kelvinhall SPT Subway Station, Partick, which is a 14 minute walk away. Free parking is available on Eastvale Place and Kelvinhaugh Street on Saturdays and Sundays.

Opening for: Studio Warehouse

Glasgow & District

7 THE GARDENS OF MILTON OF CAMPSIE
Milton of Campsie G66 8EA
The Gardeners of Milton Campsie

As well as a selection of smaller gardens, all with varying interests, we are delighted that the stunning new garden, Lillyburn will be joining us for the first time in 2024.

18 James Boyle Square G66 8JN (Hugh and Vivien Pritchard): Developed from scratch a few years ago, this peaceful, colourful garden holds a wide variety of perennial plants as well as hanging baskets, a well-stocked greenhouse and summer bedding plants, all of which can be grown by anyone who loves gardening.

56 Lochiel Drive G66 8EU (James and Ann Pert): A small garden with a variety of plants in the north-facing front garden, with herbs and geraniums under the balcony made from recycled scaffold boards by the garden owner.

Lillyburn House (NEW) 21 Campsie Road G66 8EB (Ray McKenzie): A lovely mature garden with lots of interesting features including sculptures and a summer house, gravel walkways meandering through the informal layout of colourful shrubs, flowers and trees, creating a haven for wildlife. Four lawns, one with a California-style summer house with seating areas and two magnificent champion yew trees, make this an unmissable garden to visit.

Marengo Cottage 8 Campsie Road G66 8EA (Angela Welsh): A small garden with many quirky features, it contains fruit trees, a vegetable patch, paths between flower and fauna beds, a small pond and if you can spot him, a topiary rabbit.

Milton of Campsie Community Garden
Campsie Road G66 8EU: The community garden is the creation of one man covering roughly an acre of hillside beside the Glazert water. A small beach where there are otters and kingfishers, memorial gardens and various bespoke seating, make this an unmissable garden.

Open: Sunday 23 June, 1pm - 5pm, admission £8.00, children free. Dogs on a lead welcome in some of the gardens.

Directions: From Glasgow, Kirkintilloch, Bishopbriggs bus numbers X85, 89, 88. By road, B757. By SatNav use postcode G66 8EU and follow *SGS* yellow road signs. There is free parking at the church and at other various signposted sites. **Lillyburn House** is in the corner of Campsie Road and Cottonmill Drive.

Opening for: The Trussell Trust: Food Bank Kirkintilloch

Lillyburn House

Glasgow & District

8 THE HIDDEN GARDENS

25a Albert Drive, Glasgow G41 2PE
The Hidden Gardens Trust
T: 0141 433 2722 E: info@thehiddengardens.org.uk
W: thehiddengardens.org.uk

The multi-award winning Gardens have been designed to reflect the legacy of this historic site as well as the ever-changing character and needs of the local area. The north to south borders echo the layout of the site when it was a nursery in the 1800s, supplying trees and shrubs to major gardens in Scotland, whilst the retained tramlines and the chimney reflect its industrial past. A number of artworks are integrated into the overall design, for example Alec Finlay's Xylotheque, a library of wooden books detailing 17 native Scottish trees. The Hidden Gardens is an independent charity offering learning and social activities and opportunities for the whole community to participate in its development. It is a calm, green space where you can relax away from the busy city streets: take a meditative walk along the square route path around the formal lawn; brush past the aromatic herb border; admire the white wall border with its herbaceous plantings and espalier fruit trees; stroll through the wildlife area; connect with nature in the woodland glade; and enjoy the naturalistic planting of the grassy or wild flower meadows or buy some young plants propagated here. Volunteer-led guided tours are available to book during most of the year, for free.

Open: Check the garden's website for up-to-date opening details and events.

Directions: Travel directions are available on the garden's website *thehiddengardens.org.uk/ explore/visit/*

Opening for: *Donation to SGS Beneficiaries*

Horatio's Garden © Endrick Landscapes

Inverness, Ross, Cromarty & Skye

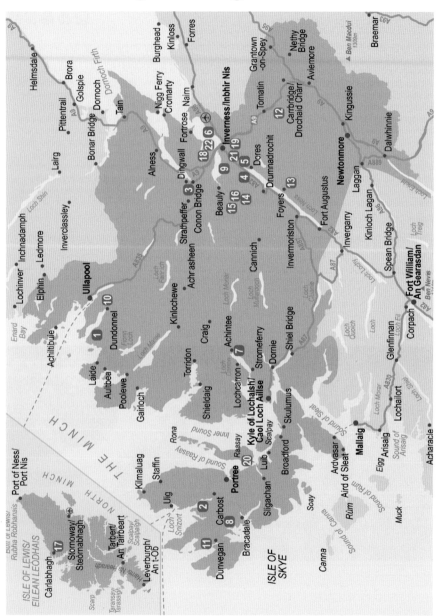

Inverness, Ross, Cromarty & Skye

OUR VOLUNTEER ORGANISERS

District Organiser:	Lucy Lister-Kaye	House of Aigas, Aigas, Beauly IV4 7AD lucy.listerkaye@gmail.com
Area Organiser:	Emma MacKenzie	Glenkyllachy, Tomatin IV13 7YA emmaglenkyllachy@gmail.com
Treasurer:	Sheila Kerr	11 Drumdevan Road, Inverness IV2 4BZ sheila.kerr@talk21.com

GARDENS OPEN ON A SPECIFIC DATE

Dunvegan Castle and Gardens, Isle of Skye	Saturday, 10 February
Dunvegan Castle and Gardens, Isle of Skye	Thursday, 15 February
Dunvegan Castle and Gardens, Isle of Skye	Tuesday, 20 February
Dundonnell House, Little Loch Broom, Wester Ross	Thursday, 11 April
Gorthleck House Garden, Stratherrick	Friday 24 May - Sunday 2 June
Dundonnell House, Little Loch Broom, Wester Ross	Thursday, 30 May
Old Allangrange, Munlochy	Sunday, 9 June
Glenkyllachy, Tomatin	Sunday, 16 June
House of Aigas and Field Centre, by Beauly	Sunday, 23 June
7 Braes of Conon, Conon Bridge	Sunday, 30 June
Kiltarlity Gardens, Kiltarlity, Beauly	Sunday, 14 July
House of Aigas and Field Centre, by Beauly	Sunday, 28 July
2 Durnamuck, Little Loch Broom, Wester Ross	Sunday, 4 August
Aldourie Castle Garden, Dores, Inverness	Sunday, 11 August
Dundonnell House, Little Loch Broom, Wester Ross	Thursday, 15 August
Old Allangrange, Munlochy	Sunday, 18 August

GARDENS OPEN REGULARLY

Raasay Walled Garden, Isle of Raasay	1 January - 31 December
Oldtown of Leys Garden, Inverness	Daily - except 1 May - 31 October (not open Thursday & Friday)
Highland Liliums, 10 Loaneckheim, Kiltarlity	1 January - 31 December
Abriachan Garden Nursery, Loch Ness Side	1 February - 30 November
Glenkyllachy, Tomatin	1 April - 31 October (Mon & Tues)
Dunvegan Castle and Gardens, Isle of Skye	1 April - 15 October
Attadale, Strathcarron	1 April - 31 October
Leathad Ard, Upper Carloway, Isle of Lewis	1 May - 30 September (not Sunday)
Balmeanach House, Balmeanach, nr Struan, Isle of Skye	1 May - 2 October
5 Knott, Clachamish, Portree, Isle of Skye	7 June - 30 September (Mon Fri & Sun)

Inverness, Ross, Cromarty & Skye

GARDENS OPEN BY ARRANGEMENT

Glenkyllachy, Tomatin	1 January - 31 December
Ar Dachaigh, Redhill Farm, Allanfearn, Inverness	1 January - 31 December
Berryfield House, Lentran, Inverness	1 April - 31 July
House of Aigas and Field Centre, by Beauly	1 April - 31 October
Dundonnell House, Little Loch Broom, Wester Ross	1 April - 31 October
Leathad Ard, Upper Carloway, Isle of Lewis	1 April - 30 April
Struanbridge, Essich Road, Inverness	1 May - 31 October
Old Allangrange, Munlochy	1 May - 31 October
The Lookout, Kilmuir, North Kessock	1 June - 31 August (not Saturday)
5 Knott, Clachamish, Portree, Isle of Skye	1 June - 30 September
2 Durnamuck, Little Loch Broom, Wester Ross	1 July - 30 September

2 Durnamuck

Inverness, Ross, Cromarty & Skye

1 **2 DURNAMUCK**
Little Loch Broom, Wester Ross IV23 2QZ
Will Soos and Susan Pomeroy
T: 01854 633761 E: sueandwill@icloud.com
W: 2Durnamuckgarden.com. You can also find us on Facebook.

Our garden is south-east facing on the edge of Little Loch Broom. It is a coastal plantsman's garden with a rich mix of herbaceous borders, trees and shrubs, vegetables, drystone wall planting, South African/Mediterranean plants, a wild meadow and stunning views. Many of the plants have been collected from all over the world, and growing them has provided obvious challenges but with a pleasing outcome. Featured in 2019 entries in *Gardens Illustrated, Homes & Gardens* and *Beechgrove.* Entry in the *English Garden* magazine in September 2020.

Open: Sunday 4 August, 11am - 4pm. Also open by arrangement 1 July - 30 September. Admission £5.00, children free. Teas by donation. A wood and stone accommodation, The Garden Bothy, is available for garden passionate people. It is small and compact but very beautiful in its own garden. Enquiries to sueandwill@icloud.com and 2Durnamuckgarden.com

Directions: On the A832, between Dundonnell and Ullapool, take the turning along the single-track road signed *Badcaul*, continue to the egg shack, turn right, go to the bottom of the hill and 2 Durnamuck is the house with the red roof. There is parking down by the house if needed.

Opening for: Scotland's Charity Air Ambulance

2 **5 KNOTT**
Clachamish, Portree, Isle of Skye IV51 9NZ
Brian and Joyce Heggie
T: 07495 442468 E: jbheggie@hotmail.co.uk
W: www.knottskye.co.uk

An informal, organic garden on a gently-sloping half-acre site. Perimeter hedging has enabled a sheltered and tranquil oasis to be created. Winding paths meander through the densely-planted borders filled with a diverse range of perennials, annuals and shrubs. There is also a vegetable area with raised beds and a large polytunnel. A developing wildflower meadow with sea loch views leads onto a sheltered bay and a shoreside walk to the headland. There are regular sightings of seals, otters, sea eagles and harbour porpoises. Garden seating in several locations. The garden is situated in an easily-reached, particularly quiet and scenic area of Skye. Featured on *Beechgrove* in 2023.

Open: 7 June - 30 September (Monday, Friday & Sunday), 2pm - 5pm. Also open by arrangement 1 June - 30 September. Admission £4.00, children free.

Directions: From Portree, take the A87 to Uig/Dunvegan. After approximately three miles, take the A850 towards Dunvegan. Six miles on, pass the *Treaslane* sign. Turn right on the bend at the signpost for *Knott.*

Opening for: Crossroads Care Skye & Lochalsh & The Way Forward Group

Inverness, Ross, Cromarty & Skye

3 7 BRAES OF CONON
Conon Bridge IV7 8AX
Mr Nigel Stanton

A beautifully-designed garden created by a professional nurseryman. Nigel Stanton moved to the Highlands in 2014. The garden needed imported local topsoil and a lot of manure. Now, eight years later, with the help of raised beds and paved paths, the fruits of his endeavours are a delight. Specialities include magnificent delphiniums, rampant sweet peas and subtly blended roses.

Open: Sunday 30 June, 2pm - 5pm, admission £5.00, children free.

Directions: Coming into Conon Bridge on the A862 from Muir of Ord, turn right into the Braes of Conon and follow the road signs to No. 7. From Dingwall, take the A835 towards Tore at the Maryburgh roundabout, then turn first right towards Conon Bridge, and follow the signs.

Opening for: Highland Hospice: Aird branch

4 ABRIACHAN GARDEN NURSERY
Loch Ness Side IV3 8LA
Mr and Mrs Davidson
T: 01463 861232 E: info@lochnessgarden.com
W: www.lochnessgarden.com

This is an outstanding garden with over four acres of exciting plantings with winding paths through native woodlands. Seasonal highlights include snowdrops, hellebores, primulas, meconopsis, hardy geraniums and colour-themed summer beds. Views over Loch Ness.

Open: 1 February - 30 November, 9am - 5pm open for Snowdrops and Winter Walks, in the spring, admission £4.00, children free.

Directions: On the A82 Inverness/Drumnadrochit road, about eight miles south of Inverness.

Opening for: Highland Hospice

Aldourie Castle Garden

Inverness, Ross, Cromarty & Skye

5 ALDOURIE CASTLE GARDEN

Dores, Inverness IV2 6DP
T: 07761 049125

Aldourie Castle garden has been designed by Tom Stuart-Smith and is an ambitious modern re-imagining of a traditional castle garden and grounds. The grounds include a walled garden, formal castle garden, arboretum and parkland. The 1.3 acre walled garden contains a large productive area which hosts a range of vegetables and cut flowers. There are espaliered apples and pears as well as soft fruit. Surrounding this area are extensive naturalistic borders, covering a range of habitats. The historic glasshouses are used to grow vegetables, tomatoes, cucumbers, figs and herbs. The castle itself is surrounded by two acres of gardens. These consist of large, late season, naturalistic herbaceous borders with beech topiaries and a central lawn with views of Loch Ness. There is an extensive terrace and smaller flower beds around the castle. Nearby is the Dell which is woodland in character and has more natural, native inspired planting. The four acre arboretum, containing some old tree specimens, is currently the subject of an interesting regeneration project.

Open: Sunday 11 August, 10am - 4pm, admission £8.00, children free.

Directions: Enter via the single track road adjacent to Aldourie Primary School, which is situated on the B862, 1.6 miles before Dores, when arriving from Inverness. Car parking is just before the electric gate on the left.

Opening for: Highland Hospice

6 AR DACHAIGH

Redhill Farm, Allanfearn, Inverness IV2 7JA
Mrs Tina Ross
T: 07920 803410 E: tinaross463@hotmail.co.uk

Ar Dachaigh has stunning views towards Kessock Bridge, the Black Isle and the Great Glen. The sloping garden is very exposed but after erecting fences, planting trees and hedging, the garden is beginning to flourish. As well as the colourful beds and borders, there are two ponds, five decks, and a large collection of plants in pots.

Open: by arrangement 1 January - 31 December, admission by donation.

Directions: Ar Dachaigh is to be found on a farm directly off the A96, 4.5 miles east of Inverness. **From Inverness** head east along the A96. Shortly after the turn off for Alturlie, there is a turn-off on the left with an old telephone box - this is the drive for Ar Dachaigh. **From the east** once you have passed the Balloch junction, the turn-off for the garden will be on your right-hand side at the old telephone box. PLEASE TAKE CARE as this is a busy stretch of the A96, and there are no filter lanes. After crossing the railway line Ar Dachaigh is ahead of you on the left.

Opening for: All proceeds to SGS Beneficiaries

Inverness, Ross, Cromarty & Skye

7 ATTADALE
Strathcarron IV54 8YX
Mr Ewen Macpherson
T: 01520 722603 E: info@attadalegardens.com
W: www.attadalegardens.com

The Gulf Stream, surrounding hills and rocky cliffs create a microclimate for 20 acres of outstanding water gardens, old rhododendrons, unusual trees and a fern collection in a geodesic dome. There is also a sunken fern garden developed on the site of an early 19th-century drain, a waterfall into a pool with dwarf rhododendrons, sunken garden, peace garden and kitchen garden. Other features include a conservatory, Japanese garden, sculpture collection and giant sundial.

Open: 1 April - 31 October, 10am - 5pm, admission £10.00, children free.

Directions: On the A890 between Strathcarron and South Strome.

Opening for: Highland Hospice

8 BALMEANACH HOUSE
Balmeanach, nr Struan, Isle of Skye IV56 8FH
Mrs Arlene Macphie
T: 01470 572320 E: info@skye-holiday.com
W: www.skye-holiday.com

Very much a plantsman's garden, begun in the early 1990s after a third-of-an-acre of croft land was fenced. A shelter belt now permits a plethora of diverse plants in exuberant herbaceous borders, which give nectar and pollen to keep the buzzing and fluttering going until autumn, plus rockeries and raised beds. Native trees rub shoulders with more exotic ornamental varieties, providing a canopy for shade-loving plants and nesting sites for the many birds who make the garden their home. A small pond in a sunken garden; a larger pond divided in two by a path over a culvert and a bog garden, give scope for marginal and moisture-loving plants. Meandering pathways lead through a small bluebell wood, an arbour garden, shrubbery and small birch wood, full of azaleas and rhododendrons. Plenty of seating throughout provides an invitation to sit, relax and enjoy the garden and stunning scenery beyond.

Open: 1 May - 2 October, 11am - 4pm, admission £4.00, children free. No teas on Saturdays and Sundays.

Directions: A87 to Sligachan, turn left and Balmeanach is five miles north of Struan and five miles south of Dunvegan.

Opening for: Scottish SPCA & Redwings

Attadale

Inverness, Ross, Cromarty & Skye

9 BERRYFIELD HOUSE
Lentran, Inverness IV3 8RJ
Lynda Perch-Nielsen
T: 01463 831346 M: 07547 960341 E: lyndazpn@gmail.com

An open garden of trees and bushes with views across the Beauly Firth to Ben Wyvis. There are large swathes of bulbs: crocus, dogtooth violets and heritage daffodils. A three-acre wildflower meadow with meandering paths adjoins the garden.

Open: by arrangement 1 April - 31 July, admission by donation.

Directions: Halfway between Inverness and Beauly on the A862. From Inverness, four-and-a-quarter miles on the left from crossing over the Clachnaharry railway bridge. From Beauly, one-and-a-quarter miles on the right from The Old North Inn.

Opening for: Action Medical Research

10 DUNDONNELL HOUSE
Little Loch Broom, Wester Ross IV23 2QW
Dundonnell Estates
T: 07789 390028 E: sueandwill@icloud.com

Camellias, magnolias and bulbs in spring, rhododendrons and laburnum walk in this ancient walled garden. Exciting planting in new borders gives all year colour, centred around one of the oldest yew trees in Scotland. A new water sculpture, midsummer roses, recently restored unique Victorian glass house, riverside walk, arboretum - all in the valley below the peaks of An Teallach.
Champion Trees: Yew and Holly.

Open: Thursday 11 April, Thursday 30 May and Thursday 15 August, 2pm - 5pm. Also open by arrangement 1 April - 31 October. Admission £5.00, children free. Teas only available on 30 May.

Directions: Turn off the A835 at Braemore on to the A832. After 11 miles take the Badralloch turn for a ½ mile.

Opening for: Multiple Sclerosis Society & Fauna & Flora International

Dundonnell House

Inverness, Ross, Cromarty & Skye

11 DUNVEGAN CASTLE AND GARDENS

Isle of Skye IV55 8WF
Hugh MacLeod of MacLeod
T: 01470 521206 E: info@dunvegancastle.com
W: www.dunvegancastle.com

Any visit to the Isle of Skye is incomplete without enjoying the wealth of history and horticultural delights at award-winning 5* Dunvegan Castle & Gardens, now an RHS partner garden. The five acres of formal gardens began life in the 18th century. In stark contrast to the barren moorland and mountains which dominate Skye's landscape, the Castle's Water Garden, Round Garden, Walled Garden and woodland walks provide an oasis for an eclectic mix of flowers, exotic plants, shrubs and specimen trees, framed by shimmering pools fed from waterfalls. After visiting the Water Garden with its ornate bridges and islands replete with colourful plants along the riverbanks, wander through the elegant formal Round Garden. The Walled Garden, formerly the Castle's vegetable garden, now has a diverse range of plants and flowers completing the attractive features, including a water lily pond, garden museum, 17th century lectern sundial, glass house and the 'Dunvegan Pebble', a rotating 2.7 ton Carrara marble sculpture. The informal areas of the garden are kept wild to encourage wildlife, creating a more natural aesthetic framed by the coastal scenery. The present Chief, Hugh MacLeod, and his dedicated team of gardeners, continue to build on this unique legacy for future generations to enjoy.

Open: Saturday 10, Thursday 15 and Tuesday 20 February, 10am - 5:30pm (last entry 5:00pm) for Snowdrops and Winter Walks (The garden and cafe will be open on these dates). Also open 1 April - 15 October, 10am - 5:30pm (last entry 5:00pm). Admission details can be found on the garden's website. The castle, gardens and cafe will open from the 1st of April until the 15th of October. Catering available from the MacLeod Tables Cafe in the car park.

Directions: One mile from Dunvegan village, 23 miles west of Portree. Follow the signs for *Dunvegan Castle.*

Opening for: *Donation to SGS Beneficiaries*

12 GLENKYLLACHY

Tomatin IV13 7YA
Mr and Mrs Philip Mackenzie
E: emmaglenkyllachy@gmail.com

In a magnificent Highland glen, 1200 feet above sea level, Glenkyllachy is a beautiful garden of shrubs, herbaceous plants, rhododendrons, trees, and spectacular views down the Findhorn River. There are some rare specimens and a recently planted arboretum. Rhododendrons and bulbs flower in May/June, herbaceous plants bloom through July/August with glorious autumn colours in September and October. There is a very productive vegetable garden, poly tunnel, fruit cage and greenhouse as well as original sculptures and a Highgrove-inspired wall which provide year round interest. Featured on TV *Beechgrove*, in *The English Garden Magazine* and recently in *Scottish Field* (November 2023). The garden is constantly evolving with new areas being developed and planting schemes changed.

Open: Sunday 16 June, 2pm - 5pm (the opening will include a plant sale with teas, stalls and live music). Also open 1 April - 31 October (Monday & Tuesday) 10am - 5pm, or any other day by arrangement.

Directions: Turn off the A9 at Tomatin and take the Coignafearn/Garbole single-track road down the north-side of the River Findhorn, there is a cattle grid and gate on the right 500 yards AFTER the humpback bridge and the sign to *Farr.*

Opening for: *Marie Curie*

Inverness, Ross, Cromarty & Skye

13 GORTHLECK HOUSE GARDEN
Stratherrick IV2 6UJ
Steve and Katie Smith
T: 07710 325903 E: gorthleckgarden@gmail.com

Gorthleck is an unusual 20-acre woodland garden built in an unlikely place, on and around an exposed rocky ridge which offers long views of the surrounding countryside in the 'borrowed landscape' tradition of Japanese gardens. The layout of the garden works with the natural features of the landscape with numerous paths, hedges and shelter belts creating clearly defined areas where a large collection of trees and shrubs are thriving. The garden includes over 400 different varieties of rhododendrons, half of which are species, and a large variety of bamboos. It is a large garden so allow sufficient time to see it properly.

Open: Friday 24 May - Sunday 2 June, 10am - 6pm, admission £5.00, children free.

Directions: From the A9, take the B851 towards Fort Augustus to join the B862. Go through the village of Errogie where there is a sharp left-hand bend on the road. After approximately one mile, there is a small church on the left. The Gorthleck drive is directly opposite the church and the house can be seen on the hill to the left as you follow the drive to the left of the new house. Visitors can park on the verges at the top of the drive.

Opening for: Maggie's

14 HIGHLAND LILIUMS
10 Loaneckheim, Kiltarlity IV4 7JQ
Neil and Frances Macritchie
T: 01463 741698 E: accounts@highlandliliums.co.uk
W: www.highlandliliums.co.uk

Highland Liliums is a working retail nursery with spectacular views over the Beauly valley and Strathfarrar hills. A wide selection of home-grown plants are available including alpines, ferns, grasses, herbaceous, herbs, liliums, primulas and shrubs.

Open: 1 January - 31 December, 9am - 5pm, admission free Also open as part of Kiltarlity Gardens, on Sunday 14 July.

Directions: Signposted from Kiltarlity village, which is just off the Beauly to Drumnadrochit road (A833), approximately 12 miles from Inverness.

Opening for: Donation to SGS Beneficiaries

Glenkyllachy

Inverness, Ross, Cromarty & Skye

15 HOUSE OF AIGAS AND FIELD CENTRE
by Beauly IV4 7AD
Sir John and Lady Lister-Kaye
T: 01463 782443 E: info@aigas.co.uk
W: www.aigas.co.uk

The House of Aigas has a small arboretum of named Victorian specimen trees and modern additions. The garden consists of extensive rockeries, herbaceous borders, ponds and shrubs. Aigas Field Centre rangers lead regular guided walks on nature trails through woodland, moorland and around a loch.
Champion Trees: Douglas fir, Atlas cedar and *Sequoiadendron giganteum*.

Open: Sunday 23 June & Sunday 28 July, 2pm - 5pm. Also open by arrangement 1 April - 31 October. Admission £5.00, children free. Homemade Teas £5.00.

Directions: Four-and-a-half miles from Beauly on the A831 Cannich/Glen Affric road.

Opening for: Highland Hospice: Aird branch

16 KILTARLITY GARDENS
Kiltarlity, Beauly IV4 7JH
Sheila Ross, Neil & Frances Macritchie and Dickon and Barbara Sandbach

Aird View 30a Camault Muir, Kiltarlity IV4 7JH (Sheila Ross): The garden at Aird View offers a mix of borders, a water feature, an arbour and a newly-added herbaceous border. There are also fruit trees and vegetable beds. Vintage tractors on display.
Highland Liliums 10 Loaneckheim, Kiltarlity IV4 7JQ (Neil and Frances Macritchie): Highland Liliums is a working retail nursery with spectacular views over the Beauly valley and Strathfarrar hills. A wide selection of home-grown plants are available including alpines, ferns, grasses, herbaceous, herbs, liliums, primulas and shrubs.
Monarda House (NEW) Kiltarlity, Beauly IV4 7HX (Dickon & Barbara Sandbach): An evolving, productive garden with a mix of ornamental and native plantings over four acres. An easy circuit, in proximity to the house on even paths, displays a variety of conifers, shrubs and herbaceous plants, with a summer house and sheltered stone circle. A wider circuit, for which stouter footwear is recommended, includes raised vegetable beds, polytunnel, chicken run, a young orchard, nuttery and mature woodland, with a pine-lined avenue along a ride up to the fledgling arboretum. Beyond is a rough-pathed area of regenerative woodlands, wildflower meadow, mature trees and willow coppice, to the old stable apiary, returning along a track sided with ornamental cherries.

Open: Sunday 14 July, noon - 5pm, admission £4.00, children free. Homemade teas and plants for sale at Highland Liliums.

Directions: Aird View take the A833 Beauly to Drumnadrochit Road, pass Brockies Lodge. Turn right at the bus shelter and follow the single-track road to the junction at the school. Turn left and go up the hill to the top, at the junction Aird View is on the right. **Highland Liliums** signposted from Kiltarlity Village, which is just off the Beauly to Drumnadrochit road (A833), approximately 12 miles from Inverness. **Monarda House** from the A833 Beauly to Drumnadrochit Road, turn into Kiltarlity. Drive right through the village, over a small bridge and take the next turn left, signed to *Clunevackie*. Continue for 1.3 miles until you see a forest track straight ahead and the road bears left; Monarda House is the next house on the right. What3words: valuables.teaches.brave

Opening for: Highland Hospice: Aird branch

Inverness, Ross, Cromarty & Skye

17 LEATHAD ARD

Upper Carloway, Isle of Lewis HS2 9AQ
Rowena and Stuart Oakley
T: 01851 643204 E: leathad.ard@gmail.com
W: www.leathadard.org.uk

A one-acre sloping garden with stunning views over East Loch Roag. It has evolved along with the shelter hedges that divide the garden into a number of areas giving a new view at every corner. With shelter and raised beds, the different conditions created permit a wide variety of plants to be grown. Features include herbaceous borders, cutting borders, bog gardens, grass garden, exposed beds, patios, a pond and vegetables and fruit grown both in the open ground and the Keder greenhouse. Some of the vegetables are grown to show standards.

Open: 1 May - 30 September (not Sunday), 10am - 6pm. Also open by arrangement 1 April - 30 April. Admission £5.00, children free.

Directions: On the A858 Shawbost-Carloway take the first right after the Carloway football pitch, and it is the first house on the right. By bus take the Westside circular bus, exit Stornoway and head for Carloway football pitch.

Opening for: British Red Cross

18 OLD ALLANGRANGE

Munlochy IV8 8NZ
J J Gladwin
T: 01463 811304 E: office@blackislegardendesign.com

We have an ornamental garden surrounding the house (new information discovered dates it from the 17th rather than 18th Century), and a three acre productive garden with two Keder greenhouses, designed using agroforestry and permaculture principles and gardened bio-dynamically using no-dig technique. The ornamental garden has different areas with distinctive characters. There is a parterre in front of the house with informal planting, a lower garden, an ornamental propagation garden, a mound and orchard. Hedges, (pleached lime, yew, beech, box, holly and mixed species field hedges) clipped in various styles connect the different areas of the garden. We have started to remove perimeter wire fences replacing them with log hedges and brash bunds. With a keen interest in gardening for biodiversity from the soil upwards, no chemicals have been used since our arrival in 1995. The development and improvement of the garden is ongoing.
Champion Trees: Yew and sweet chestnut.

Open: Sunday 9 June, 2pm - 5pm. Also open Sunday 18 August, 1:30pm - 5pm. And open by arrangement 1 May - 31 October. Admission £7.50, children free. There will be no teas, but there will be a baking stall, and visitors are welcome to bring a picnic. Guided tours given on the hour from 2pm - 4pm on open days. Tickets for self guided tours at other times can be bought from the Brewery Shop at a cost of £6.00 per head. Open by arrangement bookings for guided groups (minimum 10 people).

Directions: From Inverness head four miles north on the A9, and follow the directions for *Black Isle Brewery*. Park up at the Brewery and walk down to the garden. Directions will be given in the shop.

Opening for: Flourish

Inverness, Ross, Cromarty & Skye

19   OLDTOWN OF LEYS GARDEN
Inverness IV2 6AE
David and Anne Sutherland
T: 01463 238238 E: ams@oldtownofleys.com

Established in 2003, on the outskirts of Inverness, with views over the town, this large garden of three acres has year-round interest. Spring rhododendrons and azaleas, summer herbaceous plantings, autumn trees and shrubs and winter appeal from the conifers, evergreens and structures. Features include a rockery, ponds, musical instruments, a stumpery and a new area of late summer colour.

Open: 1 January - 31 December daily - except 1 May - 31 October (not open Thursday & Friday), dawn - dusk, admission by donation.

Directions: Turn off southern distributor road (B8082) at Leys roundabout towards Inverarnie (B861). At the T-junction turn right. After 50 metres turn right into Oldtown of Leys.

Opening for: Highland Hospice & Alzheimer Scotland

20   RAASAY WALLED GARDEN
Isle of Raasay IV40 8PB
Raasay Community
T: 07939 106426 E: raasaywalledgarden@gmail.com.
You can also find us on Facebook and Instagram
W: Raasay.com/the-walled-garden-raasay

Accessed from the road behind Raasay House, just a ten minute walk from the Ferry Terminal, is the Category A listed community owned Walled Garden. Visited by Boswell and Johnson in 1773, the garden suffered neglect before coming into community ownership. Ongoing restoration began in 2013 and the 1.43 acre garden now supplies vegetables, fruit, salad, herbs and cut flowers to the community and visitors. Features an orchard, rose beds, polytunnels, a fruit cage, wildflowers for pollinators and insects, and plenty of seats. We have a composting toilet for visitors' use. June to August provide the most colourful time and our main produce harvests take place from May to September. We run events during the year - please check our Facebook page for details. The garden isn't always staffed, so please contact us for further details.

Open: 1 January - 31 December, 9am - 7pm, admission by donation. Plants for sale occasionally, and vegetables once/twice weekly during the season.

Directions: Take the Calmac Ferry to Raasay (20 minute journey) from Sconser, between Broadford and Portree on the Isle of Skye. The garden is an easy walk from the terminal and there is plenty to do and see on Raasay on foot, although cars can also cross.

Opening for: Donation to SGS Beneficiaries

Inverness, Ross, Cromarty & Skye

21 STRUANBRIDGE
Essich Road, Inverness IV2 6AH
Marcus and Catriona Jenks
E: mjenks@greenx.co.uk

A small, well-stocked garden approximately three miles from Inverness city centre, set on three levels each with its own distinct character. The entrance to the garden includes a decking area where the hidden garden can be viewed, with a small fruit garden and raised beds. The small mid-tier area consists of mainly hydrangeas and rhododendrons and the very informal, hidden lower garden includes a wildlife pond, raised beds, and shaded garden area with a greenhouse, all framed by an old stone bridge and a small burn. Due to its layout, the garden is not suitable for wheelchairs and requires the ability to climb a number of steps to view.

Open: by arrangement 1 May - 31 October, admission £5.00, children free.

Directions: From the Inverness Southern Distributor road (A8082) exit the Essich roundabout onto Essich Road. Struanbridge is located exactly a ½ mile from the roundabout, on the left.

Opening for: Macmillan Cancer Support

Struanbridge

22 THE LOOKOUT
Kilmuir, North Kessock IV1 3ZG
David and Penny Veitch
T: 01463 731489 E: david@veitch.biz

A three-quarter-acre, elevated coastal garden, with incredible views over the Moray Firth, which is only for the sure-footed. This award-winning garden, featured on *Beechgrove*, has been created out of a rock base with shallow pockets of ground, planted to its advantage to encourage all aspects of wildlife. There is a small, sheltered courtyard, raised bed vegetable area, pretty cottage garden, scree and rock garden, rose arbour, rhododendrons, flowering shrubs, bamboos, trees and lily pond with waterside plants.

Open: by arrangement 1 June - 31 August (not Saturday), admission £4.00, children free. Teas available on request £6.00 per head. Dogs are not allowed.

Directions: From Inverness, take the North Kessock left turn from the A9, and third left at the roundabout to go on the underpass, then sharp left onto Kilmuir Road. From Tore, take the slip road for North Kessock and immediately right for Kilmuir. Follow signs for *Kilmuir* (three miles) until you reach the shore. The Lookout is near the far end of the village with a large palm tree in front, surrounded by gravel.

Opening for: Alzheimer's Research UK

Kirkcudbrightshire

Sponsored by

RATHBONES

Incorporating
Investec Wealth &
Investment (UK)

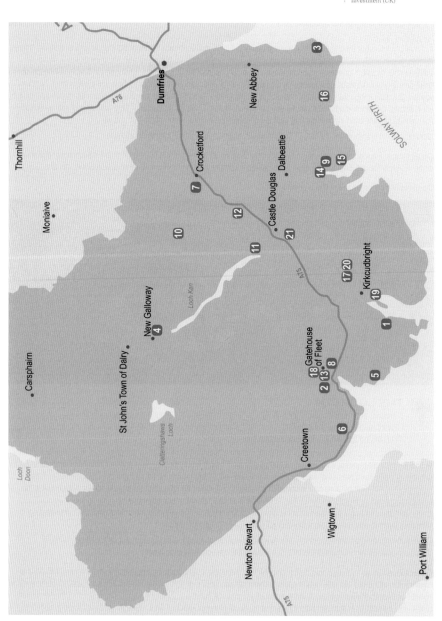

Kirkcudbrightshire

OUR VOLUNTEER ORGANISERS

District Organisers:	Julian Stanning	Seabank, Merse Road, Rockcliffe DG5 4QH
	Theodora Stanning	Seabank, Merse Road, Rockcliffe DG5 4QH
Area Organisers:	May Lockhart	25 Victoria Park, Kirkcudbright DG6 4EN
	Norman McClure	142 Cotton Street, Castle Douglas DG7 1DG
	Lesley Pepper	Anwoth Old Schoolhouse DG7 2EF
	George Thomas	Savat, Meikle Richorn, Dalbeattie DG5 4QT
Media Volunteer	Alison Forrest	Conifers, Rockcliffe, Dalbeattie DG5 4QF
District Photographer:	Stuart Littlewood	stu@f8.eclipse.co.uk
Treasurer:	Russell Allan	Braeburn, 6 Barcloy Mill, Rockcliffe DG5 4QL

GARDENS OPEN ON A SPECIFIC DATE

Danevale Park, Crossmichael	Sunday, 18 February
The Limes, Kirkcudbright	Sunday, 24 March
3 Millhall, Shore Road, Kirkcudbright	Sunday, 14 April
Balmaclellan House, Balmaclellan, Castle Douglas	Sunday, 28 April
Threave Garden, Castle Douglas	Monday, 6 May
Arbigland House, Kirkbean, Dumfries	Sunday, 12 May
Brooklands, Crocketford	Sunday, 19 May
The Limes, Kirkcudbright	Sunday, 19 May
Cally Biodiversity Gardens, Cally Avenue, Gatehouse of Fleet	Saturday, 25 May
Corsock House, Corsock, Castle Douglas	Sunday, 26 May
Seabank, The Merse, Rockcliffe	Sunday, 2 June
Southwick House, Southwick	Sunday, 30 June
3 Millhall, Shore Road, Kirkcudbright	Sunday, 1 September
Cally Biodiversity Gardens, Cally Avenue, Gatehouse of Fleet	Sunday, 29 September

Kirkcudbrightshire

GARDENS OPEN BY ARRANGEMENT

The Limes, Kirkcudbright	1 January - 31 December
Stockarton, Kirkcudbright	1 January - 31 December
Barholm Castle, Gatehouse of Fleet	1 January - 31 December
Barhill, Borgue, Kirkcudbright	1 February - 19 May
Brooklands, Crocketford	1 February - 29 February & 1 May - 30 September
Kings Grange House, Castle Douglas	1 February - 31 August
Danevale Park, Crossmichael	12 February - 24 February
Anwoth Old Schoolhouse, Anwoth, Gatehouse of Fleet	15 February - 15 November
Luckie Harg's, Anwoth, Gatehouse of Fleet, Castle Douglas	1 March - 30 September
3 Millhall, Shore Road, Kirkcudbright	1 March - 31 October
Tal-y-Fan, Laurieston Road, Gatehouse of Fleet	1 March - 31 October
Savat, Meikle Richorn, Dalbeattie	1 April - 31 October, Friday - Monday
Corsock House, Corsock, Castle Douglas	1 April - 30 June
The Waterhouse Gardens at Stockarton, Kirkcudbright	1 May - 30 September
Seabank, The Merse, Rockcliffe	27 May - 22 June
Clonyard Farm, Colvend, Dalbeattie	15 June - 30 June

Kirkcudbrightshire

1   3 MILLHALL
Shore Road, Kirkcudbright DG6 4TQ
Mr Alan Shamash
T: 01557 870352 E: shamash@freeuk.com

Impressive five-acre garden with a large collection of mature shrubs, including over 200 rhododendron species, many camellias, perennials, over 300 hydrangeas and many rare Southern Hemisphere plants. The garden has several interesting paths and is on a hillside running along the rocky shore of the Dee Estuary in Kirkcudbright Bay.

Open: Sunday 14 April & Sunday 1 September, 2pm - 5pm. Also open by arrangement 1 March - 31 October. Admission £5.00, children free.

Directions: On the B727 between Kirkcudbright and Borgue on the west shore of the Dee Estuary. Parking at Dhoon Beach public car park, about three miles south of Kirkcudbright. There is a five-minute walk to the house. Please note there will be no vehicular access to 3 Millhall and all visitors should park at Dhoon Beach and walk up to the property.

Opening for: Kirkcudbright Hospital League Of Friends & Alzheimer's Research UK

2   ANWOTH OLD SCHOOLHOUSE
Anwoth, Gatehouse of Fleet DG7 2EF
Mr and Mrs Pepper
T: 01557 814444 E: lesley.pepper@btinternet.com

Two acres of delightful cottage-style gardens behind the old schoolhouse and cottage in a picturesque setting opposite Anwoth Old Church (in ruins) and graveyard. Much of the garden provides an excellent habitat for wildlife, with winding paths alongside a burn, informally planted with unusual woodland perennials and shrubs. Wildlife pond, fish pond, rock garden, vegetable garden, wildflower area and viewpoint.

Open: by arrangement 15 February - 15 November, admission by donation.

Directions: Driving west on the A75, take the Anwoth turn off about half a mile after Gatehouse of Fleet. Anwoth Church is about half a mile along the road and Anwoth Old Schoolhouse is a little further along, opposite Anwoth Old Church (in ruins).

Opening for: Dogs for Good

© Arbigland House

Kirkcudbrightshire

3 ARBIGLAND HOUSE

Kirkbean, Dumfries DG2 8BQ
Alistair Alcock and Wayne Whittaker
T: 01387 880764 E: alcockalistair@gmail.com
W: www.arbiglandhouseandgardens.co.uk

Arbigland House is an Adam-style, 18th-century mansion surrounded by 24 acres of woodland gardens running down to a beach on the Solway Firth. The gardens date from the 18th century but the more formal areas were developed in the late 19th and early 20th centuries and are currently undergoing a programme of restoration and development. There are 200 -year-old trees lining the Broad Walk which runs down to the Solway and a huge variety of rhododendrons and azaleas. Within the woodland are a range of features including a stream-fed lake and a Japanese garden, with a more formal sundial garden and sunken rose garden, all in the process of renewal. Amongst these are a collection of mature trees and shrubs.

Open: Sunday 12 May, 2pm - 5pm, admission £5.00, children free. Teas at John Paul Jones Museum. Short tours available of the principal rooms of the house, looking at the history of the house and its pictures.

Directions: Take the A710 to Kirkbean. In the village turn off towards Carsethorn and, after 200 yards, turn right and follow signs to *John Paul Jones Cottage*. After a mile or so, turn left at the T-junction through white gates and down the drive through ornamental gates to Arbigland House.

Opening for: Absolute Classics & The Arts Society, Dumfries and Galloway

4 BALMACLELLAN HOUSE

Balmaclellan, Castle Douglas DG7 3PW
Alan and Fiona Smith
T: 01644 420227 Mob: 07769680938
E: alan.smith12345@btinternet.com

The formal garden at Balmaclellan House sits within a six-acre woodland garden with many interesting maturing trees. This formal garden was created in 2011 on the site of a redundant tennis court. The design is based on the Balmaclellan Mirror, a very early iron age mirror made of bronze which was found nearby and is currently in the National Museum of Scotland. The mirror is represented by a raised pond with other decorative features on the original replicated by raised beds and granite setts. While the planting has been designed to give year-round colour the use of daffodils and tulips brings a vibrancy to the garden in early spring. A small wooden building dates back to 1896 and is where the resident Minister is said to have written his sermons. The woodland walks and lawned areas have stone seats at appropriate points to take in the lovely views over the Rhins of Kells.

Open: Sunday 28 April, 1pm - 4pm, admission £5.00, children free.

Directions: On the B7075, just off the A712 approximately 14 miles north of Castle Douglas and two miles from New Galloway.

Opening for: Glenkens Community And Arts Trust Limited

Kirkcudbrightshire

5 BARHILL

Borgue, Kirkcudbright DG6 4UE
Guy and Jenny Houlsby
T: 07743 504981 E: jenny.houlsby@gmail.com

The garden was laid out around 1900, but had been left untouched for many years. Restoration is a work in progress with many areas still in their natural state. The garden has a lake, woodland and planted areas, including a bog garden, rockery, heather hill, herbaceous and shrub borders. There are extensive areas of snowdrops early in the year; these have been spreading and hybridising for about 100 years. The snowdrops are followed by displays of daffodils, primroses and bluebells. The garden has a healthy wildlife population and attractive views of the Isles of Fleet.

Open: by arrangement 1 February - 19 May for Snowdrops and Winter Walks, admission £5.00, children free.

Directions: From the south take the coast road from Borgue. About 500m after 'Coo Palace' the road dips into woods. The entrance is on the left 50m after some prominent white iron gates. From the north follow signs towards Carrick. Approaching the coast, with Knockbrex House ahead, stay left at the Y junction, pass Knockbrex and the entrance is next on the right after 200m. Parking is at the house.

Opening for: Loch Arthur

6 BARHOLM CASTLE

Gatehouse of Fleet DG7 2EZ
Drs John and Janet Brennan
T: 01557 840327 E: barholmcastle@gmail.com

Barholm Castle, a 16th-century tower, was restored from a ruin in 2006. The gardens surrounding the tower have been mostly developed from scratch and are now mature. There is a recently extended walled garden, with a gate designed by the artist blacksmith Adam Booth; a courtyard garden; a wooded ravine with huge hybrid rhododendrons from Benmore; a pond and a large fernery with over 100 varieties of fern, including very large tree ferns; a large Victorian-style greenhouse filled with succulents and tender perennials; and a large open garden with island beds of shrubs and perennials and a pond. Directly around the castle are rockeries and shrub borders. Views over Wigtown Bay are magnificent. The garden is planted for year-round colour, from February, when the castle ravine is a river of snowdrops, to October, when autumn colour is splendid.

Open: by arrangement 1 January - 31 December, admission £5.00, children free.

Directions: Off the A75 at the Cairn Holy turn off, fork right three times up a steep narrow road for half-a-mile.

Opening for: Home-Start Wigtownshire

Kirkcudbrightshire

7 BROOKLANDS
Crocketford DG2 8QH
Mr and Mrs Robert Herries
T: Gardener, Matthew Grieve: 07765 491902

Large old walled garden with a wide selection of plants, including some interesting shrubs and climbers and a kitchen garden. Mature woodland with many established rhododendrons and azaleas, and carpeted with snowdrops in February.

Open: Open Sunday 19 May, 2pm - 5pm (Teas will be weather dependent). Also open by arrangement 1 February - 29 February for Snowdrops and Winter Walks and 1 May - 30 September. A minimum of four adults for by arrangement openings. Admission £5.00, children free.

Directions: Turn off the A712 Crocketford to New Galloway Road one mile outside Crocketford at the Gothic gatehouse (on the right travelling north).

Opening for: All proceeds to SGS Beneficiaries

Brooklands   Corsock House

8 CALLY BIODIVERSITY GARDENS
Cally Avenue, Gatehouse of Fleet DG7 2DJ
Kevin Hughes
T: 01557 815228 E: info@callygardens.co.uk
W: www.callygardens.co.uk

A one-hectare walled garden containing an outstanding collection of rare and common plants from around the world assembled to create naturalistic habitat for our native fauna. Some plants can be found in no other Scottish garden whilst many are first introductions to gardens in the UK. This is an example of gardening harmoniously with nature where declining birds such as garden warbler can be seen nesting amongst Himalayan poppies and American Prairie plants whilst lucky people might glimpse harvest mice in our unique Grassland Ecology

Kirkcudbrightshire

Garden. We use no artificial fertiliser or pesticide and this is also true of the plants we grow for our plant sale area which has a wide range of less common plants.

Open: Saturday 25 May & Sunday 29 September, 10am - 5pm, admission £5.00, children free.

Directions: From Dumfries take the Gatehouse of Fleet turning off the A75, follow the B727 and turn left through the Cally Palace Hotel gateway from where the gardens are well signposted. A regular bus service will stop at the end of Cally Drive if requested.

Opening for: WWF-UK

 9 ## CLONYARD FARM
Colvend, Dalbeattie DG5 4QW
Matthew and Pam Pumphrey
E: clonyard@btinternet.com

Open by arrangement for wildflowers. Informal garden around traditional stone buildings with views over pasture, wetland and a loch to mature mixed forest. The garden joins a wildflower meadow dominated by black knapweed and established yellow rattle. It features three species of native orchids and a former mill pond, a notable damselfly site. Both are maintained specifically to allow native wildlife and plants to thrive. There is an ornamental vegetable garden and around the house mixed plantings merge from sun to shade and woodland planting to provide all-year-round interest. There are meadow, wetland and woodland walks to two lochs and a crannog. Refreshments available on request.

Open: by arrangement 15 June - 30 June, admission £5.00, children free.

Directions: On the north side of the A710 approximately four miles from the crossroads with the A711 in Dalbeattie, adjacent to Clonyard House Hotel and one mile from Colvend village. Parking at the Farm. Bus service from Dalbeattie but current timetables should be checked. Clonyard Farm is a request stop.

Opening for: Marie Curie: DG5 Group

 10 ## CORSOCK HOUSE
Corsock, Castle Douglas DG7 3DJ
The Ingall family
T: 01644 440250 E: jingall@hotmail.com

Corsock House garden includes an amazing variety of designed landscape, from a strictly formal walled garden, through richly planted woodlands full of different vistas, artfully designed water features and surprises to extensive lawns showing off the Bryce baronial mansion. This is an Arcadian garden with pools and temples, described by Ken Cox as 'perhaps my favourite of Scotland's many woodland gardens'.

Open: Sunday 26 May, 2pm - 5pm. Also open by arrangement 1 April - 30 June. Admission £5.00, children free.

Directions: Off the A75, Dumfries is 14 miles, Castle Douglas is ten miles, Corsock Village is half-mile on the A712.

Opening for: Corsock & Kirkpatrick Durham Church Of Scotland

Kirkcudbrightshire

11 DANEVALE PARK
Crossmichael DG7 2LP
Mrs Pam Fitton
T: 01556 670223 E: pamfitton@outlook.com

First opening for snowdrops in 1951, these mature grounds have a wonderful display of snowdrops as well as aconites and many other wildflowers. Walks through the woods and alongside the River Dee make this a memorable afternoon. We will have snowdrops for sale and home-made teas in the house.

Open: Sunday 18 February, noon - 4pm for Snowdrops and Winter Walks. Also open by arrangement 12 February - 24 February. Admission £5.00, children free. By arrangement opening for a minimum of four adults.

Directions: On the A713 two miles from Castle Douglas and one mile short of Crossmichael.

Opening for: Crossmichael Community Trust SCIO

12 KINGS GRANGE HOUSE
Castle Douglas DG7 3EU
Christine and Peter Hickman
T: 07787 535889

An extensive garden surrounded by mature trees and shrubberies, with views to the south west over the surrounding countryside. Originally Victorian, the garden is being restored by the present owners with a colourful variety of herbaceous mixed borders, beds and rockeries. There are snowdrops in February and banks of daffodils and a carpet of white narcissus in the lawns and around the pergola in springtime.

Open: by arrangement 1 February - 31 August, admission £5.00, children free.

Directions: Take the B794 north off the A75, two miles east of Castle Douglas. Kings Grange House is approximately one mile on the left.

Opening for: RNLI & Marie Curie

13 LUCKIE HARG'S
Anwoth, Gatehouse of Fleet, Castle Douglas DG7 2EF
Drs Carole and Ian Bainbridge
T: 01557 814141 E: luckiehargs@btinternet.com

A new and developing garden on the outskirts of Gatehouse of Fleet. A rock and spring herbaceous garden of around an acre, with a wide range of alpines, Himalayan and New Zealand plants, shrubs and small trees. There is a rock garden, modern crevice gardens, troughs, a large alpine house and bulb frame. New boulder, scree and stumpery beds, a pond and a woodland area are being developed. Small productive vegetable and fruit garden, plus a bluebell bank in May.

Open: by arrangement 1 March - 30 September, admission £5.00, children free.

Directions: From Gatehouse High Street, turn north onto Station Road, immediately west at the Fleet Bridge by The Ship Inn. After almost one mile turn left signed to *Anwoth Old Church*. Luckie Harg's is the first on the right after 400 yards. The nearest bus stop is on Gatehouse High Street, walk about 15 minutes to Luckie Harg's.

Opening for: Scottish Rock Garden Club

Kirkcudbrightshire

14 **SAVAT**
Meikle Richorn, Dalbeattie DG5 4QT
George Thomas
T: 01556 612863 Mob. 07866 392150 E: georgethomas6@icloud.com

. . . .

A generally informal garden of about two thirds of an acre with mature trees, exposed Dalbeattie granite and winding paths. The garden houses a unique summerhouse, artist Sue Thomas's studio and a greenhouse. Planting caters for sun to shade and dry to very moist, with shrubs – including rhododendrons, herbaceous and minimal summer bedding with an eye to keeping maintenance requirements to a minimum! There is a paved area around the house in which there are two water features, and may display potted plants.

Open: by arrangement 1 April - 31 October (Fridays to Mondays inclusive) admission £5.00, children free.

Directions: Leave Dalbeattie along the A710 south towards Kippford. After about 1.7 miles pass *Gorsebank* on the left and 200 yards further on turn right into a large lay-by. Enter the lane marked with cul de sac signs and proceed straight ahead along the paved road for about 500 yards. Limited parking is available at the property entrance. Savat is the sixth house on the left.

Opening for: All proceeds to SGS Beneficiaries

15 **SEABANK**
The Merse, Rockcliffe DG5 4QH
Julian and Theodora Stanning
T: 01556 630244

. . . .

This one-and-a-half-acre garden extends to the high water mark with westerly views across a wildflower meadow to the Urr Estuary, Rough Island and beyond. The house is flanked by raised beds, and overlooks a cottage-style garden; peripheral plantings of mixed shrubs and perennials are interspersed with spring bulbs and summer annuals for all-year-round interest. There is a greenhouse with a range of succulents and tender plants. To the rear of the property is a new walled garden stocked with top and soft fruit, perennial vegetables (sea kale, asparagus and globe artichokes), a range of annual vegetables and flower borders. A further greenhouse is used for tomatoes and cucumbers, and has peaches growing against the back wall. A plantswoman's garden with a range of interesting and unusual plants.

Open: Sunday 2 June, 2pm - 5pm. Also open by arrangement 27 May - 22 June. Admission £5.00, children free.

Directions: Park in the public car park at Rockcliffe. Walk down the road about 50 yards towards the sea and turn left along The Merse, a private road. Seabank is the sixth house on the left.

Opening for: Marie Curie: DG5 Group

Kirkcudbrightshire

Seabank

16 SOUTHWICK HOUSE
Southwick DG2 8AH
Mr and Mrs R H L Thomas

The extensive gardens at Southwick House comprise three main areas. The first is a traditional formal walled garden with potager and large glasshouse producing a range of fruit, vegetables and cutting flowers. Adjacent to this is a hedged formal garden with herbaceous, shrub and rose beds centred around a lily pond, with roses being a notable feature. Outwith the formal gardens there is a large water garden with two connected ponds with trees, shrubs and lawns running alongside the Southwick Burn.

Open: Sunday 30 June, 2pm - 5pm, admission £5.00, children free.

Directions: On the A710 near Caulkerbush. Dalbeattie 7 miles, Dumfries 17 miles.

Opening for: Loch Arthur

Southwick House

Kirkcudbrightshire

17 STOCKARTON
Kirkcudbright DG6 4XS
Lt Col and Mrs Richard Cliff
T: 01557 330430

This garden was started in 1995 by Carola Cliff, a keen and knowledgeable plantswoman, and contains a collection of unusual shrubs and small trees, which are growing well. Her aim has been to create different informal gardens around a Galloway farm house, leading down to a lochan. Above the lochan there is a sweet cottage, used for holiday retreats, with its own interesting garden. In 1996 a three-acre arboretum was planted as a shelter belt and it now contains some rare oak trees.

Open: by arrangement 1 January - 31 December, admission £5.00, children free.

Directions: On the B727 Kirkcudbright to Gelston Road. Kirkcudbright three miles, Castle Douglas seven miles.

Opening for: Loch Arthur

Stockarton © Stuart Littlewood

Kirkcudbrightshire

18 TAL-Y-FAN
Laurieston Road, Gatehouse of Fleet, Kirkcudbrightshire DG7 2BE
Janet & Sarah Wood
T: 01557 815287 E: woodhill2uk@yahoo.co.uk

An over-mature, one-acre plot is being developed into a many faceted garden with a varied mix of interesting plants. The Secret Path leads to Acer Valley and the Won-Kei Parterre, overlooked by the Loch Corbie Monster. A narrow log-lined way leads to West Wood, from where you follow the Burnside Path by the Flame Tree Forest and through the bamboo arch to Dry Wood to find Wood's Henge. Then up through Bluebell Wood to the top of The Rock, where Big Red, the giant squirrel resides, with views across the Fleet Valley. Back down and cross the lawns below the pond before heading up the granite path to the greenhouse, polytunnel, compost bins and the car park, with its collection of pots and troughs. Visit the front lawn and its well-stocked beds on your way out. Light refreshments may be available by arrangement.

Open: by arrangement 1 March - 31 October, admission £5.00, children free.

Directions: Take the Laurieston Road north from Gatehouse of Fleet. After 1 mile fork right and then right at postcode sign. Turn left at top of slope. Tal-y-Fan (red roof) is at the very end.

Opening for: All proceeds to SGS Beneficiaries

19 THE LIMES
Kirkcudbright DG6 4XD
David and Carolyn McHale
E: carolyn.mchale@btinternet.com

This one-and-a-quarter acre plantswoman's garden has a variety of different plant habitats: woodland, dry sunny gravel beds, rock garden, crevice garden and mixed perennial and shrub borders. There is also a large productive vegetable garden. The McHales like to grow most of their plants from seed obtained through various international seed exchanges. You can expect to see a large number of unusual and exciting plants. The garden is full of colour with an abundance of spring flowers in March, and in late May and early June the meconopsis should be at their best. The gravel garden comes into its own in July and continues through until winter. Hardy cyclamen are a big favourite and one species or another is in flower in almost every month of the year. Winter is a good time to admire their varied leaf forms.

Open: Sunday 24 March and Sunday 19 May, 2pm - 5pm. Also open by arrangement 1 January - 31 December. Admission £5.00, children free.

Directions: In Kirkcudbright go straight along St Mary Street towards Dundrennan. The Limes is on the right, about half a mile from the town centre crossroads, on the edge of the town.

Opening for: Friends Of Kirkcudbright Swimming Pool

Kirkcudbrightshire

20 THE WATERHOUSE GARDENS AT STOCKARTON

Kirkcudbright DG6 4XS
Martin Gould and Sharon O'Rourke
T: 01557 331266 E: waterhousekbt@aol.com
W: www.waterhousekbt.co.uk

One acre of densely planted, terraced, cottage-style gardens attached to a Galloway cottage. Three ponds surround the oak-framed eco-polehouse, The Waterhouse. Climbing roses, clematis and honeysuckles are a big feature as well as a pond-side walk. There are over 50 photos on their website. Featured on *The Beechgrove Garden* in 2007.

Open: by arrangement 1 May - 30 September, admission £5.00, children free.

Directions: On the B727 Kirkcudbright to Gelston/Dalbeattie road. Kirkcudbright is three miles and Castle Douglas is seven miles.

Opening for: Loch Arthur

21 THREAVE GARDEN

Castle Douglas DG7 1RX
National Trust for Scotland
T: 01556 502 575 E: threave@nts.org.uk
W: www.nts.org.uk/visit/places/threave-garden

Threave Garden & Nature Reserve SGS Open Day is a one-day event at the home of the National Trust for Scotland's School of Heritage Gardening in Dumfries & Galloway, celebrating all aspects of horticulture. There will be plant nurseries, a craft fair, local producers, and plant-related talks from Threave's Garden Instructors. In addition to this there will be children's activities including a storyteller, face painting and bug hunting. Threave Garden Café, gift shop and plants sales will be open as normal on the day.

Champion Trees: *Acer platanoides* 'Princeton Gold'; *Carpinus caroliniana*; X *Cuprocyparis leylandii* 'Picturesque' and a further 25 Scottish Champion Trees.

Open: Monday 6 May, 10am - 5pm, admission £5.00, children free.

Directions: Off the A75, one mile west of Castle Douglas.

Opening for: The National Trust for Scotland: School of Gardening Heritage

Tal-y-Fan   Luckie Harg's

Lanarkshire

Sponsored by

RATHBONES

Incorporating
Investec Wealth &
Investment (UK)

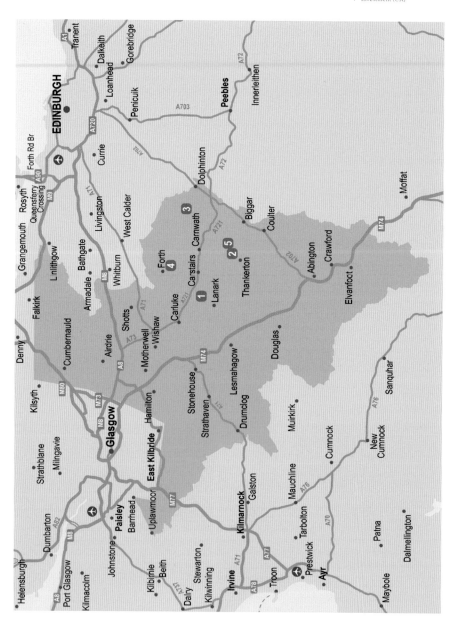

Lanarkshire

OUR VOLUNTEER ORGANISERS

District Organiser:	Vanessa Rogers	8 Springdale Drive, Biggar, Lanarkshire ML12 6AZ info@scotlandsgardens.org
Area Organiser:	Nicky Eliott Lockhart	Stable House, Cleghorn Farm, Lanark ML11 7RW
District Photographers:	Alistair McNeill	57 Sherifflats Road, Thankerton, Biggar ML12 6PA
Treasurer:	Sheila Munro Tulloch	Castlegait House, Castlegait, Lanarkshire, Strathaven ML10 6FF

GARDENS OPEN ON A SPECIFIC DATE

Cleghorn, Stable House, Cleghorn Farm, Lanark	Sunday, 3 March
Covington Gardens, Covington Village	Sunday, 16 June
Little Sparta, Stonypath, Dunsyre	Tuesday, 25 June
Little Sparta, Stonypath, Dunsyre	Tuesday, 2 July
The Walled Garden, Shieldhill, Quothquan, Biggar	Sunday, 4 August
Stobwood Cottage Garden, Stobwood Cottage, Stobwood, Forth	Saturday/Sunday, 10/11 August
Little Sparta, Stonypath, Dunsyre	Tuesday, 27 August
Little Sparta, Stonypath, Dunsyre	Tuesday, 3 September

GARDENS OPEN BY ARRANGEMENT

The Walled Garden, Shieldhill, Quothquan, Biggar	1 July - 31 August

Lanarkshire

1 CLEGHORN
Stable House, Cleghorn Farm, Lanark ML11 7RN
Mr and Mrs R Eliott Lockhart
T: 01555 663792 E: eliottlockhart.nicky@gmail.com
W: www.cleghornestategardens.com

Eighteenth-century garden gradually being returned to its former layout. Lawns with mature trees, shrubs, abundant snowdrops and a woodland walk along the valley, formed by 12th-century dams that were originally built to form fish ponds. The valley has been totally cleared in the last couple of years and the burn and snowdrops are now visible from both sides of the valley. Visitors are welcome to return when the daffodils are in flower.

Open: Sunday 3 March, 2pm - 4pm for Snowdrops and Winter Walks, admission by donation.

Directions: Cleghorn Farm is situated two miles north of Lanark off the A706.

Opening for: Hope and Homes for Children

Covington Mill Farmhouse

Lanarkshire

2 COVINGTON GARDENS

Covington Village ML12 6NE
Sharon Pearson
T: 07827 236771 E: sharon.pearson69@outlook.com

A group of three gardens in and close to Covington Village.

Covington Mill Farmhouse (NEW) (Sharon Pearson) Set amongst eight acres, the gardens have been transformed since 2019 from pastureland to a landscape of woodlands, wildlife habitats: formal gardens and recently, a prairie-inspired garden. A restored watermill building and lade runs through the whole area, creating a meditative backdrop to the matrix and drift planting schemes surrounding them. Changing seasons and environmental challenges we face, are reflected in different planting responses to the garden's varied site aspects and aesthetic aims.
Hawk House Gardens (NEW) (Angus and Angela Milner-Brown) The two plus acres of Hawk House gardens were formed in 2009. Protective mixed hedges, a wildflower meadow and lawns were planted on an exposed hillside with far reaching views. Since then the new owners have designed and planted additional gardens with extensive borders and herbaceous plants bringing much of their sizeable collection from the nearby manse. The new gardens include an alpine garden, hosta beds, a pond, new formal hedging leading to the wildflower meadows (80 species in 2023) and a hilltop pavilion nestled into a woodland.
Weavers Cottage (NEW) (Sharon Paton) This quaint cottage garden with picket fencing, topiary and stone and brick paths and walls, is the canvas for a Grade B listed thatched cottage. Lovingly interpreted and restored over 30 years, following the original layout of these modest cottages whose long plots and 'vennels' lead to a little woodland and pond. The Newtown's row of cottages dating to the mid 1820s, some with original thatch under tin roofing, are now a rarity in Scotland.

Open: Sunday 16 June, 1pm - 5pm, admission £6.00, children free. Artist Tansy Lee Moir (www.tansyleemoir.co.uk) will be running an open studio and moth expert Jo Davies will be on hand to show the different species of moth found in the gardens. On-road parking will be beyond Covington Village. A minibus will be provided for those who are unable to walk the 300-400m to the gardens.

Directions: From the A73 turn off at Tinto Hill into the village of Thankerton and follow the SGS signs.

Opening for: Buglife - The Invertebrate Conservation Trust, The Linda Norgrove Foundation & Pancreatic Cancer UK

Hawk House Gardens

Lanarkshire

3 LITTLE SPARTA

Stonypath, Dunsyre ML11 8NG
Pantea Cameron
T: 01899 810711 E: contact@littlesparta.org.uk
W: www.littlesparta.org.uk

Little Sparta is Ian Hamilton Finlay's greatest work of art. Ian and Sue Finlay moved to the farm of Stonypath in 1966 and began to create what would become an internationally acclaimed garden across seven acres of a wild and exposed moorland site. Collaborating with stone carvers, letterers and other artists and poets, the numerous sculptures and artworks created by Finlay explore themes as diverse as the sea and its fishing fleets, our relationship to nature, classical antiquity, the French Revolution and the Second World War. Individual poetic and sculptural elements, in wood, stone and metal, are sited in relation to carefully structured landscaping and planting. Please note that there is a 700m uphill walk from the car park and livestock grazing in the fields. For visitors with limited mobility, it may be possible to book a space near the house; call the garden for details.

Open: Tuesday 25 June, Tuesday 2 July, Tuesday 27 August & Tuesday 3 September, 1pm - 4pm, admission £9.00, children £5.00. Last entry 3pm. Pre-booking of tickets is required, please see **scotlandsgardens.org/little-sparta/** to book

Directions: Check www.littlesparta.org.uk/visit/ for directions.

Opening for: Little Sparta Trust

4 STOBWOOD COTTAGE GARDEN

Stobwood Cottage, Stobwood, Forth, South Lanarkshire ML11 8ET
Jamie and Kayleigh Robertson
T: 07885 701642 E: jamierobertson04@hotmail.co.uk

A four times winner of West Lothian Gardener of the year, Jamie invites you to Stobwood Cottage. In just four years he has established a hugely impressive garden in the South Lanarkshire countryside. Just shy of half an acre, colour dominates this garden. Wide herbaceous borders surround a velvet lawn. Stunning hanging baskets and tubs clothe the front of the cottage and are dotted around elsewhere. There is also a feature pond with a bridge, a cacti house, a polytunnel growing corn, pumpkins and squashes plus there is a productive vegetable plot to explore. A must for those less experienced gardeners, and a delight for those who have a little more knowledge.

Open: Saturday 10 and Sunday 11 August, 1pm - 5pm, admission £6.00, children free. Refreshments included in admission fee.

Directions: Travelling from the south, 1 ½ miles north of Braehead on the B7016. From the north, turn off the A706 onto the B7016 at Wilsontown.

Opening for: Braehead Village Trust

Lanarkshire

5 THE WALLED GARDEN, SHIELDHILL
Quothquan, Biggar ML12 6NA
Mr and Mrs Gordon
T: 01899 221961 E: nicolagord@gmail.com

This 200-year-old walled garden was completely redesigned and planted in 2014/15 with contemporary features within a classic design. The garden incorporates a modern rill and banks of colour with perennial flowers in a variety of borders. The resident bees enjoy the large area of traditional meadow flowers as well as the rose garden planted with lavenders, salvias and stocks. Outside the wall you will find mature woodland including a giant sequoia and a wildlife pond. If you are interested in fruit and vegetables, take a look at the raised beds and the peach tree and vine in the greenhouse. There are many secluded spots around the garden to sit and enjoy a cup of tea and a homemade cake.

Open: Sunday 4 August, 2pm - 5pm. Also open by arrangement 1 July - 31 August. Admission £5.00, children free.

Directions: Turn off the B7016 between Biggar and Carnwath towards Quothquan. After about a mile, look for signs and turn right at the lodge.

Opening for: Médecins Sans Frontières

The Walled Garden, Shieldhill

Moray & Nairn

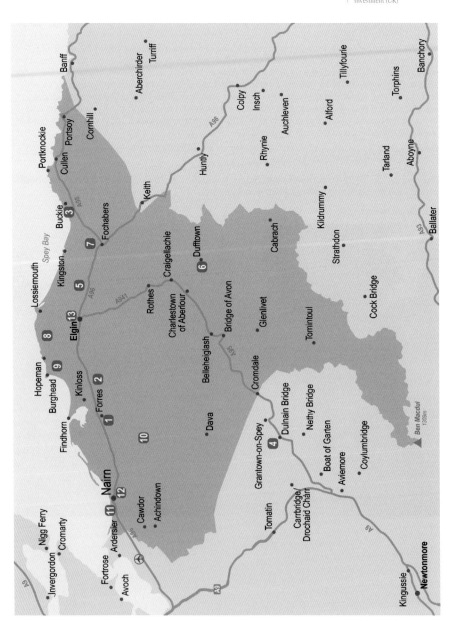

Moray & Nairn

OUR VOLUNTEER ORGANISERS

District Organiser:	James Byatt	info@scotlandsgardens.org
Area Organisers:	Lorraine Dingwall	
	David Hetherington	
	Gwynne Hetherington	
	Jo Mackenzie	
	Annie Stewart	
Treasurer:	David Barnett	

GARDENS OPEN ON A SPECIFIC DATE

The Biblical Garden, King Street, Elgin, Moray	Saturday, 4 May
Cuthberts Brae, 84 Seatown, Buckie	Saturday/Sunday, 6/7 July
Sunflower Dreams, 2 Househill Drive, Nairn	Saturday, 13 July
Glebe House, Main Street, Urquhart	Sunday, 14 July
Glenrinnes Lodge, Dufftown, Keith, Banffshire	Sunday, 28 July
Easter Laggan, Dulnain Bridge, Grantown-on-Spey	Saturday, 24 August
Gordonstoun, Duffus, near Elgin	Date to be confirmed

GARDENS OPEN REGULARLY

Burgie Arboretum, Between Forres and Elgin	1 January - 31 December
Logie House, Dunphail, Forres	1 January - 29 February (not Monday & Tuesday)
Gordon Castle Walled Garden, Fochabers, Moray	2 January - 31 December
Logie House, Dunphail, Forres	1 March - 31 December

GARDENS OPEN BY ARRANGEMENT

10 Pilmuir Road West, Forres	25 January - 11 March
Glenrinnes Lodge, Dufftown, Keith, Banffshire	1 April - 30 September
Ruthven Cottage Hardy Plant Nursery, Denies, Nairn	1 April - 30 September
Haugh Garden, College of Roseisle	1 May - 31 July
10 Pilmuir Road West, Forres	1 June - 1 September

Moray & Nairn

10 PILMUIR ROAD WEST
Forres IV36 2HL
Mrs Lorraine Dingwall
T: 01309 674634 E: fixandig@aol.com

Plantswoman's small town garden with over 300 cultivars of hostas, an extensive collection of hardy geraniums together with many other unusual plants. Managed entirely without the use of artificial fertilisers or chemicals, the owner encourages hedgehogs, toads and wild birds to control slugs. In early spring there are approximately 150 named snowdrops to be seen, some of which are very rare.

Open: by arrangement 25 January - 11 March for Snowdrops and Winter Walks. Also open by arrangement 1 June - 1 September. Admission £5.00, children free. There is a well-stocked sales area.

Directions: From Tesco roundabout at Forres continue along Nairn Road. Take the first left onto Ramflat Road, then go right at the bottom and first left onto Pilmuir Road West.

Opening for: Macmillan Cancer Support

BURGIE ARBORETUM
Between Forres and Elgin IV36 2QU
Hamish Lochore
T: 01343 850231 E: hamish@burgie.org

A rare opportunity to see a sizeable woodland garden/arboretum in its infancy. It has a good collection of rhododendrons, Sorbus, alder, birch and Tilia but also includes many unusual trees from around the world. The arboretum is zoned into geographic areas and species type. It includes a Japanese Garden, bog garden, bog wood, loch and quarry garden. First created in 2005 and is ongoing. Most plants are grown from hand-collected seed and propagated in the Georgian greenhouse.

Open: Open 1 January - 31 December, 8am - 5pm. Admission by donation. Also open for snowdrops during the Scottish Snowdrop Festival

Directions: A96 between Forres and Elgin. Four miles east of Forres. Six miles west of Elgin. Sign to *Burgie Mains* along the A96 is set in wrought iron decorated with horses and cattle. South off the main road and one mile to the Woodland Garden car park.

Opening for: Sandpiper Trust & World Horse Welfare

Easter Laggan © James Byatt

Moray & Nairn

 CUTHBERTS BRAE
84 Seatown, Buckie AB56 1JS
Elizabeth and Malcolm Schofield
T: 07878 486093 E: malcolmsgsp@gmail.com
W: www.instagram.com/cuthbertsbrae_garden

. . . .

Gardeners' World Magazine, Readers' Garden of the Year 2020, Judges' Choice Winner. *'In the small seaside town of Buckie in the north east Moray Coast, what was once a wild hill, overgrown with brambles, has now been transformed into a beautiful colourful haven for all to admire.' - Gardeners' World Magazine.* The garden is sited on a steep hill with a small flat terrace with gravel garden wrapping around the house. The path then takes you down the bank into a terraced cottage garden that is a magnet for bees, butterflies and other wildlife. As you continue into the newer section of the garden you discover the greenhouse, rabbit enclosure and veg beds. *'This garden is a really good lesson in what you can achieve in inhospitable conditions with limited knowledge and money.' - Alan Titchmarsh.*

Open: Saturday/Sunday, 6/7 July, 1pm - 5pm, admission by donation.

Directions: Arriving from the Tesco road turn left at the Town Square. Take the next right. Use the car park at the *Seatown* sign. Follow the signage to our garden. The garden is a short walk (five minutes) from the Town Square.

Opening for: Scottish Association For Mental Health

 EASTER LAGGAN
Dulnain Bridge, Grantown-on-Spey PH26 3NU
Rob and Julie Forrest

. . . .

A garden under development, designed by Jens Nielsen. It has stunning views of the River Spey and the Cairngorm mountains and is a haven for wildlife, including red squirrels. Five acres in size, the garden consists of some formal lawns with herbaceous borders, newly-created rockeries and drystone walls and the beginnings of a Japanese garden. A stream enters the garden and flows into a newly-restored pond. The stream then winds its way through the garden back into the surrounding fields. Gravel driveways allow some wheelchair access with assistance.

Open: Saturday 24 August, 12:30pm - 5pm, admission £5.00, children free.

Directions: From Grantown-on-Spey take the A95 towards Aviemore. Take the first turn signed to Dulnain Bridge, then turn immediately right on to the old road. Turn immediately left up the track signed to Easter Laggan. Parking is available in a paddock by the house.

Opening for: Parkinsons UK

Moray & Nairn

5 GLEBE HOUSE
Main Street, Urquhart IV30 8LG
Melanie Collett
E: mel.collett2015@outlook.com

Early 19th-century formal walled garden of the former manse by Alexander Forteath, also incorporating a unique doocot in its construction of clay dab. The garden consists of colourful herbaceous borders within the walled garden and box hedge symmetry. A wide variety of roses together with an orchard and kitchen garden area to the south.

Open: Sunday 14 July, noon - 3pm, admission £6.00, children free.

Directions: Off the main street in Urquhart, find the walled entrance at the end of the street. Follow parking signs.

Opening for: The Royal Air Force Benevolent Fund

6 GLENRINNES LODGE
Dufftown, Keith, Banffshire AB55 4BS
Mrs Kathleen Locke
T: 01340 820384/073939 28049
W: www.glenrinnes.com

The garden and policies surrounding Glenrinnes Lodge are typical of a Victorian lodge. They are full of exciting colourful borders. Newly-developed areas are now beginning to establish and give year-round seasonal interest in the kitchen garden and glasshouse, the secret garden, labyrinth and bog garden. There are also woodland walks and a flight pond and meadow. If you are lucky, you may spot our red squirrel, otter and pine marten. All caught on woodland trail camera.

Open: Sunday 28 July, 2pm - 5pm. Also open by arrangement 1 April - 30 September. Admission £5.00, children free. Teas £5. Please phone to arrange a visit.

Directions: In the centre of Dufftown at the Clock Tower take the B9009 road to Tomintoul for about one mile. After passing Dufftown Golf Club on your right there is a lane to the left, which leads to two stone pillars to Glenrinnes Lodge.

Opening for: Alzheimer's Research UK

Glenrinnes Lodge

Moray & Nairn

7 GORDON CASTLE WALLED GARDEN

Fochabers, Moray IV32 7PQ
Angus and Zara Gordon Lennox
T: 01343 612317 E: info@gordoncastlescotland.com
W: www.gordoncastle.co.uk

At almost eight acres in size, Gordon Castle has one of the oldest and largest walled gardens in Britain. Lovingly restored to its former glory with a modern design by award-winning designer Arne Maynard, this beautiful garden is overflowing with vegetables, fruit, herbs, and cut flowers. The onsite cafe has a 'Plant, Pick, Plate' ethos using wonderful fresh produce grown in the garden. There is a children's natural play area and shop.

Open: 2 January - 31 December, 10am - 4pm, admission details can be found on the garden's website. The cafe is open from Wednesday to Sunday.

Directions: The main entrance is at the western end of the village of Fochabers, just off the A96, nine miles east of Elgin and 12 miles west of Keith.

Opening for: Donation to SGS Beneficiaries

8 GORDONSTOUN

Duffus, near Elgin IV30 5RF
The Principal
E: principalpa@gordonstoun.org.uk
W: www.gordonstoun.org.uk

Gordonstoun is famous for educating the Royal Family, but its history dates much further back and was the 18th century Georgian home of the first Marquis of Huntly. The school gardens consist of formal herbaceous borders, an ornamental lake and an apple orchard. Visitors can take a self-guided tour of the extensive school grounds including the unique 'Round Square' former farm building (now boarding house) which has an unusual echo and can stroll down the 'silent walk' to the 17th century kirk where former students including members of the Royal Family would have worshipped.

Open: Date to be confirmed. Refreshments included in entry price.

Directions: Entrance off B9012, four miles from Elgin at Duffus village.

Opening for: All proceeds to SGS Beneficiaries

Gordonstoun © James Byatt

Ruthven Cottage Hardy Plant Nursery

Moray & Nairn

9 HAUGH GARDEN
College of Roseisle IV30 5YE
Gwynne and David Hetherington
T: 01343 835790

A lovely two acre garden to enjoy and to relax in. Wander through woodland and meadows, and in and around eye-catching perennial borders with unusual plants and shrubs, a pond and an orchard, all attracting a diversity of insects and birds. Our organic vegetable garden and polytunnel keep us well supplied and using the no-dig method, without need for artificial fertiliser or chemicals. Our garden delights us with year-round interest starting with various spring bulbs and flowering shrubs and continuing through to late autumn colours.

Open: by arrangement 1 May - 31 July, admission £6.00, children free. Home made teas and plants for sale.

Directions: From Elgin take the A96 west, then the B9013 Burghead Road to the crossroads at the centre of College of Roseisle. The garden is on the right, enter from the Duffus Road. Car parking at the village hall off Kinloss road. Drop off and disabled parking is available at the house.

Opening for: CHAS & Alzheimer Scotland

10 LOGIE HOUSE
Dunphail, Forres IV36 2QN
Alasdair and Panny Laing
E: panny@logie.co.uk
W: www.logie.co.uk

Originally a traditional formal garden, Logie House walled garden has been developed since 1991 with emphasis on trees, shrubs and hardy perennials, giving all-year-round interest. The meandering burn and dry stone walls support the creation of a wide variety of planting habitats from dry sunny banks to damp shady areas. Many of the unusual plants are propagated for sale in the Garden Shop at Logie Steading. Also features woodland and river walks.

Open: 3 January - 29 February (not Monday & Tuesday), 2pm - 5pm. Also open 1 March - 31 December, 2pm - 5pm. Admission details can be found on the garden's website.

Directions: Six miles south of Forres off the A940. Follow signs to *Logie Steading*.

Opening for: Donation to SGS Beneficiaries

11 RUTHVEN COTTAGE HARDY PLANT NURSERY
Denies, Nairn IV12 5NT
Mari and Kevin Reid
T: 07874 779705 E: kevin.mari@gmail.com

The garden has exciting interest all year round. It features several large colourful herbaceous borders and many of the plants are sold at the nursery. The naturalistic style of planting with grasses and perennials looks good from late spring to late summer. There is also a pond, greenhouse and chickens.

Open: by arrangement 1 April - 30 September, admission by donation.

Directions: From Inverness take the A96 to Nairn, Ruthven Cottage is on your left just before the *Sandown Road Crossroads*. From Nairn the entrance is on your right off the A96. Ruthven Cottage is at the end of the lane.

Opening for: All proceeds to SGS Beneficiaries

Moray & Nairn

 12 SUNFLOWER DREAMS
2 Househill Drive, Nairn IV12 5RX
Heather Lansdell

This cottage-style, wildlife-friendly garden is filled with character, featuring several murals, repurposed items, upcycled furniture, whisky barrels, archways, and many different cosy seating areas. The front of the property contains many beds and borders filled with rhododendrons and perennials, all hemmed in by a white picket fence. Wildlife is welcome in our garden, with pollinator-friendly planting, many tall grass areas, miniature wildflower meadows, a pond and a hedgehog habitat. In mid to late summer, expect to see a minimum of 65 sunflowers planted throughout the garden, as well as dahlias, helichrysum, nicotiana and bedding plants all grown from seed in our greenhouse. This is definitely a three-season garden, full of surprises, and providing large amounts of interest on all but the coldest winter months.

Open: Saturday 13 July, 10am - 5pm, admission £5.00, children free.

Directions: From Inverness or Nairn, take the A96 through Nairn towards Forres. Go over the river and under the railway bridge. At the lights turn right onto the A939 to Grantown. After ½ mile there is a sharp 90-degree bend to the left. Take the first right after this bend into Househill Drive. Sunflower Dreams is on your right with a white picket fence. **From Forres** turn left onto the Grantown A939 road at the lights after Sainsburys. There is limited parking in Househill Drive. You can also park along the lane leading to Househill Meadows and Househill Gate and on the street in Househill Meadows. There is a bus stop beyond the A939 turning at Sainsburys and it is about a one mile walk from there.

Opening for: Borneo Nature Foundation

 13 THE BIBLICAL GARDEN
King Street, Elgin, Moray IV30 1HU
The Friends of the Biblical Garden
W: biblicalgardenelgin.co.uk

The Biblical Garden opened to the public in June 1996. The success of the garden since its opening relies on a good working partnership among the Friends of the Biblical Garden, Moray Council and UHI Moray. The Garden is used by the horticulture students to develop their skills. The gardens have grown and developed over the years and are now host to a broad range of garden features, interesting plants and mature trees. The main central area is paved and together with the surrounding borders reflects a Celtic cross. A large rose arbour represents the neighbouring cathedral. The gardens also host a rock garden, woodland garden, winter border, herbaceous border and an oriental-themed garden.

Open: Saturday 4 May, 11am - 3pm, admission by donation. Student-led tours will be available on the open day.

Directions: The gardens are on King Street, off North College Street and are adjacent to Elgin Cathedral. Parking along King Street is limited. All main bus routes stop along the A96 and the garden is in easy walking distance from these.

Opening for: All proceeds to SGS Beneficiaries

Peeblesshire & Tweeddale

Sponsored by

RATHBONES

Incorporating
Investec Wealth &
Investment (UK)

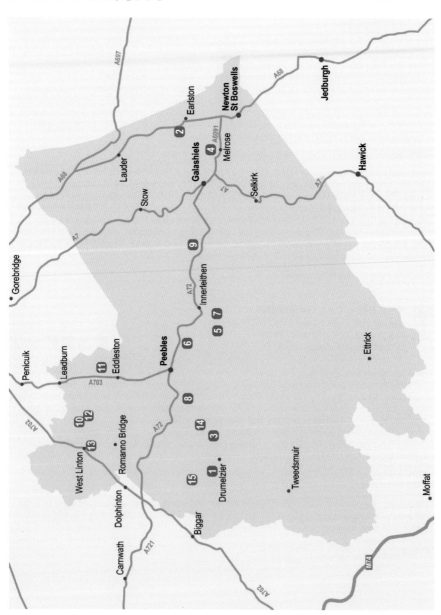

Peeblesshire & Tweeddale

OUR VOLUNTEER ORGANISERS

District Organiser:	Lesley McDavid	Braedon, Medwyn Road, West Linton EH46 7HA info@scotlandsgardens.org
Deputy District Organiser:	John Bracken	Gowan Lea, Croft Road, West Linton EH46 7DZ
Area Organisers:	Jennifer Barr	Allerly, Gattonside, Melrose TD6 9LT
	Jenny Litherland	Laidlawstiel House, Clovenfords TD1 1TJ
Treasurer:	Marie Gilmour	1 Kittlegairy Place, Peebles EH45 9LW

GARDENS OPEN ON A SPECIFIC DATE

Kailzie Gardens, Peebles	Sunday, 3 March
Quercus Garden Plants, Whitmuir Farm, West Linton	Sunday, 2 June
Stobo Japanese Water Garden, Stobo Farm, Stobo	Sunday, 2 June
Macbiehill Gardens, The Walled Garden, Macbiehill	Sunday, 2 June
Laidlawstiel House, Clovenfords, Galashiels	Wednesday/Thursday, 5/6 June
Srongarbh, The Loan, West Linton	Sunday, 9 June
Kirkhouse, Traquair	Sunday, 16 June
Carolside, Earlston	Sunday, 7 July
Glen House, Glen Estate, Innerleithen	Sunday, 7 July
Kailzie Gardens, Peebles	Sunday, 21 July
Gattonside Village Gardens, Gattonside	Sunday, 28 July
Quercus Garden Plants, Whitmuir Farm, West Linton	Sunday, 25 August
Dawyck Botanic Garden, Stobo	Sunday, 6 October

GARDENS OPEN REGULARLY

Kirkton Manor House, Peebles	14 February - 10 July (Wednesday only)
The Potting Shed, Broughton Place, Broughton, Biggar	5 June - 3 July (Wednesday only)
Beechwood, Broughton, Peeblesshire	5 June - 3 July (Wednesday only)
Portmore, Eddleston	3 July - 28 August (Wednesday only)

GARDENS OPEN BY ARRANGEMENT

Kirkton Manor House, Peebles	14 February - 10 July
The Potting Shed, Broughton Place, Broughton, Biggar	1 May - 31 October
Beechwood, Broughton, Peeblesshire	1 May - 31 October
Portmore, Eddleston	1 June - 31 August

Peeblesshire & Tweeddale

1 BEECHWOOD

Broughton, Peeblesshire ML12 6HH
Susheila and James Gordon
T: 07810 837068 or 01899 830443 E: susheilarachan@gmail.com
W: www.rachan.co.uk

An informal, sculptor's garden adjacent to a mature woodland and pond. A well-planted stream runs through the garden. There are varied perennial meadows to encourage wildlife and provide forage for the resident bees and it also features many examples of the owners' artworks which are inspired by the natural world.

Open: 5 June - 3 July (Wednesday only), 2pm - 5pm. Also open by arrangement 1 May - 31 October. Admission £5.00, children free.

Directions: Approximately one mile south of Broughton take the B712 off the A701. Then first left turn onto unmade road.

Opening for: MND Scotland

Beechwood

Peeblesshire & Tweeddale

2 CAROLSIDE

Earlston TD4 6AL
Mr and Mrs Anthony Foyle
T: 01896 849272 E: info@carolside.com
W: www.carolside.com

A traditional and romantic garden set in a beautiful 18th-century landscape. This garden is best known for its historically important collection of roses, with a national collection of pre-19th century Gallica roses and for its design of garden rooms with soft delicate herbaceous planting. Visit the oval walled garden, spilling with roses and billowing herbaceous borders, the herb garden with yellow and white roses set against acid green herbs or sit in the secret garden, planted in silver and pale pink. Walk to the apple orchard of historic apple trees and wild flowers or through the rose gates to the 18th century bridge and into the park and sit by the river. Carolside is said to be one of Scotland's finest private gardens.
National Plant Collection: Pre-19th century *Rosa* Gallica.

Open: Sunday 7 July, 11am - 5pm, admission £8.00, children free. Dogs on leads in the park only.

Directions: One mile north of Earlston on the A68. Entrance faces south. Garden accessible by Borders Bus 51, ask to get off at Carolside gate.

Opening for: Marie Curie

3 DAWYCK BOTANIC GARDEN

Stobo EH45 9JU
A Regional Garden of the Royal Botanic Garden Edinburgh
T: 01721 760254
W: www.rbge.org.uk/dawyck

Dawyck is a regional garden of the Royal Botanic Garden Edinburgh which had its 350th anniversary in 2020. Stunning collection of rare trees and shrubs. With over 300 years of tree planting, Dawyck is a world-famous arboretum with mature specimens of Chinese conifers, Japanese maples, Brewer's spruce, the unique Dawyck beech and sequoiadendrons from North America which are over 150 feet tall. Bold herbaceous plantings run along the burn. Range of trails and walks. Fabulous autumn colours.
National Plant Collection: *Larix* spp. and *Tsuga* spp.
Champion Trees: Numerous.

Open: Sunday 6 October, 10am - 5pm, admission details can be found on the garden's website.

Directions: Eight miles south-west of Peebles on the B712.

Opening for: Donation to SGS Beneficiaries

Peeblesshire & Tweeddale

4 GATTONSIDE VILLAGE GARDENS
Gattonside TD6 9NP
The Gardeners of Gattonside

A group of varied gardens situated on a south facing slope with views across the River Tweed to Melrose and its famous Abbey. Gattonside is known for its roses and fruit trees, once the fruit growing slopes for the Abbey monks. Walled gardens, herbaceous borders, fruit cages and vegetable gardens. Old and new gardens mixed together in this pretty village. Beautiful listed trees copper birch, oak trees, fruit trees and espalier trees within the village and gardens - some dating back to the time of Walter Scott!

Open: Sunday 28 July, 2pm - 5pm, admission £6.00, children free. Refreshments served in the village hall. Plants for sale at Allerly.

Directions: On the B6360 just outside the village of Gattonside on the LHS. First house after the 30mph sign. Short walk from Melrose over the chain bridge. Twenty minute walk along the River Tweed from Tweedbank railway station. By car access off A68, signposted *Gattonside*. Parking within the village.

Opening for: Borders General Hospital, Margaret Kerr Unit

5 GLEN HOUSE
Glen Estate, Innerleithen EH44 6PX
The Tennant family
T: 01896 830210 E: info@glenhouse.com
W: www.glenhouse.com

Surrounding the outstanding Scots Baronial mansion designed by David Bryce in the mid-19th century, Glen House gardens are laid out on shallow terraces overhanging the glen itself. It offers one of the loveliest designed landscapes in the Borders. The garden expands from the formal courtyard through a yew colonnade, and contains a fine range of trees, long herbaceous border and a pool garden with pergola, all arranged within the curve of slopes sheltering the house.

Open: Sunday 7 July, 1pm - 4pm, admission £8.00, children free.

Directions: Follow the B709 out of Innerleithen for approximately 2½ miles. Right turn at signpost for *Glen Estate*.

Opening for: WFGA

Carolside

Peeblesshire & Tweeddale

6 KAILZIE GARDENS

Peebles EH45 9HT
Susan and Steve Plag
T: 01721 720682
W: kailziegardens.com

Kailzie Gardens sits at the heart of the Tweed Valley just a mile east of Peebles occupying a beautiful position on the River Tweed. At its heart lies the stunning walled garden with plantings of many unusual shrubs, laburnum arches, an enchanting rose garden and spectacular herbaceous borders and one of the best examples of a Mackenzie and Moncur glasshouse still in existence, filled with fuchsias, pelargoniums and exotics. The garden also features prize winning show vegetables. The surrounding woodlands have one of the best laid arboretums in Scotland, with champion trees and specimens (including the oldest larch), providing acres of captivating woodland and burnside walks and spectacular vistas. Champion Trees: Larch planted 1725.

Open: Sunday 3 March, 10am - 4pm for Snowdrops and Winter Walks. Also open Sunday 21 July, 10am - 4pm. Admission details can be found on the garden's website. See website for other opening times.

Directions: A mile east of Peebles on the B7062.

Opening for: Tweed Togs SCIO

7 KIRKHOUSE

Traquair EH44 6PU
Mr and Mrs H Panton
T: 07793 019518

The Panton family moved into Kirkhouse in 2017 and have been enjoying working (with some help!), learning and experimenting with the 8 acres of varied garden. The garden is a mixture of formal and wild, with some areas having existed and evolved over many years. A delightful network of paths will lead you through a series of 'rooms' including a newly-planted large herbaceous border, a formal terraced lawn surrounded by mature trees and shrubs, a kitchen garden and greenhouse. There is a gently sloping path through mature woodland to the most recent project – a wildflower meadow. The garden is home to much wildlife and if you are lucky, you may meet one of the local red squirrels.

Open: Sunday 16 June, 2pm - 5pm, admission £6.00, children free.

Directions: Follow the B709 out of Innerleithen for approximately 2½ miles until you reach the hamlet of Kirkhouse and look for the yellow signs. Parking in the church car park, beyond Traquair Kirk on right hand side.

Opening for: Peeblesshire Youth Trust

Peeblesshire & Tweeddale

8 KIRKTON MANOR HOUSE
Peebles EH45 9JH
Mrs Rosemary Thorburn
T: 01721 740220 E: rpthorburn@icloud.com

Kirkton Manor House has a delightful, three-acre, informal country garden set in the beautiful Manor Valley. It enjoys spectacular open views and calling curlews from its riverside position. Bluebells flank the impressive entrance leading to a new shrub border. Stone steps continue through to terraced slopes filled with bulbs, roses and hellebores providing height, interest and fragrance. Grass paths meander along the burn where snowdrops, blue and white camassia, meconopsis, and ligularia thrive in this sunny meadow environment. Later, in June, sisyrinchiums, irises, orchids and many flowering shrubs and roses are abundant. The natural woodland includes many interesting trees.

Open: 14 February - 10 July (Wednesday only), 1pm - 4pm. Admission £5.00, children free. Visits can be made by arrangement on other days between mid-February and mid-July. Individuals and small groups are welcome.

Directions: Turn off the A72 west of Neidpath Castle, signposted to *Kirkton Manor*. After crossing the River Tweed, enter a garden gate which is a mile downhill, opposite a *Beware Horses* sign.

Opening for: All proceeds to SGS Beneficiaries

9 LAIDLAWSTIEL HOUSE
Clovenfords, Galashiels TD1 1TJ
Mr and Mrs P Litherland

Walled garden containing herbaceous border, fruit and vegetables in raised beds. There are colourful rhododendrons and azaleas as well as splendid views down to the River Tweed.

Open: Wednesday/Thursday, 5/6 June, 2pm - 5pm, admission £5.00, children free.

Directions: On the A72 between Clovenfords and Walkerburn turn up the hill signposted for *Thornielee*. The house is on the right at the top of the hill.

Opening for: Young Lives vs Cancer

Srongarbh

Peeblesshire & Tweeddale

10 MACBIEHILL GARDENS

The Walled Garden, Macbiehill EH46 7AZ
Simone Lyon
T: 07933 113067

Three very different gardens in the hamlet of Macbiehill which sits at some 1000 feet above sea level, very exposed to the copious wind and rain.

Alderbank: Alderbank is a large garden containing a mix of wild flower meadows and trees, a herbaceous border and a productive area of fruit and vegetables. It is very much a family garden used by our children to explore nature and play.

Birchbrae: The house was built on this site by the owners in 2019 and thereafter the garden was created from rough moorland ground. The enrichment of the soil and planting became a 'Lockdown' project in June 2021.

The Walled Garden: A contemporary walled garden paved with multi-hued sandstone enlivened by plants in raised beds and containers, plus a variety of ceramic and large one-off sculptures.

Open: Sunday 2 June, 2pm - 5pm, admission £6.00, children free. There will be a courtesy bus running from Whitmuir Farm on the A701 where there will be ample parking.

Directions: From the A701 take the turning opposite the entrance to Whitmuir Farm, signposted Macbiehill. After the narrow bridge go uphill and take the first entrance on the left, signposted Macbiehill Farm. There will be signs to the gardens and limited parking at the far end of the driveway. Alternatively, see opening section above for details of the available courtesy bus from Whitmuir Farm.

Opening for: Macmillan Cancer Support

11 PORTMORE

Eddleston EH45 8QU
Mr and Mrs David Reid
T: 07825 294388
W: www.portmoregardens.co.uk

Lovingly created by the current owners over the past 30 years; the gardens surrounding the David Bryce-designed mansion house contain mature trees and offer fine views of the surrounding countryside. Large walled garden with box-edged herbaceous borders is planted in stunning colour harmonies, potager, rose garden, pleached lime walk and ornamental fruit cages. The Victorian glasshouses contain fruit trees, roses, geraniums, pelargoniums and a wide variety of tender plants. There is also an Italianate grotto and water garden with shrubs and *Meconopsis*. The woodland walks are lined with rhododendrons, azaleas and shrub roses. Starred in *Good Gardens Guide* and featured in Kenneth Cox's book *Scotland for Gardeners* and on *Beechgrove*.

Open: 3 July - 28 August (Wednesday only), 1pm - 5pm. Also open by arrangement 1 June - 31 August. Admission £7.00, children free (3 July - 28 August) and details can be found on the garden's website (1 June - 31 August). Self-service refreshments for Wednesday openings. Homemade cream teas for groups over 15 people by prior arrangement. Please consult the garden's website.

Directions: Off the A703 one mile north of Eddleston. Bus 62.

Opening for: Chest Heart & Stroke Scotland

Peeblesshire & Tweeddale

12 ### QUERCUS GARDEN PLANTS
Whitmuir Farm, West Linton EH46 7BB
Rona Dodds
T: 01968 660708 E: quercusgardenplants@gmail.com
W: www.quercusgardenplants.co.uk

We are a small, independent nursery growing and selling a wide range of happy, healthy plants propagated from our nursery gardens. At just under two acres, these gardens were started in 2015 to show visitors and customers what can be grown in our conditions here on a north-west-facing hill at 850 feet above sea level. Explore our herb garden, scented garden, wildlife garden, prairie-style garden, winter garden and all the other inspirational smaller borders. Our new woodland garden opened in Spring 2023. Many of the plants seen in the gardens are available to buy in the nursery.

Open: Sunday 2 June & Sunday 25 August, 10am - 5pm, admission by donation. A percentage of plant sales on these dates will be donated to Scotland's Garden Scheme and Breast Cancer Now. The 16mm narrow gauge garden railway will be running from 2pm. Garden books and succulents will be available for a donation. On **2nd June,** a minibus will run from Whitmuir Farm to Macbiehill for those visitors interested in visiting the three Macbiehill Gardens also. Please park at Whitmuir Farm if you wish to visit Macbiehill.

Directions: On the A701, four miles south of the Leadburn junction or two miles north of West Linton.

Opening for: Breast Cancer Now

13 ### SRONGARBH
The Loan, West Linton EH46 7HE
Mr and Mrs O Arnesen

The property consists of an Arts and Crafts house (not open) with a large, well-established garden dating from the 1930s surrounded by woodland, with many trees and shrubs within the garden. This garden is approximately 1,000 feet above sea level, with acidic soil, high rainfall and low winter temperatures. In spring, the azaleas and rhododendrons provide a beautiful array of colours and the wide herbaceous borders continue flowering throughout the year. There is a formal rose garden with hybrid teas and old varieties of climbing, rambling and shrub roses. Below the formal terracing there is an original swimming pool as well as an ornamental pool under Japanese acers. The new owners are opening up areas of the garden with naturalistic paths.

Open: Sunday 9 June, 2pm - 5pm, admission £5.00, children free. Teas served in the village hall. Owing to access problems, a continuous minibus service will ferry visitors from the clock tower in West Linton village centre, just 50 yards from the village hall.

Directions: A701 or A702 and follow the signs.

Opening for: Ben Walton Trust & Borders General Hospital, Margaret Kerr Unit

Peeblesshire & Tweeddale

14 STOBO JAPANESE WATER GARDEN
Stobo Farm, Stobo EH45 8NX
Agnete Samdahl
E: enquiries@stobofarmestate.com

This is a mature, secluded woodland garden created in the early 1900s. Its most prominent feature is the constant presence of water that adds to the tranquillity of the garden, beginning with the drama of a waterfall at its head through a cascade of ponds, punctuated along the way by stepping stones and bridges. The garden was brought to life when Japanese style was the height of fashion – hence its cherry trees, maples, and iconic Japanese lanterns, 'tea house' and humpback bridge. The azaleas and rhododendrons provide a spectacular display in the spring. Limited disabled access due to gravel paths and steps. Visitors are advised to wear appropriate footwear.

Open: Sunday 2 June, 2pm - 5pm, admission £5.00, children free.

Directions: Off the B712 (Peebles/Broughton road) via *Stobo Castle* entrance. Bus 91

Opening for: Stobo and Drumelzier Church of Scotland & Scotland's Charity Air Ambulance

15 THE POTTING SHED
Broughton Place, Broughton, Biggar ML12 6HJ
Jane and Graham Buchanan-Dunlop
T: 01899 830574 E: buchanandunlop@btinternet.com

A one-acre garden begun from scratch in 2008, on an exposed hillside at 900 feet. It contains herbaceous plants, climbers, shrubs and trees - all selected for wind resistance and ability to cope with the poor, stony soil. There are usually fine views to the Southern Uplands.

Open: 5 June - 3 July (Wednesday only), 11am - 5pm. Also open by arrangement 1 May - 31 October. Admission £5.00, children free.

Directions: Signposted from the main A701 Edinburgh - Moffat Road, immediately north of Broughton village.

Opening for: Macmillan Cancer Support: Borders General Hospital

The Potting Shed © Kathy Henry

Perth & Kinross

Sponsored by

RATHBONES

Incorporating
Investec Wealth &
Investment (UK)

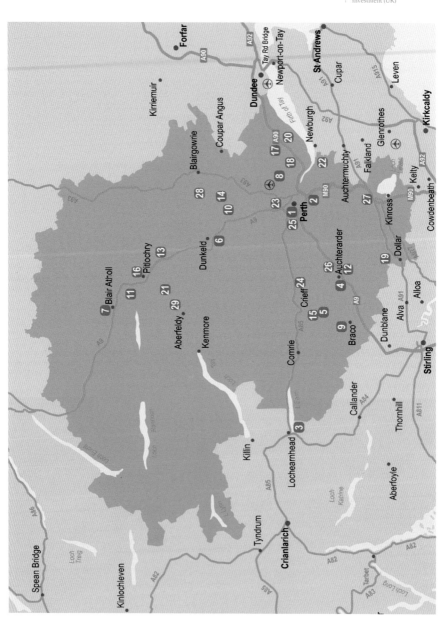

Perth & Kinross

OUR VOLUNTEER ORGANISERS

District Organiser:	Fiona Stewart	7 Craigend Cottages, Craigend, Perth PH2 8PX info@scotlandsgardens.org
Area Organisers:	Gill Boardman	16 Acremoar Drive, Kinross KY13 8RE
	Jane Gallier	The Old Farmhouse, Dunning Road, Auchterarder PH3 1DU
	Henrietta Harland	Easter Carmichael Cottage, Forgandenny Road, Bridge of Earn PH2 9EZ
	Ruth Howell	Tomandroighne, Edradynate, Aberfeldy PH15 2JS
	Alex Lindsay	19 St Serfs Place, Auchterarder PH3 1QS
	Judy Norwell	Dura Den, 20 Pitcullen Terrace, Perth PH2 7EQ
	Kareen Robertson	2 The Orchard, Bridge of Earn PH2 9DX
	Mary Jane Thompson	Mosspark House, Rumbling Bridge KY13 0QE
	Heather Wood	Mill of Forneth, Forneth, Blairgowrie PH10 6SP
Treasurer:	Michael Tinson	Parkhead House, Parkhead Gardens, Burghmuir, Road, Perth PH1 1JF

GARDENS OPEN ON A SPECIFIC DATE

Cloan, by Auchterarder	Sunday, 18 February
Scone Palace Garden, Perth	Saturday, 24 February
Fingask Castle, Rait	Sunday, 7 April
Megginch Castle, Errol	Sunday, 14 April
Birnam Bank Walled Garden, Birnam Bank, Birnam Glen, Dunkeld	Saturday, 11 May
Cloan, by Auchterarder	Sunday, 12 May
Cloan, by Auchterarder	Saturday/Sunday, 8/9 June
36 Muirfield, Perth	Sunday, 9 June
Mouse Cottage, Strathtay, Pitlochry	Friday/Saturday, 14/15 June
Blair Castle Gardens, Blair Atholl	Saturday, 15 June
Bradystone House, Murthly	Saturday, 15 June
The Abercairny Garden, Abercairny House, Crieff	Saturday, 15 June
The Bield at Blackruthven, Blackruthven House, Tibbermore	Saturday, 29 June
Tomandroighne, Edradynate, Aberfeldy	Saturday/Sunday, 27/28 July
Drummond Castle Gardens, Muthill, Crieff	Sunday, 4 August
Cloan, by Auchterarder	Sunday, 11 August
Auchterarder Allotments Association,	Saturday, 24 August

Perth & Kinross

GARDENS OPEN REGULARLY

Fingask Castle, Rait	22 January - 7 March (not Friday, Saturday & Sunday)
Braco Castle, Braco	1 February - 31 October
Glendoick Garden Centre, Glencarse	1 April - 31 May
Explorers Garden, Port Na Craig, Pitlochry	2 April - 26 October (not Monday & Sunday)
Ardvorlich, Lochearnhead	1 May - 2 June
Bradystone House, Murthly	6 June - 26 September (Thursday only)
Blair Castle	28 March - 27 October

GARDENS OPEN BY ARRANGEMENT

Mouse Cottage, Strathtay, Pitlochry	1 January - 29 November (not Sunday)
Delvine, Murthly	2 January - 29 December
The Pond Garden, Pond Cottage, Middleton, Milnathort	1 February - 31 December
Bonhard House, Perth	1 April - 31 October
Hollytree Lodge, Muckhart, Dollar	1 April - 31 October
The Steading at Clunie, The Steading	6 April - 7 July
Craigowan, Ballinluig	7 April - 31 July
Pitcurran House, Abernethy	1 May - 1 September
Beech Cottage, The Wynd, Muthill	1 May - 1 September
Carig Dhubh, Bonskeid, Pitlochry	1 May - 30 September
The Old Farmhouse, Dunning Road, Auchterarder	1 May - 30 June
7 Craigend Cottages, Craigend, Perth	1 June - 31 July

The Abercairny Garden

Perth & Kinross

1 **36 MUIRFIELD**
Perth PH1 1JJ
Rob Mackay and Amanda Brown
T: 01738 636527 E: mackaybrownjoint@gmail.com

A small suburban garden with a Japanese theme. The garden was designed and planted in 2019 with the aim of being low maintenance and offering a fun and safe environment for children. The Japanese features include a stone lantern, a water bowl, the placing of rocks, raked gravel and a timber building. The planting includes prunus, acer, bamboo, hostas, ferns and flowering plants. Foliage and texture are important elements. Views of the distant hills are seen as an extension of the garden in the Japanese tradition.

Open: Sunday 9 June, 2pm - 5pm, admission £5.00, children free.

Directions: Muirfield connects Muirend Road with Burghmuir Road. 36 Muirfield is the white bungalow near the junction with Muirend Road on the left-hand side as you travel up the hill. The number 8 bus from Mill Street in the centre runs every hour, alight at Fairies Road just before the junction with Viewlands Road West. Go straight over the mini roundabout continuing along Fairies Road. At the next mini roundabout turn left into Muirend Road. Muirfield is the first turning on the right with number 36 the second house on the right. If coming by car please park on Muirend Road to avoid blocking neighbours' access.

Opening for: Amnesty International UK Section Charitable Trust

2 **7 CRAIGEND COTTAGES**
Craigend, Perth PH2 8PX
Fiona Stewart
T: 07468 303506 E: munro283@btinternet.com

This south-west-facing garden has a sunny, open aspect with an extended landscape to the front and back. It is an informal cottage garden with a dedicated, productive vegetable growing area including fruit bushes, dahlias and the lovely scent of sweet peas growing alongside. There are herbaceous borders with a colourful mix of flowers and shrubs many of which attract bees and butterflies. The soil is acid and so rhododendrons and pieris grow well. Also included are climbers such as clematis and honeysuckle, mixed hedges and a rose bed along with lawns, a productive greenhouse and a wildlife-attracting pond with beautiful water lilies.

Open: by arrangement 1 June - 31 July, admission £5.00, children free.

Directions: From Bridge of Earn follow the main street and drive north on the A912 for about 1 ½ miles passing the Earn Cafe on your left. Craigend Cottages are on the main road on the left-hand-side with number 7 at the Perth end of the row. From Perth take the Edinburgh Road (A912). Continue on the road passing Tesco on your left and straight on at mini roundabout. Continue with Craigclowan School on your right, pass under two flyovers and Craigend cottages are immediately on your right.

Opening for: Alzheimer Scotland

Perth & Kinross

3 ARDVORLICH
Lochearnhead FK19 8QE
Mr and Mrs Sandy Stewart
T: 01567 830335

Beautiful hill garden featuring over 170 different species of rhododendrons and many hybrids, grown in a glorious setting of oaks and birches on either side of the Ardvorlich Burn. The paths are quite steep and rough in places and boots are advisable, especially when wet.

Open: 1 May - 2 June, 9am - dusk, admission £5.00, children free.

Directions: On South Loch Earn Road three miles from Lochearnhead, five miles from St Fillans.

Opening for: The Ghurka Welfare Trust

4 AUCHTERARDER ALLOTMENTS ASSOCIATION
PH3 1JH
Located behind St Margaret's Hospital, Auchterarder PH3 1JH

Embark on a journey from abandoned field to flourishing oasis at Auchterarder Allotments, transformed over eight years, hidden away off the High Street. Turning stony, weedy clay soil into a verdant haven of approximately 22 diverse plots, we champion the growth of local, nourishing, organic food, harmonising with nature both body and soul. Join us for a day of inspiration; indulge in tea and cakes (made from our own produce), explore with a guided tour, and engage in conversation with our passionate allotmenteers. Get inspired and embark on your own 'grow your own' journey.

Open: Saturday 24 August, 1pm - 3pm, admission £6.00, children free.

Directions: Located behind St Margaret's Hospital. Access by foot from the High Street (Townhead) along a private lane between St Margaret's Hospital and Beechtree Place. Various parking places on the High Street.

Opening for: Auchterarder Community Sports and Recreation: Supporting green spaces project in the community.

5 BEECH COTTAGE
The Wynd, Muthill PH5 2AP
Rosalyn Serex
T: 07590 813509 E: rosalyn@serex.me

Nestled at the foot of The Wynd in the conservation village of Muthill, the garden is surrounded by the ancient trees of Lindores. The main attraction of the garden is the collection of 200 roses interspersed with companion perennials. A well-planted Koi pond provides a relaxing area to be seated.

Open: by arrangement 1 May - 1 September, admission by donation. Open from 11am - 5pm

Directions: The Wynd is a street perpendicular to Drummond Street. The cottage is at the bottom of The Wynd approx 80 metres slightly down hill. Please note, The Wynd is very narrow and is not suitable for large vehicles and is extremely difficult to turn around. Recommend using Drummond Street to park where there are usually sufficient spaces. Bus routes in Muthill: 18 – Auchterarder/Crieff; 45 - Town Service/Crieff; 15A – Perth/ St Fillans or Stirling; 615 – Perth/ St Fillans or Stirling. Bus stops are on Drummond Street - from here, head east towards the church/old church monuments.

Opening for: The Dystonia Society

Perth & Kinross

Beech Cottage

6

BIRNAM BANK WALLED GARDEN
Birnam Bank, Birnam Glen, Dunkeld PH8 0BW
Kirsty Binnie

This large walled garden was added to Birnam Bank in 1986, with new entrances, namely a stone archway with apple arch and wooden gate, leading onto an existing cobbled patio. A beech hedge was subsequently planted providing a boundary. The owners moved here in July 2022 and began the process of restoring the garden to its former glory. Large areas are under development but there is a productive vegetable section, fruit bushes, a cut-flower border, a herbaceous border and many mature apple trees. A variety of well-established trees include two specimen copper beeches and an original fruiting walnut.

Open: Saturday 11 May, 10am - 4pm, admission £5.00, children free.

Directions: There is limited parking at the house. Please park at Birnam village or at Dunkeld and Birnam train station and walk to the garden up Birnam Glen footpath which is a five-minute walk.

Opening for: Tayside Health Fund: Cornhill Macmillan Centre

Perth & Kinross

Bradystone House © Mike Nicoll

7 BLAIR CASTLE GARDENS
Blair Atholl PH18 5TL
Blair Charitable Trust
T: 01796 481207 E: office@blair-castle.co.uk
W: www.blair-castle.co.uk

Blair Castle stands as the focal point in a designed landscape of some 2,500 acres within a Highland estate. Hercules Garden is a walled enclosure of about nine acres recently restored to its original 18th-century design with landscaped ponds, a Chinese bridge, contemporary plantings, and an orchard of more than 100 fruit trees. The glory of this garden in summer is the herbaceous border, which runs along the 275 yard south-facing wall. A delightful sculpture trail incorporates contemporary and 18th-century sculpture as well as eight new works, letter-carving on stone from the *Memorial and Commemorative Arts* charity's 'Art and Memory Collection'. Diana's Grove is a magnificent stand of tall trees including grand fir, Douglas fir, larch and wellingtonia running along the Banvie Burn, with the 12th-century ruins of St Bride's Church on the far bank.

Open: Saturday 15 June, 10am - 5pm, admission details can be found on the garden's website. Also open 28 March - 27 October, 10am - 5pm (7 days a week).

Directions: Off A9, follow signs to *Blair Castle, Blair Atholl.*

Opening for: SGS

Perth & Kinross

8 BONHARD HOUSE

Perth PH2 7PQ
Stephen and Charlotte Hay
T: 07990 574570 E: stephenjohnhay@me.com

Traditional 19th-century garden of five acres approached through an avenue of magnificent oaks. Mature trees, six classified by the National Tree Register as 'remarkable', including a monkey puzzle, sequoias, Douglas fir and a variety of hollies. Reinstated and new herbaceous borders. Rhododendron and azalea beds. Recently planted spring and summer flowering meadow areas with a variety of fruit and nut trees. Beehive and a productive vegetable garden. A new larch arbour with climbing roses and clematis. Grass paths meander through a pond area with shrubs and mature trees. A pinetum with 25 different varieties. Garden emphasis on wildlife habitat as well as aesthetics. Resident red squirrels. Plentiful and varied birdlife.

Open: by arrangement 1 April - 31 October, admission £5.00, children free. Groups welcome to enquire.

Directions: On the A94 just under a mile north of Perth take the right turn, signed *Murrayshall Country Estate*. After approximately one mile take the entrance right marked *Bonhard House*, at a sharp left turn. From Balbeggie turn left, signposted for *Bonhard*, one mile north of Scone. Turn right in a half-a-mile, pass any sign for *Bonhard Nursery*, and enter the drive at sharp right turn.

Opening for: Freedom from Fistula Foundation

9 BRACO CASTLE

Braco FK15 9LA
Mr and Mrs M van Ballegooijen
T: 01786 880437

A 19th-century landscaped garden with a plethora of wonderful and interesting trees, shrubs, bulbs and plants. An old garden for all seasons that has been extensively expanded over the last 35 years. The partly walled garden is approached on a rhododendron and tree-lined path featuring an ornamental pond. Spectacular spring bulbs, exuberant shrub and herbaceous borders and many ornamental trees are all enhanced by the spectacular views across the park to the Ochils. From snowdrops through to vibrant autumn colour, this garden is a gem. Look out for the embothrium in June, hoheria in August, eucryphia in September and an interesting collection of rhododendrons and azaleas with long flowering season.

Open: 1 February - 31 October, 10am - 5pm. February to early March for Snowdrops and Winter Walks. Admission £5.00, children free. No dogs please.

Directions: Drive for 1 ½ miles from the gates at the north end of Braco Village, just west of the bridge on the A822. Parking at the castle is welcome.

Opening for: The Woodland Trust Scotland

Perth & Kinross

10 BRADYSTONE HOUSE
Murthly PH1 4EW
Mrs James Lumsden
T: 01738 710308 E: pclumsden@me.com

A unique cottage garden converted from a derelict farm steading. Imaginative and abundant planting with unusual and special perennials, clematis, roses, abutilons and shrubs. There is an interesting and bountiful plant stall. Small vegetable garden and orchard, meandering woodland walks and a duck pond. A garden oasis in which to sit and dream. Garden groups welcome by arrangement. Dogs on leads please.

Open: Open 6 June to 26 September, Thursdays only, 11am - 4pm. Admission £5.00, children free. Also open Saturday 15 June 11am - 4pm as a special plant sale day.

Directions: From south/north follow the A9 to Bankfoot, then signs to *Murthly*. At the crossroads in Murthly take the private road to Bradystone.

Opening for: Scotland's Charity Air Ambulance

11 CARIG DHUBH
Bonskeid, Pitlochry PH16 5NP
Jane and Niall Graham-Campbell
T: 01796 473469 E: niallgc@btinternet.com

'I don't know how Niall and Jane manage to grow their splendid meconopsis on the sand and rock of their garden but they do, most successfully.' In this stunning situation, when not admiring the views, you will find wonderful primulas, cardiocrinum and meconopsis, all interspersed between beautiful shrubs and other herbaceous plants. Look up and in July you will see roses flowering 40 feet up in the tree. This is a gem of a garden and you will be welcomed by Niall and Jane Graham-Campbell with all their expert knowledge.

Open: by arrangement 1 May - 30 September, admission £5.00, children free.

Directions: Take the old A9 between Pitlochry and Killiecrankie, turn west on the Tummel Bridge Road B8019, Carig Dhubh is ¾ mile on the north side of the road.

Opening for: Earl Haig Fund Poppy Scotland

Carig Dhubh © Camelia Hudema

Perth & Kinross

12 CLOAN
by Auchterarder PH3 1PP
Neil Mitchison
T: 07958 155831 E: niall@fastmail.co.uk

Two acres of wild garden, with a wide variety of rhododendrons and azaleas, and an impressive collection of trees, including metasequoia, cryptomeria, *Acer cappadocicum*, *Sequoia sempervirens*, *Quercus robur* 'Filicifolia', liriodendron, several Japanese maples, magnificent beech and Scots pine trees, and extensive yew topiary; also an acre of walled garden with embothriums, *Acer griseum*, liquidambar, several sorbus varieties, parrotia and a large herbaceous border. Fine views of Strathearn from the front of the house.

Open: Sunday 18 February 11am - 3pm for Snowdrops and Winter Walks. Also open Sunday 12 May, Saturday/Sunday, 8/9 June and Sunday 11 August 10am - 5pm. Admission £4.00, children free.

Directions: From the A823, just south of the A9, follow the small road heading north-east, signposted *Duchally*. Continue for approximately 2 ½ miles, turn right at the sign *Coulshill*. Continue for just under ½ mile. Follow the signs for *car parking*.

Opening for: Tiphereth Limited: Camphill Scotland

13 CRAIGOWAN
Ballinluig PH9 0NE
Ian and Christine Jones
T: 01796 482244 E: i.q.jones@btinternet.com

This is a specialist garden with a major collection of rhododendrons put together over the last 40 years; initially, mainly species from Glendoick following the plant hunting and discoveries of Peter Cox and the late Sir Peter Hutchison and others. In the last 20 years there have been added noteworthy hybrids sourced from Glendoick and the major English nurseries. Each year further additions are made and earlier introductions which have outgrown their original or secondary planting spot are moved to new locations. With growth rates tending to increase, this is a major exercise but the result is a constantly changing garden and more plants are developing into a spectacular presentation. Other plant types include magnolias, ornamental acers and a collection of unusual trees. There are areas of more formal beds where there is a large collection of meconopsis and lilies including cardiocrinum with roughly a hundred flowering each year. The rhododendron flowering period lasts from January to August but the best months are April, May and June. There is adjoining woodland which is being replanted with disease resistant trees and with the larger rhododendrons which have outgrown the more formal areas. In June and July two large herbaceous borders give summer colour and interest.

Open: by arrangement 7 April - 31 July, admission £5.00, children free.

Directions: From the north or south of the A9 to Ballinluig junction. Follow sign for *Tulliemet* and *Dalcapon*. Pass the filling station and Ballinluig Hotel. Turn right following the *Tulliemet/Dalcapon* sign; this is a steep narrow road so take care. About ½ mile up the road take a left turning with fields on either side and Craigowan is the first house on the left about ½ mile along. Park on paviours adjoining the house.

Opening for: LUPUS UK

Perth & Kinross

14 DELVINE

Murthly PH1 4LD
Mr and Mrs David Gemmell
T: 07748 207647 E: gemmell.david@googlemail.com

The gardens and arboretum at Delvine cover about 20 acres. The old gardens are on the Inchtuthil plateau, leading down to the more recent garden and arboretum which is situated on a flood plain, flanked by oxbow lakes on each side. This is the place to visit for those who seek a remote and peaceful setting. As one proceeds in a westerly direction, one departs from the traditional and enters an area of great drifts of chimonobambusa and miscanthus grasses with water and wildlife in abundance. The walking is easy. This garden will appeal to those seeking the unusual and also for those with an adventurous spirit.

Open: by arrangement 2 January - 29 December, admission by donation. Surfaces are level grass. Dogs on leads, please.

Directions: On the A984, seven miles east of Dunkeld, four miles south-west of Blairgowrie.

Opening for: ABF The Soldiers' Charity

15 DRUMMOND CASTLE GARDENS

Muthill, Crieff PH7 4HN
Grimsthorpe & Drummond Castle Trust Ltd
T: 01764 681433
W: www.drummondcastlegardens.co.uk

Activities and events for a great family day out. The gardens of Drummond Castle were originally laid out in 1630 by John Drummond, second Earl of Perth. In 1830 the parterre was changed to an Italian style. One of the most interesting features is the multi-faceted sundial designed by John Mylne, Master Mason to Charles I. The formal garden is said to be one of the finest in Europe and is the largest of its type in Scotland.

Open: Sunday 4 August, 1pm - 5pm, admission details can be found on the garden's website.

Directions: Entrance two miles south of Crieff on Muthill road (A822).

Opening for: BLESMA

16 EXPLORERS GARDEN

Port Na Craig, Pitlochry PH16 5DR
Pitlochry Festival Theatre
T: 01796 484626
W: www.pitlochryfestivaltheatre.com

Designed as a Theatricum Botanicum, to showcase art and horticulture in one place. The Explorers Garden celebrates the rich history of Scottish Plant Explorers of the past. Across our serene, seven-acre woodland garden, you will find each area is dedicated to regions across the world including a large Himalayan section which houses our meconopsis, beautiful Himalayan blue poppies. There are breathtaking views, buildings and stone structures with unique odes to Pitlochry's Pictish past. The garden is a sanctuary for our resident red squirrels and there is visiting art throughout each garden space. We have live theatre performances in summer in our very own amphitheatre. This really is a garden like no other.
National Plant Collection: *Meconopsis*.

Perth & Kinross

Open: 2 April - 26 October (not Monday & Sunday), 10am - 5pm, admission £5.00, children under 12 free. Last entry 4:00 pm. Cafe at Pitlochry Festival Theatre.

Directions: Take the A9 to Pitlochry town, then follow signs to *Pitlochry Festival Theatre*, (tickets available at the Theatre Box Office). Bus and rail travel are both available to Pitlochry from further afield.

Opening for: Donation to SGS Beneficiaries

17 FINGASK CASTLE
Rait PH2 7SA
Mr and Mrs Andrew Murray Threipland
T: 01821 670777 ext 4 & 6 E: andrew@fingaskcastle.com
W: www.fingaskcastle.co.uk

Scotland's only surrealist garden: spectacular topiary staggers across the garden bumping into stone globes, marble balls, statues and a figure of Alice (in Wonderland). Other literary and historical characters are scattered among the 17th-century pleasure gardens. Bonnie Prince Charlie and his father are said to have approached the castle up the long yew avenue known as 'The King's Walk'. A 15-minute walk takes you down to the dell beneath the castle and St Peter's Well – a stopping place for medieval pilgrims on their way to the bones of the saintly Queen Margaret at Dunkeld Cathedral. Return via a Chinese bridge, Gabriel's bridge, an iron age fort, along a stream, past Sir Stuart's House and back to the castle via the Old Orchard. There are large drifts of snowdrops, daffodils and flowering shrubs in season. A wollemi pine has recently been planted. Giant 120 year old Redwoods: both Sempervirens and Giganteum Champion Trees: *Pinus wallichiana* (Bhutan Pine) Metasequoia glyptostroboides and the handsome remnants of what was the largest walnut in Scotland.

Open: 22 January - 7 March (not Friday, Saturday & Sunday), 10am - 4pm for Snowdrops and Winter Walks. Also open Sunday 7 April, 1pm - 4:30pm. Admission for all dates £6.00, children free. Homemade teas on 7 April only.

Directions: Half-way between Perth and Dundee. From the A90 follow signs to *Rait* until small crossroad, turn right and follow signs to *Fingask*.

Opening for: All Saints Episcopal Church & Fingask Follies

Fingask Castle © Carolyn Bell

Perth & Kinross

 18 **GLENDOICK GARDEN CENTRE**
Glencarse, Perthshire PH2 7NS
Cox Family
T: 01738 860260 E: gardencentre@glendoick.com
W: www.glendoick.com

Glendoick's gardens and garden centre with its award-winning café is the ideal spring day out in April and May. 2023 sees Glendoick Garden Centre celebrate 50 years. Glendoick boasts a unique collection of plants from three generations of Cox plant-hunting expeditions in China and the Himalaya. Enjoy one of the finest collections of rhododendrons and azaleas, magnolias and other acid-loving plants in the woodland garden and the gardens surrounding the house. Many of the rhododendron and azalea species and hybrids have been introduced from the wild or bred by the Cox family. There are fine waterfall views in the woodland gardens. The award-winning Glendoick Garden Centre has one of Scotland's best selections of plants including their world-famous rhododendrons and azaleas as well as a gift shop and café.

Open: 1 April - 31 May, 10am - 4pm, admission £5.00, children free. For garden visit group bookings email gardencentre@glendoick.com. Café bookings (run separately) E: manager@garden-cafe.co.uk. Please note the woodland garden is not easily accessible to wheelchairs but some of the gardens by the house are. Toilets and refreshments are at the garden centre only. No dogs.

Directions: Follow the *brown* signs to Glendoick Garden Centre off the A90 Perth - Dundee road. The gardens are ½ mile behind the Garden Centre. After buying tickets at the Garden Centre, please drive up and park at the gardens (free parking).

Opening for: Donation to SGS Beneficiaries

 19 **HOLLYTREE LODGE**
Muckhart, Dollar FK14 7JW
Liz and Peter Wyatt
T: 07973 374687 E: elizwyatt@aol.com

A tranquil one-acre garden in the centre of the village. The garden is divided by internal hedges into different areas. Highlights include a small Japanese garden, mini orchard, naturalised spring bulbs and wildflowers, mixed herbaceous borders, rill and a wildlife pond. We have an interesting collection of rhododendrons and azaleas. A variety of other unusual trees and shrubs including various acers, giving wonderful autumn colours, a handkerchief tree, eucalyptus snow gum, and a *Parrotia persica* (Persian Ironwood) amongst others. We garden organically, aiming to keep the garden as pollinator friendly as possible, by working with nature, complementing our beekeeping interests.

Open: by arrangement 1 April - 31 October, admission £5.00, children free. Always worth a call if you are in the area outwith these dates.

Directions: Approximately 100 yards from the A91 (between Dollar and Milnathort) down the small lane directly opposite the entrance to the Inn at Muckhart.

Opening for: The Royal Air Force Benevolent Fund

Perth & Kinross

20 MEGGINCH CASTLE

Errol PH2 7SW
Giles Herdman and Catherine Drummond-Herdman
T: 01821 642222 E: info@megginch.com
W: megginchcastle.com

There really is no place like home! Come and spend time walking through the daffodils, across the green lawns, peek into the serene ancient stone chapel, walk through the peaceful walled garden and into the 10-acre heritage orchard. Then back into the warmth of the conservatory for a good blether and hot cup of tea or two - not forgetting some cake of course! Another Magical Megginch afternoon which we want to share with you, your family and friends – two and four-legged!
National Plant Collection: Scottish cider apples, Scottish Heritage apples and pears.
Champion Trees: *Acer palmatum.*

Open: Sunday 14 April, 2pm - 5pm, admission £6.00, children free.

Directions: Ten miles from Perth and Dundee directly off the A90, Perth-bound carriageway, 600 yards after the Errol/Rait flyover, on the left hand side, 300 yards after *Beware Pedestrians Crossing* sign, or signed entrance just before the level crossing in Errol Station.

Opening for: SGS and beneficiaries

21 MOUSE COTTAGE

Strathtay, Pitlochry PH9 0PG
Penny Kennedy
T: 07799 678067 E: mymousecottage@outlook.com
W: mousecottage.co.uk

Mouse Cottage sits on a south-facing hill overlooking Strathtay. Small but packed with interesting features, it is a semi-wild haven of secret places where self-seeders mix with annuals and more formal planting. The owner is an artist who adores her garden space and collects quirky planting containers such as dustbins and dolly tubs. Her Pear Parasol and Holly Brolly are amongst her favourite features. Gravel paths wind through shady places full of joyous surprises such as *Crambe cordifolia.*

Open: Friday/Saturday, 14/15 June, 10am - 4pm. Also open by arrangement 1 January - 29 November (not Sunday). Admission £5.00, children free. (Ice cream, home-made lemonade and homebaking available on 14/15th June only.)

Directions: From the A9 take the exit at Ballinluig signposted Aberfeldy. Go through Logierait, after about 4 miles turn right at T junction. At Grandtully turn right, over the bridge, up the hill to Strathtay Post Office. Turn right passing the golf course up to the red telephone box. Mouse Cottage is next opening on the left, signposted. Please beware of flying golf balls!
NB: No parking at Mouse Cottage. On street parking possible at Strathtay. Bus 23 (Aberfeldy to Perth) stops at Grandtully Bridge.

Opening for: SGS and beneficiaries

Perth & Kinross

22 **PITCURRAN HOUSE**
Abernethy PH2 9LH
The Hon Ranald and Mrs Noel-Paton
T: 01738 850933 E: patricianp@pitcurran.com

This end-of-village garden was created 20 years ago. It includes an interesting combination of trees, rare shrubs and herbaceous plants including azaleas, rhododendrons, tree peonies, trillium and veratrum. Also a rose pergola, eucryphias and a large west-facing hydrangea border for the later summer. Above the pond there is a good collection of pink and white-barked birch, and a young arboretum, from which there are fine views over the Earn and Tay valleys.

Open: by arrangement 1 May - 1 September, admission £6.00, children free.

Directions: South-east of Perth. From the M90 (exit nine) take the A912 towards Glenfarg, go left at the roundabout onto the A913 to Abernethy. Pitcurran House is at the far eastern end of the village. Buses run through Abernethy from Perth and the surrounding districts.

Opening for: Juvenile Diabetes Research Foundation Limited

Pitcurran House © Camelia Hudema

23 **SCONE PALACE GARDEN**
Perth PH2 6BD
The Earl & Countess of Mansfield
W: www.scone-palace.co.uk

Scone Palace will be hosting a day to celebrate the snowdrop display that grows in the gardens and grounds of this historic site. A waymarked 'Snowdrop Walk' will guide you through the Friars Den, Victorian Pinetum and down the old drive lined with an avenue of lime trees. Join the Palace gardens team as they plant up a wooded area of the grounds for a new snowdrop display. Here you will learn how to increase your own snowdrop display at home where lifting, splitting and transplanting will be demonstrated. As a thank you, a gift of a few snowdrops will be given to improve or start your own collection.

Open: Saturday 24 February, 10am - 3pm for Snowdrops and Winter Walks, free access but an entry donation of £5.00 is requested. A small selection of specialised snowdrops will be for sale from our gift shop with our coffee shop open for a selection of refreshments.

Directions: Two miles from Perth on the A93 Perth/Braemar road. Well signposted.

Opening for: All proceeds to SGS Beneficiaries

Perth & Kinross

 24 ## THE ABERCAIRNY GARDEN

Abercairny House, Crieff PH7 3NQ
Liz O'Donnell
T: 01764 652706 E: info@abercairny.com

The Abercairny garden, originally designed by Lewis Kennedy, is in the shape of a horseshoe and set within a wall. It is edged by huge trees that include Douglas firs and *Sequoia sempervirens* and it is laid out on three terraces. The top terrace is mostly formal, with mature informal beds on either side; these beds contain roses, rhododendrons, and azaleas. The second (originally called the Bowling Green) includes rhododendrons and fruit trees. The third is made up of gardens that have been created in the last sixteen years. Here you will see, amongst many new plants, a paulownia tree, different kinds of cornus and eight magnolias. There are lots of different varieties of candelabra primulas in the primula garden. At the bottom of this garden there is a stream and Kennedy's two Swiss bridges. Look out for red squirrels.

Open: Saturday 15 June, noon - 5pm, admission £5.00, children free. Paths can be rough underfoot. Sensible footwear advised. Dogs on a lead please.

Directions: Turn south off the A85 at the New Fowlis crossroads, following signs. Turn right into the estate grounds after 1.2 miles (opposite Kintocher Farm on the left) and follow the drive for one mile past Abercairny House on the left. Car parking for the gardens is in the car park opposite the castellated stables venue.

Opening for: Anchor House Cyrenians: Perth

 25 ## THE BIELD AT BLACKRUTHVEN

Blackruthven House, Tibbermore PH1 1PY
The Bield Christian Co Ltd
T: 01738 583238 E: info@bieldatblackruthven.org.uk

The Bield is set in extensive grounds with well-maintained lawns, hedges, flower meadow and specimen trees. A labyrinth is cut into the grass of the old orchard and there is also a wheelchair-friendly labyrinth. Traditional walled garden with colourful, richly-stocked borders and lawns, cut-flower garden, healing garden, glasshouse, trained fruit trees and organic vegetable plot. Walk through extensive woodland and visit the old curling pond. Southton Smallholding is a social enterprise ten minutes walk away, featuring vegetable plots, polytunnels and a number of animals (not staffed on the day).

Open: Saturday 29 June, 2pm - 5pm, admission £5.00, children free.

Directions: From Dundee or Edinburgh, follow signs for *Glasgow, Stirling* and *Crianlarich* which lead onto the Perth bypass. Head west on the A85 signed to *Crieff/Crianlarich* to West Huntingtower. Turn left at the crossroads to *Madderty/Tibbermore*. The entrance is left after a ½ mile passing the gate lodge on your right. Parking signed to right at the steading.

Opening for: Ripple Effect

Perth & Kinross

26 THE OLD FARMHOUSE

Dunning Road, Auchterarder PH3 1DU
Jane and Nigel Gallier
T: 01764 662471 E: thegalliers@msn.com

A garden of approximately one acre with herbaceous borders, a gravel garden, vegetable garden, trained fruit trees in half-wine barrels, wild areas under-planted with bulbs, and woodland areas, with other areas still being developed. As you approach the house, look out for our kamikaze hens. The garden is not always immaculate; a well-ordered winter garden and a floriferous summer garden.

Open: by arrangement 1 May - 30 June, admission £5.00, children free.

Directions: From the A9 take the A824 and halfway between Auchterarder and Aberuthven take the B8062 at Grand Eagles and head towards Dunning. We are on the left just before the A9 bridge.

Opening for: ABF The Soldiers' Charity

27 THE POND GARDEN

Pond Cottage, Middleton, Milnathort KY13 0SD
Fay Young & Ray Perman
T: 07767 407396 E: fay@fayyoung.org
W: fayyoung.org/category/pond-cottage/

A wild woodland and wetland garden creatively adapting to the challenges of climate change. We learn from resilient plants and thriving communities of birds, bats, bees, butterflies, red squirrels, swans and other wildlife. Woodland paths lead through seasonal highlights: snowdrops, daffodils, bluebells, foxgloves and ferns. Grand old beeches and oaks mark the boundaries of a former Victorian estate. Since the mid 1990s we have rebuilt and recently retrofitted derelict farm cottage with external insulation and renewable energy. New plantings of native trees add spring and autumn colour. There are stone and willow features to discover and benches to rest by the pond.

Open: by arrangement 1 February - 31 December, admission £5.50, children free. Open for seasonal highlights.

Directions: From Milnathort village: At the mini roundabout in the centre of the village take the north exit (signed for Path of Condie) up Wester Loan, then North Street. At the top of the hill, past the church on your left, you will cross the motorway again. Carry straight on for ½ mile, the gate to Pond Cottage is on the right after a field opening.

Opening for: CHAS: Children's Hospices Across Scotland

Perth & Kinross

28 THE STEADING AT CLUNIE
The Steading PH10 6SG
Jean and Dave Trudgill
T: 01250 884263 E: davetrudgill@googlemail.com

The Steading at Newmill is on the north bank of the Lunan Burn midway between Lochs Clunie and Marlee. There are paths that extend for 800yds along the Lunan, a small, colourful cottage garden with a fish pond, and 6 acres of woodland, ponds and a wildflower meadow. There are banks of wild daffodils that are at their best in early April. By early May there are primroses, carpets of cuckoo flower, wood anemones, and cowslips in the meadow. Mid-May sees some of the banks covered with bluebells. In the meadow there are 14 species of wild orchids that come into flower from mid-May until early July. A video of Newmill, lasting 8 minutes, can be seen by going to Youtube and searching for 'Newmill: creating and managing an orchid meadow'

Open: by arrangement 6 April - 7 July, admission by donation. There are narrow paths, bridges and flowing water. One dog on lead only.

Directions: Three miles west of Blairgowrie on the A923. About 600 metres west of the Kinloch Hotel take the track on the left, just after a mobile phone mast and a breeze-block wall.

Opening for: Save the Children UK

29 TOMANDROIGHNE
Edradynate, Aberfeldy PH15 2JS
Ruth Howell

Tomandroighne is a garden of just under two acres located on a steep bank overlooking the River Tay. Quirky sculptures, stonework and salvaged items add interest as this challenging site is gradually improved. The garden hosts a collection of rhododendrons and azaleas, flowering in sequence late spring and early summer. A spring-fed water garden is home to many bog-loving plants including gunnera, rodgersia, candelabra primulas and ligularia. In May a carpet of native Scottish bluebells gives way to herbaceous planting and flowering shrubs which give colour and texture all summer. There are many quiet areas for peaceful contemplation.

Open: Saturday/Sunday, 27/28 July, noon - 4pm, admission £5.00, children free. Not suitable for wheelchairs or those with mobility issues. Parking is limited and not suitable for large vehicles.

Directions: Coming from the A9, take the Ballinluig exit heading for Aberfeldy. At Grandtully turn right, crossing the River Tay via the metal bridge to Strathtay. From there turn left, following the signs to Cluny House Gardens for about three miles alongside the river. At the turning to Cluny House Gardens, turn right and then immediately left up a short steep drive. Tomandroighne is the white house at the top of the steep bank. Please note the SATNAV map location is not correct, we are about a ¼ of a mile east of the location given, at the bottom of the road up to Cluny House Gardens.

Opening for: The Aberfeldy Dementia-Friendly Collaborative

Renfrewshire

Sponsored by

RATHBONES

Incorporating
Investec Wealth &
Investment (UK)

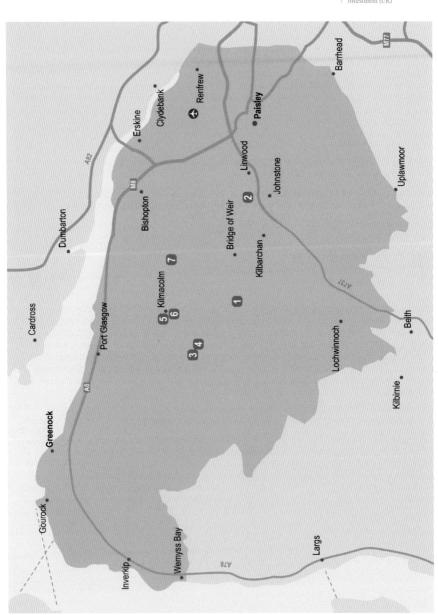

Renfrewshire

OUR VOLUNTEER ORGANISERS

District Organiser:	Alexandra MacMillan	Langside Farm, Kilmacolm, PA13 4SA
		info@scotlandsgardens.org
Area Organisers:	Helen Hunter	2 Bay Street, Fairlie, KA29 0AL
	Barbara McLean	49 Middlepenny Road, Langbank, PA14 6XE
Treasurer:	Jean Gillan	Bogriggs Cottage, West Kilbride, KA23 9PS

GARDENS OPEN ON A SPECIFIC DATE

SGS Kilmacolm Plant Sale, Outside Kilmacolm Library, Kilmacolm	Saturday, 27 April
Highwood, off Lochwinnoch Road, Kilmacolm	Sunday, 12 May
Barnbeth House, Clevans Road, Bridge of Weir	Sunday, 2 June
The Bishop's House, Glencairn Road, Kilmacolm	Sunday, 9 June
Craig Hepburn Memorial Garden, Linwood High School, Linwood	Wednesday/Thursday, 12/13 June
SGS Kilmacolm Plant Sale, Outside Kilmacolm Library, Kilmacolm	Saturday, 13 July
North Newton Farm, Kilmacolm	Sunday, 11 August

GARDENS OPEN BY ARRANGEMENT

Wraes, Corseliehill Road, nr Houston	1 May - 1 September

Renfrewshire

BARNBETH HOUSE
Clevans Road, Bridge of Weir PA11 3RS
Laura Brown, Head Gardener; Dylan Brown, Assistant Gardener

Barnbeth Estate is a country estate in Renfrewshire with an Arts & Crafts mansion at its heart. Extensive formal gardens with sweeping lawns and mature trees, formal patio area with pond, rockery with unusual alpines/shrubs, herbaceous borders running down the stream edge leading to a large pond. Large woodland with rhododendrons, eucryphias, azaleas and laurel, and a new topiary themed garden. This is a traditional garden with a modern twist - full of surprises.

Open: Sunday 2 June, 2pm - 5pm, admission £5.00, children free.

Directions: From the A761 in Bridge of Weir, turn onto Prieston Road leading to Clevans Road, drive past Ranfurly Castle Golf Club. Turn right to stay on Clevans Road. Barnbeth is approx 1 mile outside Bridge of Weir on Clevans Road. There are cross country routes here from Lochwinnoch but this is the easiest route.

Opening for: St Vincents Hospice Limited

Barnbeth House

Renfrewshire

2 CRAIG HEPBURN MEMORIAL GARDEN

Stirling Drive, Linwood PA3 3NB
Linwood High School
T: 01505 336146 E: gw07hindelesley@glow.sch.uk
W: facebook.com/welovegardening14/

The Craig Hepburn Memorial Garden and Outdoor Learning Centre is located in Linwood High School. Our original garden with an outdoor classroom has been expanded to include community raised beds, an orchard, greenhouse and presentation area. We work with all years in the school, reconnecting them to the natural world, whether through growing in our organic garden, encouraging biodiversity or learning about sustainability. Winners of the *Cultivation Street* competition 2020.

Open: Wednesday/Thursday, 12/13 June, 4pm - 6pm, admission £5.00, children free. Admission charge to include tea/cake/refreshments.

Directions: Exit the M8 at St James Interchange and take the A737. Take the exit for Linwood onto the A761, follow to Clippens Road and then Stirling Drive where you will see the high school. Accessible by McGill's buses.

Opening for: Teenage Cancer Trust

3 HIGHWOOD

off Lochwinnoch Road, Kilmacolm PA13 4TF
Dr Jill Morgan

A beautiful woodland walk around 50 acres of native bluebells, primroses and wild garlic in a delightful setting bordering the Green Water river with tumbling waterfalls. Great outdoor space for children to run and explore and splash in the burn (under supervision). A haven of tranquillity only three miles from the centre of Kilmacolm. This opening is raising funds for Buildher (buildher.org) a social enterprise owned by Orkidstudio.

Open: Sunday 12 May, 2pm - 5pm, admission £5.00, children free. Stout footwear is recommended as the footpath is uneven and can be muddy in inclement weather. Dogs are welcome on a lead. Fantastic opportunity for lovers of wildflowers and photography.

Directions: Take the B786 Lochwinnoch road out of Kilmacolm and continue for approximately two miles. From Lochwinnoch take the B786 Kilmacolm road for approximately six miles. Turn up the road signposted for Killochries. Then follow the yellow SGS signs.

Opening for: Orkidstudio

Renfrewshire

North Newton Farm

4 NORTH NEWTON FARM

Kilmacolm PA13 4TE
Carole Cameron
E: carole.cameron100@btinternet.com

In six years, the new owners have transformed North Newton Farm garden. 'No straight lines' and 'any colour so long as it is pink, purple, blue or white' are the guidelines. Many 'finds' abandoned by the previous owners in and around the barns have been repurposed under the 'let's use what we have' philosophy. To suit the topography, the garden now has cultivated and wilder parts with stunning views. Many climbing plants and herbaceous borders surround the wildlife pond below a rockery. A small wooded area provides a lovely view. A Victorian style greenhouse and cold frames flank stone-built raised beds in a fruit and vegetable garden. The resident goats, chickens and donkeys provide ample fertiliser.

Open: Sunday 11 August, 1pm - 5pm, admission £5.00, children free.

Directions: Take the B786 Lochwinnoch road out of Kilmacolm and continue for approximately two miles. From Lochwinnoch take the B786 Kilmacolm road for approximately six miles. Turn up the road signposted to Killochries at this point following the yellow SGS signs

Opening for: Pancreatic Cancer Action

5 SGS KILMACOLM PLANT SALE

Outside Kilmacolm Library, Kilmacolm PA13 4LE
Scotland's Gardens Scheme

Spring and summer plant sales in the middle of Kilmacolm.

Open: Saturday 27 April and Saturday 13 July, 10am - noon. Donations welcome.

Directions: The plant sale will be held at the Cross outside the Library and Cargill centre in the middle of Kilmacolm. Accessible by McGill's buses.

Opening for: Pancreatic Cancer Action

Renfrewshire

 6 THE BISHOP'S HOUSE
Glencairn Road, Kilmacolm PA13 4PD
Paula Macgee and Paul Yacoubian

The Bishop's House is one of six villas in Kilmacolm designed by James Salmon in 1905. It was originally named Miyanoshta but renamed when it became the official residence of the Catholic Bishops of Paisley (1948-1993). The house is now a family home and much care has been taken in preserving the house and garden, both in landscaping and planting, which remain mostly as designed by Salmon. The house sits at the top of the garden and is framed by mature beech trees. There is a burn running down the side of the property (children should be supervised).

Open: Sunday 9 June, 2pm - 5pm, admission £5.00, children free. Please note there are gravel paths. Depending on the weather, there may be 'entertainment' at the garden opening. Please check website nearer the time.

Directions: Please access the garden from the Glencairn Road entrance. Turn off the A761 in the centre of Kilmacolm onto Houston Road or Porterfield Road for access to the garden on Glencairn Road. Follow SGS signage. Parking on-road. McGill's buses run through Kilmacolm on the A761.

Opening for: Glasgow Samaritans

 7 WRAES
Corseliehill Road, nr Houston PA6 7HU
Tim and Jo Mack
T: 07985 156555 E: jomack22@gmail.com

Varied seven-acre rural garden with far-reaching views and a variety of planting areas designed to take advantage of the natural terrain and be actively wildlife friendly. Raised formal herbaceous beds, several wildlife ponds, burnside walks, grass maze, spring garden, woodland with rhododendron collection (100 species). For those interested in growing their own food, there is a large no-dig productive area, with vegetables, fruit cage, orchard and wildflower meadow. There are lots of seating places to relax and enjoy the tranquility while the kids tackle the maze or just have a good run around!

Open: by arrangement 1 May - 1 September, admission £5.00, children free.

Directions: From Houston follow Barochan Road towards Langbank B789 for about a mile, turn left down Corseliehill Road. From Kilmacolm leave the village on Houston Road, past the golf course, turn left down Corseliehill Road for about a mile.

Opening for: Breast Cancer Care

Roxburghshire

Sponsored by

RATHBONES

Incorporating
Investec Wealth &
Investment (UK)

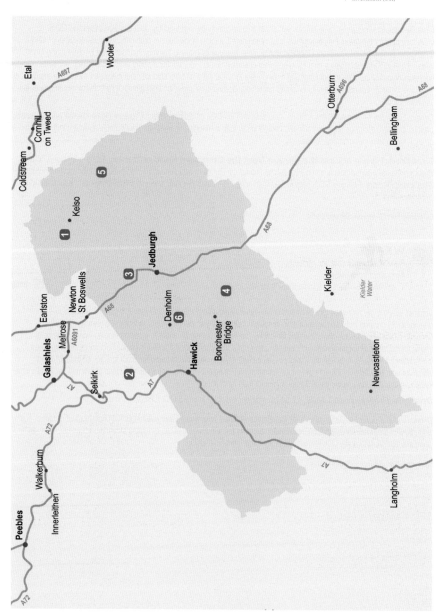

Roxburghshire

OUR VOLUNTEER ORGANISERS

District Organiser: Penny Wright info@scotlandsgardens.org

District Photographer: Malcolm Ross

Treasurer: David Douglas

GARDENS OPEN ON A SPECIFIC DATE

West Leas, Bonchester Bridge	Sunday, 2 June
Southdean Mill, Southdean Mill, Chesters, Hawick	Saturday/Sunday, 22/23 June
West Leas, Bonchester Bridge	Sunday, 4 August
Southdean Mill, Southdean Mill, Chesters, Hawick	Saturday/Sunday, 10/11 August
Thirlestane, Kelso	Saturday/Sunday, 26/27 October

GARDENS OPEN REGULARLY

Monteviot, Jedburgh	1 April - 31 October
Floors Castle, Kelso	1 May - 30 September

GARDENS OPEN BY ARRANGEMENT

Thirlestane, Kelso	31 March - 31 October
West Leas, Bonchester Bridge	1 May - 31 October
Larch House, Clerklands, Near Lilliesleaf	1 July - 31 August

Would you like to get involved?

We're always looking for new gardens and people to help out with our garden opening programme.

If you're interested and would like to find out more, please visit scotlandsgardens.org/join-in/ or call the office on **0131 226 3714** for a friendly chat.

Roxburghshire

1 FLOORS CASTLE
Kelso TD5 7SF
The Duke of Roxburghe
T: 01573 223333
W: www.floorscastle.com

The gardens are situated within the grounds of Floors Castle. Meander through to the formal Millennium Parterre and soak up the spectacular visions of colour, texture and the most delicious scents around the four herbaceous borders in one of the finest Victorian kitchen gardens in Scotland. Features include perennial gardens, fruit cage, Tapestry Garden and glasshouse access as well as the Terrace Cafe, Apple Shed Gift Shop and Deli and children's play area. Explore the grounds, which offer woodland and riverside walks from May to the end of September.

Open: 1 May - 30 September, 10am - 5pm, admission details can be found on the garden's website.

Directions: Floors Castle can be reached by following the A6089 from Edinburgh; the B6397 from Earlston; or the A698 from Coldstream. Go through Kelso, up Roxburgh Street to the Golden Gates.

Opening for: *Donation to SGS Beneficiaries*

Floors Castle

Roxburghshire

2 LARCH HOUSE

Clerklands, Near Lilliesleaf TD6 9JR
David and Julia King
T: 01835 870888 M: 07985 691775 E: northcorner14@btinternet.com

New for 2024, the garden at Larch House is constantly evolving. Extending to over three acres and building on a layout, design and planting by the previous owners, further landscaping and renovation is ongoing. It includes a terraced area of vegetables and cut flowers edged by fruit trees, several mixed borders surrounding a lawn, a large natural wildlife pond and a newly-planted bog garden. The garden leads into a mixed wood planted about six years ago where meandering paths, sometimes steep, lead to extensive views of the Cheviots. Many of the paths are gravel and may prove difficult for wheelchairs.

Open: by arrangement 1 July - 31 August, admission £5.00, children free. We welcome small groups of up to approximately ten people. There may be plants for sale and light refreshments available on request - enquire when booking.

Directions: Clerklands is a small hamlet approximately two miles from Lilliesleaf. On the A7 from Selkirk, turn left and follow signs to Clerklands. After approximately three miles the house will be clearly signed. On the A7 from Hawick, turn right and follow signs to Lilliesleaf and the house will be clearly signed. Car parking is on site.

Opening for: All proceeds to SGS Beneficiaries

3 MONTEVIOT

Jedburgh TD8 6UQ
Marquis and Marchioness of Lothian
T: 01835 830380
W: www.monteviot.com

A series of differing gardens displaying rose and herbaceous plants surrounded by foliage plants. A water feature linked by bridges and falls passes through the Dene Garden and Water Garden. The Garden of Persistent Imagination is planted with rose and clematis beside paths which meander across a bridge and under the Moonstone Gate, past the Dali-style clock.

Open: 1 April - 31 October, noon - 5pm, admission £6.00, children free. Card payment only.

Directions: Turn off the A68, three miles north of Jedburgh on to the B6400. After one mile turn right.

Opening for: Donation to SGS Beneficiaries

Roxburghshire

4 SOUTHDEAN MILL
Southdean Mill, Chesters, Hawick TD9 8TL
Linda and Brian Falconer
T: 07930 199552 E: linda@beastieassemblage.co.uk
W: https://www.beastieassemblage.co.uk

An unruly, secluded family garden complete with mill ruins situated within 10 acres of young woodland. Approached down an avenue of crab apples, it features a romantic walled garden in front of the rose-covered, former miller's cottage, where perennials tussle with pretty annuals and biannuals. The old mill lade runs into a semi-wild pond with a turf bridge by the front lawn with its standing stones that depict the family. Behind the cottage, and sheltered by stone barn walls, is a very productive vegetable garden for the family with a wooden greenhouse, poly-tunnel and raised beds. The old farm courtyard makes an idyllic spot for a cream tea next to the stone barn where Linda will be displaying her assemblage art inspired by her garden.

Open: Saturday/Sunday, 22/23 June, 11am - 5pm. Also open Saturday/Sunday, 10/11 August, 11am - 5pm. Admission £5.00, children free.

Directions: 400m from Chesters village on the A6088 heading towards Newcastle, there is a farm track on the left.

Opening for: Southdean Hall

Larch House

Southdean Mill

Roxburghshire

5 THIRLESTANE
Kelso TD5 8PD
Catherine Ross and John Wylie
T: 01573 420487

Thirlestane is a large informal garden. There is a walled garden with colour-themed borders and an orchard with many old varieties of fruit trees. In front of the house prairie planting is surrounded by high beech hedges. The young nine-acre wood has trees and shrubs selected for autumn colour and for decorative bark and fruit. These include Persian Ironwood, Golden Rain Tree, Scarlet Oak, Monarch Birch, Himalayan Birch, Tibetan Cherry, Chinese Hawthorn and various maples.

Open: Saturday/Sunday, 26/27 October, 11am - 4pm. Also open by arrangement 31 March - 31 October. Admission £5.00, children free. Please feel free to bring a picnic to enjoy in the garden. Dogs welcome.

Directions: Thirlestane is near Yetholm, not to be confused with Thirlestane, Lauder. Do not follow SatNav, it will try to take you to Lochside. From Kelso, take the B6352 towards Yetholm for about six miles. Continue past a cottage on the edge of the road. Thirlestane is next on the left, opposite the road to Lochside. From Yetholm, take the road to Kelso for about two miles. After a very sharp corner, Thirlestane is on the right.

Opening for: Alzheimer Scotland

6 WEST LEAS
Bonchester Bridge TD9 8TD
Mr and Mrs Robert Laidlaw
T: 01450 860711 E: ann@johnlaidlawandson.co.uk

The visitor to West Leas can share in an exciting and dramatic project on a grand scale, still in the making. At its core is a passion for plants, allied to a love and understanding of the land in which they are set. Collections of perennials and shrubs, many in temporary holding quarters, lighten up the landscape to magical effect. New lily pond and woodland planting added in 2019 and a new courtyard garden is under construction.

Open: Sunday 2 June, 2pm - 5pm. Also open Sunday 4 August, 2pm - 5pm. And open by arrangement 1 May - 31 October. Admission £4.00, children free. Teas for the specific date openings will be served in Bedrule Village Hall, Bonchester Bridge, Hawick TD9 8TE.

Directions: Signposted off the Jedburgh/Bonchester Bridge Road.

Opening for: Macmillan Cancer Support: Borders Appeal

Stirlingshire

Sponsored by
RATHBONES
Incorporating
Investec Wealth &
Investment (UK)

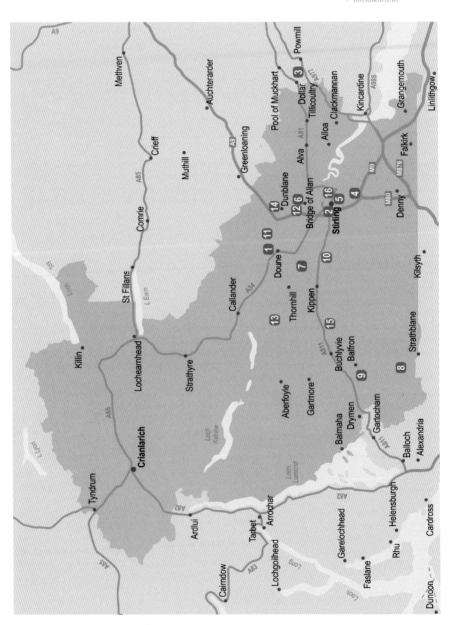

Stirlingshire

OUR VOLUNTEER ORGANISERS

District Organiser:	Willie Campbell	13 Fir Road, Doune FK16 6HU info@scotlandsgardens.org
District Administrator:	Jo Dormer	
Area Organisers:	Sylvia Broomfield	
	Morna Knottenbelt	Gardener's Cottage Walled Garden, Ballochruin Road, Killearn G63 9QB
	Rosemary Leckie	Auchengarroch, 16 Chalton Road, Bridge of Allan FK9 4DX
Media Officer:	Fiona Campbell	13 Fir Road, Doune FK16 6HU
Treasurer:	Carol Freireich	18 Netherblane, Blanefield, Glasgow G63 9JW

GARDENS OPEN ON A SPECIFIC DATE

3 Southfield Gardens, Stirling	Sunday, 28 April
Oakmore, Blairhoyle, Port of Menteith	Sunday, 5 May
18 Buchany, Doune	Sunday, 12 May
Bridge of Allan Gardens, Bridge of Allan	Sunday, 19 May
Kilbryde Castle, Dunblane	Sunday, 26 May
Coldoch, Blairdrummond	Sunday, 2 June
Thorntree, Arnprior	Sunday, 9 June
Tiny Farm, St Modan's High School, Royal Stuart Way, Stirling	Sunday, 23 June
Oakmore, Blairhoyle, Port of Menteith	Sunday, 14 July
18 Buchany, Doune	Sunday, 21 July
Braehead Community Garden, Broom Road, Braehead	Sunday, 4 August
Bannockburn House Gardens, Stirling	Sunday, 25 August

GARDENS OPEN BY ARRANGEMENT

Gargunnock House Garden, Gargunnnock	1 February - 30 September
Duntreath Castle, Blanefield	1 February - 30 September
Kilbryde Castle, Dunblane	1 February - 30 September
Thorntree, Arnprior	1 May - 1 September
Milseybank, Bridge of Allan	1 May - 31 May
Arndean, by Dollar	6 May - 7 June
St Blane's House, High Street, Dunblane	6 May - 28 June
Gardener's Cottage Walled Garden, Ballochruin Road, Killearn	15 June - 15 October

Stirlingshire

18 BUCHANY
Doune FK16 6HG
John and Sarah Burrows
E: wackwack1@btinternet.com

This is a cottage garden with perennial and fruit tree borders, along with raised beds for vegetables. Extensive use is made of pots and tubs planted with spring bulbs, herbaceous plants, annuals as well as shrubs and vegetables making them more accessible. The owners are well known for showing prize-winning vegetables and flowers at flower shows in Stirlingshire. Visit in May and you can see the start of this process and then come back to the second open day in July to see the results of the TLC this garden has had.

Open: Sunday 12 May & Sunday 21 July, 1pm - 5pm, admission £5.00, children free.

Directions: As there is no parking available at the garden, visitors must go to Moray Estate Office FK16 6HG which is situated on the A84, 1.5 miles west of Doune through Buchany towards Callander. Turn into the Estate Office grounds where visitors can take the shuttle bus to the garden.

Opening for: British Heart Foundation

3 SOUTHFIELD CRESCENT
Stirling FK8 2JQ
Mary Menzies McCaig
E: maryming@yahoo.com

This charming town garden has a variegated privet hedge in the front and behind this there are numerous pots and planters of spring bulbs to see in the beds and borders. The garden has a frog pond and many interesting specimen trees such as acers, magnolia black tulip, Cytisus (pineapple tree), Hoheria (snowdrop tree) and monkey puzzle planted throughout the garden. The sheltered semi-walled garden has raised beds along with a summer house and chicken run.

Open: Sunday 28 April, 1pm - 5pm, admission £5.00, children free.

Directions: Southfield Crescent is close to Stirling's King's Park. From King's Park Road roundabouts, opposite the park gates turn into Drummond Place and Southfield Crescent is 200 yards along on the left, facing the grassy area ahead.

Opening for: CRY

ARNDEAN
by Dollar FK14 7NH
Johnny and Katie Stewart
T: 07940 530499 E: johnny@arndean.co.uk

Opening for more than 40 years, this is a beautiful mature garden extending to 15 acres including the woodland walk. There is a formal herbaceous part, a small vegetable garden and an orchard. In addition, there are flowering shrubs, abundant and striking rhododendrons and azaleas as well as many fine specimen trees. There is a tree house for children.

Open: by arrangement 6 May - 7 June, admission £5.00, children free.

Directions: Arndean is well signposted off the A977.

Opening for: Marie Curie

Stirlingshire

4 BANNOCKBURN HOUSE GARDENS

Stirling FK7 8EY
Bannockburn House Trust
E: admin@bannockburnhouse.scot
W: www.bannockburnhouse.scot

Bannockburn House, an A-listed mansion built in 1675 by Sir Hugh Paterson, now sits in 26 acres of woodland and gardens. Bonnie Prince Charlie visited in 1746 where he met Clementina Walkinshaw who would become his mistress. Local boy, John McLaren, creator of The Golden Gate Park in San Francisco, began his gardening career here in 1860. The house and gardens suffered from 50 years of neglect before coming into community ownership in 2017 with restoration ongoing. Features include an enclosed kitchen garden supplying fruit and vegetables to two local food banks; herb gardens, an orchard, fruit cages, pollinator garden, wisteria border, labyrinth, polytunnels and raised beds. A short woodland walk passes 'The Five Sisters' - our fabulous giant redwood trees; the Fountain Walk passes our veteran lime trees, a cast-iron fountain (built by Steven in 1888), and our award-winning apiary.

Open: Sunday 25 August, 10am - 4pm. **All house visits must be booked in advance on www.bannockburnhouse.scot**. House, gardens and teas £15.00, under 12s £5.00; garden and teas £10.00, under 12s £3.00; garden only £7.00, under 12s free. Concessions available, see the ticketing website for details.

Directions: The house entrance is 0.2 miles from the Bannockburn Interchange (M9/Junction 9 roundabout) off the A91. Please car share where possible as parking is limited.

Opening for: Bannockburn House Trust

5 BRAEHEAD COMMUNITY GARDEN

Broom Road, Braehead FK7 7GU
Nikki Thomas, Development Officer
E: garden@braehead.org

Braehead Community Garden is an 11,000 square metre outdoor space, offering an array of activities and facilities including 126 micro allotments for hire, a communal toolshed, an apiary producing local honey, a large polytunnel for social events and free-range eggs from our resident chickens. We have a multitude of nectar beds and wild spaces, ensuring we are giving back to our environment and supporting and encouraging local wildlife. Our extensive rain water harvesting system keeps the garden running whilst reducing our carbon footprint. Produce is available for the local community at affordable prices. Come and enjoy home baking and take home fresh produce from the gardens.

Open: Sunday 4 August, 11am - 4pm, admission £5.00, children free.

Directions: From north on the A9 towards Bannockburn, take the first exit on Linden Avenue leading to Broom Road, turn right and the gardens are on the left. From south, on the A91 turn left on Pike Road leading to Broom Road.

Opening for: Braehead, Broomridge & District Community Development Trust

Stirlingshire

6   BRIDGE OF ALLAN GARDENS
Bridge of Allan FK9 4AT
The Gardeners of Bridge of Allan

Bridge of Allan gardens will again feature a selection of larger and smaller gardens. They will highlight various species of rhododendrons and azaleas and many varieties of spring blossoms, plants and flowers. Some have water features showing an interesting variety of plants. One of the gardens features a variety of sculpture, with quirky quotations placed around the garden, while another is divided into 'rooms', each having a different theme. The Gardens of Bridge of Allan were featured on *Beechgrove* last year.

Open: Sunday 19 May, 1pm - 5pm, admission £6.00, children free. Tickets and maps will be available only at the Episcopal Church, Keir Street, Bridge of Allan FK9 4AT. There will be a plant sale at the Church Garden and teas will be served in the Church Hall.

Directions: Gardens will be signposted in the village on the day.

Opening for: Artlink Central Ltd & St Saviours Episcopal Church: Bridge Of Allan

13 Henderson Street, Bridge of Allan

Stirlingshire

7 COLDOCH
Blairdrummond, Stirling FK9 4XD
David & Kim Stewart and Tim Black
T: 01786 841217

The garden at Coldoch is sheltered by belts of mature woodland on three sides and looks south over the Carse of Stirling. The parterre courtyard garden and border have replaced the old farm buildings and lead on to a kitchen garden created by using the three old walls of an earlier rose garden. The less formal areas include a stream, a pond, paddocks and woodland. The drives are lined with old oaks and sycamores mixed with new trees from Eastern Europe, Central Asia and some fine, mature cherry trees.

Open: Sunday 2 June, 2pm - 5pm, admission £5.00, children free.

Directions: Signed from the A84. Take the A873 for Aberfoyle, after just under one mile turn left on to Coldoch Road, B8031 and continue for approximately half a mile. Wrought iron gates on the left mark the entrance.

Opening for: Forth Valley Welcome

8 DUNTREATH CASTLE
Blanefield G63 9AJ
Sir Archibald and Lady Edmonstone
T: 01360 770215 E: juliet@edmonstone.com
W: www.duntreathcastle.co.uk

Extensive gardens with mature and new plantings. Ornamental landscaped lake and bog garden. Sweeping lawns below formal fountain and rose parterre with an herbaceous border leading up to an attractive waterfall garden. Swathes of yellow daffodils and other colourful spring bulbs together with rhododendrons and many other ornamental shrubs surround the formal lawns. There is also a woodland walk. The garden has horticultural interest throughout the year and enjoys superb autumn colours.

Open: by arrangement 1 February - 30 September (Snowdrops and Winter Walks February/March), admission £5.00, children free. Groups welcome.

Directions: A81 north of Glasgow between Blanefield and Killearn.

Opening for: All proceeds to SGS Beneficiaries

Stirlingshire

9 GARDENER'S COTTAGE WALLED GARDEN

Ballochruin Road, Killearn G63 9QB
Morna Knottenbelt
T: 01360 551682 E: mornaknottenbelt@hotmail.com

The walled garden, acquired in 2013 by the present owners, has been planted with extensive herbaceous borders, box hedging, roses and many unusual plants. There is a White Garden, a long shrub border with primulas and gentians and a former fernery with a collection of salvias and peach and pear trees. June is a good time to visit when the roses are in bloom and borders with lupins, peonies and other perennials are in flower. By late summer, the borders have argyranthemums as well as dahlias, Michaelmas daisies, rudbeckias and blue aconitums. The Celtic Cross Garden was planted in May 2021 with a range of new plants including echinaceas, cardoons, lobelias, anthemis and lavender for mid to late summer colour. There are fine views of the Campsie Hills and the garden is surrounded by the conifers of the Designed Landscape of Carbeth.

Open: by arrangement 15 June - 15 October, admission £5.00, children free. The Garden Owners welcome visitors at short notice (the day before planned visits). Small numbers and individuals are welcome.

Directions: Follow Sat Nav to G63 0LF, which is Carbeth Home Farm. We are the next entrance below the farm. Turn left on to the gravel road and follow yellow *SGS* signs.

Opening for: The British Horse Society: Scotland

10 GARGUNNOCK HOUSE GARDEN

Gargunnnock FK8 3AZ
The Gargunnock Trustees
T: Garden contact: William Campbell 01786 842538
E: william.campbellwj@btinternet.com

Large mature garden five miles from Stirling, with a walled garden, well-established house garden, woodland walks with species and hybrid rhododendrons, massed plantings of azaleas and wonderful specimen trees. Snowdrops in February/March are followed by over 40 varieties of daffodils and the glorious displays of azaleas and rhododendrons in May. The three-acre walled garden contains perennial borders, cut-flower beds, greenhouses, fruit orchard and newly planted arboretum of specimen trees. The Walled Garden is now used by the charity Green Routes to give gardening education to adults with learning difficulties.

Open: by arrangement 1 February - 30 September (Snowdrops and Winter Walks February/March), admission £5.00, children free. Group tours are welcomed.

Directions: Five miles west of Stirling on the A811. Car parking is at the entrance by the lodge.

Opening for: Rhododendron Species Conservation Group

Stirlingshire

11 KILBRYDE CASTLE

Dunblane FK15 9NF
Sir James and Lady Campbell
T: 01786 824897 E: carolaandjames@googlemail.com
W: www.kilbrydecastle.com

Kilbryde Castle gardens cover some 12 acres and are situated above the Ardoch Burn and below the castle. The gardens are split into three parts: informal, woodland and wild. Natural planting (azaleas, rhododendrons, camellias and magnolias) is found in the woodland garden. There are glorious snowdrops, spring bulbs, and autumn colour provided by clematis and acers.

Open: Open Sunday 26 May, 11am - 5pm, when there will be plants for sale and refreshments. Also open by arrangement 1 February - 30 September (1 February - 15 March for Snowdrops and Winter Walks). Admission £5.00, children free.

Directions: Three miles from Dunblane and Doune, off the A820 between Dunblane and Doune. On Scotland's Gardens Scheme open days the garden is signposted from the A820.

Opening for: Leighton Library Trust

Kilbryde Castle © Carolyn Bell

12 MILSEYBANK

Bridge of Allan FK9 4NB
Murray and Sheila Airth
T: 07799 036367 E: smairth@hotmail.com

Wonderful and interesting sloping garden with outstanding views, terraced for ease of access. Woodland with bluebells, rhododendrons, magnolias and camellias, and many other unusual plants, including a big variety of meconopsis. This is a true plantsman's garden with quiet corners to sit, admire and reflect. A garden to inspire you and give you ideas to take home. National Plant Collection: Meconopsis.

Open: by arrangement 1 May - 31 May, admission £5.00, children free.

Directions: Situated on the A9, one mile from junction 11, M9 and ¼ mile from Bridge of Allan. Milseybank is at the top of the lane at Lecropt Nursery, 250 yards from the Bridge of Allan train station.

Opening for: Strathcarron Hospice

Stirlingshire

13 OAKMORE

Blairhoyle, Port of Menteith, Stirling FK8 3LF
Rachel Nunn
T: 07872 068080

In 2014 this garden was a 3.5 acre field with a small wood and lots of rushes. Under the hands of a gardening fanatic and her willing husband you will see a maturing garden with raised herbaceous borders, young orchards, a developing shrubbery, a rose garden, a bog garden and a variety of species trees. This is a garden for real plant enthusiasts and to enjoy it to the full, good footwear is recommended, particularly if it has been raining.

Open: Sunday 5 May & Sunday 14 July, 11am - 5pm, admission £5.00, children free.

Directions: Blairhoyle is on the Thornhill to Port of Monteith road.

Opening for: Radical Weavers

Oakmore © R Nunn

14 ST BLANE'S HOUSE

High Street, Dunblane FK15 0ER
Guy and Maud Crawford
E: maud.crawford@btinternet.com

This is a well-established two-acre garden with a wide variety of trees, rhododendrons, azaleas and other shrubs and herbaceous perennials. There is a short walk through a wooded area.

Open: by arrangement 6 May - 28 June, admission £5.00, children free.

Directions: St Blanes House is almost directly opposite Dunblane Library.

Opening for: Strathcarron Hospice

Stirlingshire

 15 THORNTREE
Arnprior FK8 3EY
Mark and Carol Seymour
T: 01786 870710 E: carolseymour666@gmail.com
W: www.thorntreebarn.co.uk

In 2024, Thorntree looks forward to welcoming visitors to the garden opening on Sunday 9 June as well as by arrangement on other dates. Carol will happily walk round the garden with you or you can wander on your own. The garden continues to evolve and cotoneasters by the saltire beds have been cut back which means the four flower beds are no longer hidden behind a hedge! Also, the view past the summerhouse can be seen and the Annabelle hydrangea has popped up now that there are fewer branches above it. It is an inspiring garden to visit at any time of the year. From the garden you can see panoramic views from Ben Lomond to Doune, watching the Forth meander down the bottom of the valley.

Open: Sunday 9 June, 2pm - 5pm. Also open by arrangement 1 May - 1 September. Admission £5.00, children free. There will be a huge plant stall as plants are always available for sale as part of the trainee experience under the WRAGS scheme.

Directions: On the A811, to Arnprior, then take the Fintry Road; Thorntree is second on the right.

Opening for: Forth Driving Group RDA SCIO

 16 TINY FARM
St Modan's High School, Royal Stuart Way, Stirling FK7 7WS
Alison Poole
E: poolea05s@glow.sch.uk

Tiny farm was created to support learners within the Autism Provision at St Modan's High School. The space is a mixture of raised beds, planted grass and small woodland areas. Learning for sustainability is embedded within the Tiny Farm. Planting is decided by the learners and includes a range of flowers and vegetables. 2023 was a bumper year for the strawberry crops and we will be selling some of our delicious homemade strawberry jam! The Tiny Farm enables our curriculum to come to life, allowing interdisciplinary learning to flourish as learners nurture the plants, harvest them, donate to the community and make products such as jam and soap to sell. The Tiny Farm is opening to showcase what is being undertaken.

Open: Sunday 23 June, 11am - 5pm, admission £5.00, children free.

Directions: From the A91, take exit off Muirton Roundabout to Holiday Express Inn. At Springkerse roundabout take exit to the Peak. Keep right, and turn right at approach to Forthbank Stadium carpark and follow the road to the car park for St Modan's High School.

Opening for: Strathcarron Hospice

Wigtownshire

Sponsored by

RATHBONES

Incorporating
Investec Wealth &
Investment (UK)

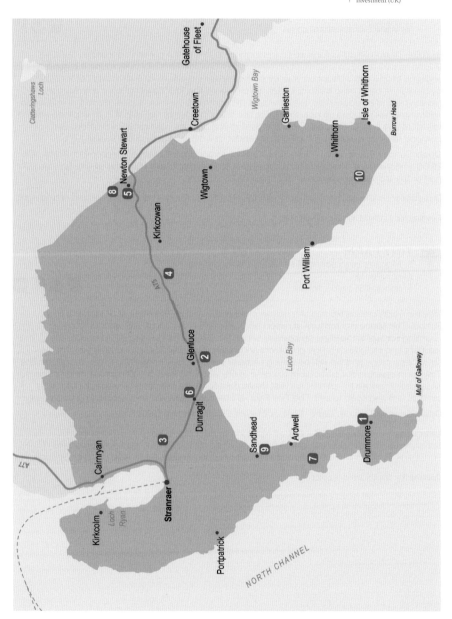

Wigtownshire

OUR VOLUNTEER ORGANISERS

District Organiser:	Ann Watson	Doonholm, Cairnryan Road, Stranraer DG9 8AT info@scotlandsgardens.org
Area Organisers:	Colin Belton	Amulree, 8 Mill Street, Drummore DG9 9PS
	Teri Birch	The Old Manse, Gruisey House, Sandhead DG9 9JT
	Eileen Davie	Whitehills House, Minnigaff DG8 6SL
	Mary Gladstone	Craichlaw, Kirkcowan DG8 0DQ
	Annmaree Mitchell	Cottage 2, Little Float, Sandhead DG9 9LD
District Photographer:	Stuart Littlewood	Tayvallich, West Port, New Galloway DG7 3SB
Treasurer:	Marilyn Sime	1 Weir Terrace, Sandhead, Stranraer DG9 9JH

GARDENS OPEN ON A SPECIFIC DATE

Logan Botanic Garden, Port Logan, by Stranraer	Sunday, 19 May
Woodfall Gardens, Glasserton	Sunday, 19 May
Castle Kennedy Gardens, Stranraer	Sunday, 9 June
Woodfall Gardens, Glasserton	Sunday, 16 June
Woodfall Gardens, Glasserton	Sunday, 7 July
Amulree, 8 Mill Street, Drummore, Stranraer	Saturday/Sunday, 13/14 July
Lutra Holt, Penninghame, Newton Stewart	Saturday/Sunday, 17/18 August

GARDENS OPEN REGULARLY

Glenwhan Gardens & Arboretum, Dunragit, by Stranraer	1 January - 31 December
Castle Kennedy Gardens, Stranraer	3 February - 24 March (Sat & Sun) and 29 March - 3 November (daily)
Logan Botanic Garden, Port Logan, by Stranraer	4 February - 26 February (Sat & Sun) 1 March - 15 November (daily)

GARDENS OPEN BY ARRANGEMENT

Craichlaw, Kirkcowan, Newton Stewart	1 January - 31 December
Amulree, 8 Mill Street, Drummore, Stranraer	1 January - 31 December
Fernlea Garden, Corvisel Road, Newton Stewart	1 April - 30 September
Barlockhart Lodge, Glenluce	1 May - 30 September
The Old Manse, Sandhead, Stranraer	1 May - 30 September

Wigtownshire

1 AMULREE

8 Mill Street, Drummore, Stranraer DG9 9PS
Colin Belton and Gabrielle Reynolds
T: 0789 909 2070 E: gabygardeners@btinternet.com

Amulree is home to two complete plantaholics who probably should start taking their own advice and stop collecting quite so many plants! Starting from a blank canvas in 2017 the garden now consists of a sunny terrace with displays of half-hardy and tender plants, exuberantly planted borders separated by serpentine grass patches, a small vegetable patch, a glasshouse and a 'wild' bit. Amulree contains many unusual plants including a National Plant Collection. National Plant Collection: *Nicotiana* species.

Open: Saturday/Sunday, 13/14 July, 10am - 4pm. Groups also welcome at other times by prior arrangement. Admission £5.00, children free.

Directions: Follow the A716 signposted *Drummore and Mull of Galloway.* At the T-junction in Drummore turn right. Amulree is on the left, a few doors up from the shop. Bus route 407 from Stranraer.

Opening for: Kirkmaiden Old Kirk

2 BARLOCKHART LODGE

Glenluce DG8 0JG
Barlockhart Gardeners
T: 07821 776226 E: neilharper1962@btinternet.com

A newly-created garden, which is very much a work in progress. The main part is a reclaimed riding manege, which has been transformed with meandering paths around borders planted with perennials and grasses to reflect the local undulating landscape. An alpine border and greenhouse are to one side of the house and traditional cottage-style borders are to the front and other side. A small vegetable plot with no-dig beds and raised areas is to the rear. The garden is situated about a mile from Luce Bay and has the benefits of the Gulf Stream, but the disadvantages of an exposed, shadeless position.

Open: by arrangement 1 May - 30 September, admission £5.00, children free. There is plenty of off-road parking. Please do not park on the lane.

Directions: Take the A75 to Glenluce. On the hill which links the two Glenluce turnoffs, take the single-track unmarked lane, signposted for *Whithorn Way.* Property is roughly one mile along the lane, on the left.

Opening for: Galloway Music Festival

Wigtownshire

Barlockhart Lodge

 3

CASTLE KENNEDY GARDENS
Stranraer DG9 8SJ
The Earl and Countess of Stair
T: 01581 400225
W: www.castlekennedygardens.com

Romantically situated, these famous 75 acres of landscaped gardens are located on an isthmus surrounded by two large natural lochs. At one end, the ruined Castle Kennedy overlooks a beautiful herbaceous walled garden with Lochinch Castle at the other end. With over 300 years of planting, there is an impressive collection of rare trees, rhododendrons, exotic shrubs and many spectacular Champion Trees. The stunning snowdrop walks, daffodils, spring flowers, rhododendron and magnolia displays and herbaceous borders make this a 'must visit' garden throughout the year.
Champion Trees: 95 in total; including 12 British, 30 Scottish, 44 for Dumfries and Galloway and 9 trees described as 'otherwise remarkable'.

Open: 3 February - 24 March (Saturday & Sunday), also open daily 29 March - 3 November, 10am - 5pm (open for Snowdrops and Winter Walks February and March). And open Sunday 9 June, 10am - 5pm. Admission details can be found on the garden's website.

Directions: On the A75, five miles east of Stranraer. The nearest train station is in Stranraer. The garden is on a local bus route.

Opening for: Home-Start Wigtownshire

Wigtownshire

4 CRAICHLAW
Kirkcowan, Newton Stewart DG8 0DQ
Mr and Mrs Andrew Gladstone
T: 01671 830208 E: craichlaw@aol.com

Formal garden with herbaceous borders around the house. Set in extensive grounds with lawns, lochs and woodland. A path around the main loch leads to a water garden returning past a recently planted arboretum in the old walled garden. The best times to visit the garden are early February for snowdrops, May to mid-June for the water garden and rhododendrons, and mid-June to August for herbaceous borders.

Open: by arrangement 1 January - 31 December. Snowdrops and Winter Walks February - mid-March, admission £5.00, children free.

Directions: Take the B733 for Kirkcowan, off the A75 at the Halfway House eight miles west of Newton Stewart and Craichlaw House is the first turning on the right.

Opening for: All proceeds to SGS Beneficiaries

Craichlaw

5 FERNLEA GARDEN
Corvisel Road, Newton Stewart DG8 6LW
Mrs Jenny Gustafson
T: 07909 951 885/ 01671 638273 E: jennygustafson2@hotmail.com

A secluded town garden of a third-of-an-acre, it was created in 2006 to complement a new house. There are many rare and unusual trees and shrubs. Two herbaceous borders, one with hot colours and the other pastels. A Chinese-inspired corner, small pond, fruit trees including a Galloway pippin apple and soft fruit. The upper part of the garden is hidden behind a tall beech hedge, where there is a summer house and adjacent woodland planting.

Open: by arrangement 1 April - 30 September, admission £5.00, children free. We welcome enquiries from individuals and small groups for our openings by arrangement. Teas are available by prior arrangement.

Directions: Turn right at the roundabout on the A75 if coming from Dumfries direction. Go left at the cattle market (opposite the Crown Hotel) and it is the first through road on the right.

Opening for: GDI: Red Squirrels

Wigtownshire

6 GLENWHAN GARDENS & ARBORETUM

Dunragit, by Stranraer DG9 8PH
Tessa and Ian Knott Sinclair
T: 07787 990702
W: www.glenwhangardens.co.uk

Described as one of the most beautiful gardens in Scotland, Glenwhan Gardens is situated at 300 feet and overlooks Luce Bay and the Mull of Galloway, with clear views to the Isle of Man. Forty-five years ago there was wild moorland, but now, following considerable dedication and vision, you can see glorious collections of plants from around the world. There is colour in all seasons and the winding paths, well-placed seats and varied sculptures, set around small lochans, add to the tranquil atmosphere. There is a 17-acre moorland wildflower walk, the chance to see red squirrels and well-marked garden and tree trails. Glenwhan has now been added to the Inventory of Gardens and Designed Landscapes, a record of nationally important gardens and designed landscapes and a major resource for enhancing appreciation and understanding of these sites, as well as promoting education and stimulating further research. Dara Parsons, Head of Designations at HES, said: 'Glenwhan Gardens is an excellent addition to the inventory.'

Open: 1 January - 31 December, 2pm - 5pm, Snowdrops and Winter Walks 25 January - 11 March. Admission details can be found on the garden's website. Admission to gardens a the entrance. Tearoom and locally grown plants for sale.

Directions: Seven miles east of Stranraer, one mile off the A75 at Dunragit (follow brown *VisitScotland* and *yellow SGS arrows*).

Opening for: Donation to SGS Beneficiaries

Glenwhan

Wigtownshire

7 LOGAN BOTANIC GARDEN
Port Logan, by Stranraer DG9 9ND
A Regional Garden of the Royal Botanic Garden Edinburgh
T: 01776 860231 E: logan@rbge.org.uk
W: www.rbge.org.uk/logan

Logan Botanic Garden lies at the south-western tip of Scotland, unrivalled as 'Scotland's Most Exotic Garden'. Warmed by the Gulf Stream, a remarkable collection of southern hemisphere plants flourish, making this a plantsman's paradise. Logan enjoys an almost subtropical climate where the garden's avenues and borders feature a spectacular and colourful array of half-hardy perennials. The garden is warmed by the Gulf Stream which enables plants from Australia, New Zealand, South and Central America and Southern Africa to thrive. Voted 'Best Garden in the UK' 2021, Logan promises a delightful day out for all.
National Plant Collection: *Gunnera, Leptospermum, Griselinia, Clianthus* and *Sutherlandia*. Champion Trees: *Polylepis* and *Eucalyptus*.

Open: Open weekends in February 10am - 4pm for Snowdrops and Winter Walks. Also open Sunday 19 May, 10am - 5pm. And open daily from 1 March - 15 November 10am - 5pm (4pm in November) Admission details can be found on the garden's website.

Directions: Ten miles south of Stranraer on the A716 then 2½ miles from Ardwell Village.

Opening for: Board Of Trustees Of The Royal Botanic Garden Edinburgh

8 LUTRA HOLT
Penninghame, Newton Stewart DG8 6RD
Mark and Heidi Platts

When we moved into the property six years ago, the garden was a completely blank canvas having had no work done to it. We have done extensive landscaping and improvements trying to encourage local wildlife. The garden has many flowers beds, and recent additions include a stone-built cold frame and large outdoor chess board. The property has a large decking area around the property overlooking the River Cree where the extensive views can be enjoyed.

Open: Saturday/Sunday, 17/18 August, 2pm - 5pm, admission £5.00, children free.

Directions: From Newton Stewart we are four miles north on the A714. Look for the *Portequip* sign on your left and we are the first property on your right. **From Girvan** travel south on the A714 for about 20 miles. The Girvan to Newton Stewart bus number 359 runs on Saturdays.

Opening for: The Royal Scottish Agricultural Benevolent Institution

Wigtownshire

9 THE OLD MANSE

Sandhead, Stranraer DG9 9JT
Mrs Teri Birch
T: 01776 830455 E: birchteri@gmail.com

Recently designed, landscaped and replanted by the current owners who are keen to develop the garden to its full potential. Comprising about half-an-acre, the garden is surrounded by stone walls and has a burn running through it. Features include a formal parterre, a rose garden, herbaceous borders, rockeries and a shady woodland area. The planting is creative and thoughtful, using grasses, bulbs, annuals, herbaceous perennials and alpines to make full use of the temperate climate enjoyed in this location.

Open: by arrangement 1 May - 30 September, admission £6.00, children free.

Directions: From Stranraer take the A716 south following signs for *Drummore*; past Sandhead, look for a tourist sign for *Kirkmadrine Stones and Clachanmore* and turn immediately right. The Old Manse is on the corner on the right (known locally as *Doctors' Corner*). A bus service is available from Stranraer and stops at Doctors' Corner.

Opening for: Board Of Trustees Of The Royal Botanic Garden Edinburgh

The Old Manse

10 WOODFALL GARDENS

Glasserton DG8 8LY
Ross and Liz Muir
E: woodfallgardens@btinternet.com
W: www.woodfall-gardens.co.uk

This lovely, three-acre, 18th-century triple walled garden has been thoughtfully restored to provide year-round interest. It contains many mature trees and shrubs, including some less common species, herbaceous borders and shrub roses which surround the foundations of original greenhouses, grass borders, a parterre, extensive beds of fruit and vegetables, a herb garden and a small woodland walk. This unusual garden is well worth a visit.

Open: Sundays 19 May, 16 June and 7 July, 10:30am - 4:30pm. Admission £5.00, children free. Please check the garden's website for details of further openings.

Directions: Two miles south-west of Whithorn at junction off A746 and A747 (directly behind Glasserton Church).

Opening for: Whithorn Primary School

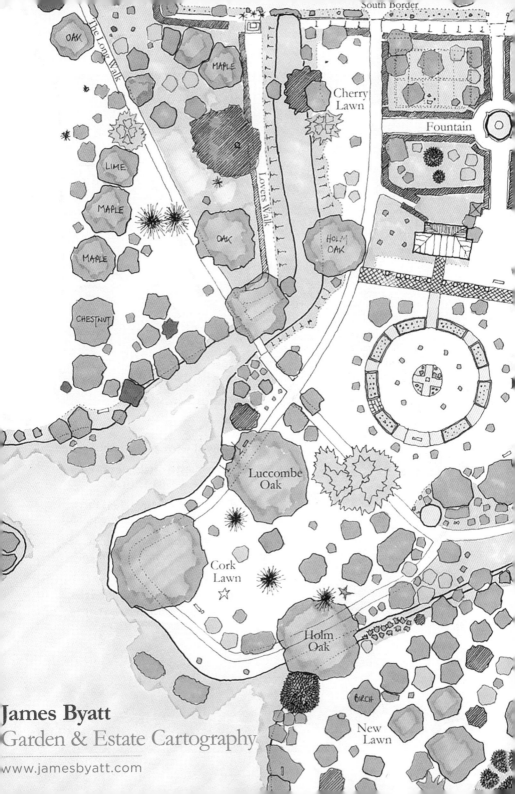

South Border

OAK

The Long Walk

MAPLE

Cherry
Lawn

Fountain

LIME

Lovers Walk

MAPLE

OAK

HOLM
OAK

MAPLE

CHESTNUT

Luccombe
Oak

Cork
Lawn

Holm
Oak

BIRCH

James Byatt
Garden & Estate Cartography

New
Lawn

www.jamesbyatt.com

DISC♣VER
SCOTTISH GARDENS

Discover us online at
discoverscottishgardens.org

Get inspiration for your garden visits & trips in 2024 by joining our mailing list.

- Learn of garden trails & festivals
- Explore where to visit, stay & eat
- Discover over 200 Scottish gardens
- Read about some of Scotland's best gardens

Be sure to pick-up one of our stunning free maps for on-the-go inspiration.

Gardens open on a specific date

FEBRUARY

Tuesday 6 February
East Lothian — Shepherd House, Inveresk, Musselburgh

Thursday 8 February
East Lothian — Shepherd House, Inveresk, Musselburgh

Saturday 10 February
Fife — Dunimarle Castle, Balgownie West, Culross
Inverness, Ross, Cromarty & Skye — Dunvegan Castle and Gardens, Isle of Skye

Sunday 11 February
Fife — Dunimarle Castle, Balgownie West, Culross

Tuesday 13 February
East Lothian — Shepherd House, Inveresk, Musselburgh

Wednesday 14 February
Peeblesshire & Tweeddale — Kirkton Manor House, Peebles

Thursday 15 February
East Lothian — Shepherd House, Inveresk, Musselburgh
Inverness, Ross, Cromarty & Skye — Dunvegan Castle and Gardens, Isle of Skye

Saturday 17 February
Dumfriesshire — Tinnisburn Plants, Upper Millsteads, Canonbie
Edinburgh, Midlothian & West Lothian — Preston Hall Walled Garden, Pathhead

Sunday 18 February
Dumfriesshire — Craig, Langholm
Dumfriesshire — Tinnisburn Plants, Upper Millsteads, Canonbie
East Lothian — Shepherd House, Inveresk, Musselburgh
Edinburgh, Midlothian & West Lothian — Preston Hall Walled Garden, Pathhead
Kirkcudbrightshire — Danevale Park, Crossmichael
Perth & Kinross — Cloan, by Auchterarder

Tuesday 20 February
East Lothian — Shepherd House, Inveresk, Musselburgh
Inverness, Ross, Cromarty & Skye — Dunvegan Castle and Gardens, Isle of Skye

Wednesday 21 February
Peeblesshire & Tweeddale — Kirkton Manor House, Peebles

Thursday 22 February
East Lothian — Shepherd House, Inveresk, Musselburgh

Saturday 24 February
Angus, Dundee & The Mearns — Kinblethmont House, by Arbroath, Angus
Fife — Lindores House, by Newburgh
Perth & Kinross — Scone Palace Garden, Perth

Sunday 25 February
Angus, Dundee & The Mearns   Kinblethmont House, by Arbroath, Angus
Dunbartonshire   Stuckenduff, Shore Road, Shandon

Tuesday 27 February
East Lothian   Shepherd House, Inveresk, Musselburgh

Wednesday 28 February
Peeblesshire & Tweeddale   Kirkton Manor House, Peebles

Thursday 29 February
Angus, Dundee & The Mearns   Lawton House, Inverkeilor, by Arbroath
East Lothian   Shepherd House, Inveresk, Musselburgh

MARCH

Friday 1 March
Angus, Dundee & The Mearns   Lawton House, Inverkeilor, by Arbroath

Saturday 2 March
Angus, Dundee & The Mearns   Lawton House, Inverkeilor, by Arbroath

Sunday 3 March
Angus, Dundee & The Mearns   Ecclesgreig Castle, St Cyrus
Lanarkshire   Cleghorn, Stable House, Cleghorn Farm, Lanark
Peeblesshire & Tweeddale   Kailzie Gardens, Peebles

Wednesday 6 March
Peeblesshire & Tweeddale   Kirkton Manor House, Peebles

Wednesday 13 March
Peeblesshire & Tweeddale   Kirkton Manor House, Peebles

Wednesday 20 March
East Lothian   Humbie Dean, Humbie
Peeblesshire & Tweeddale   Kirkton Manor House, Peebles

Saturday 23 March
Dumfriesshire   Tinnisburn Plants, Upper Millsteads, Canonbie

Sunday 24 March
Dumfriesshire   Tinnisburn Plants, Upper Millsteads, Canonbie
Kirkcudbrightshire   The Limes, Kirkcudbright

Wednesday 27 March
Peeblesshire & Tweeddale   Kirkton Manor House, Peebles

Friday 29 March
Berwickshire   Bughtrig, near Leitholm, Coldstream

Saturday 30 March
Berwickshire   Bughtrig, near Leitholm, Coldstream

Sunday 31 March
Berwickshire   Bughtrig, near Leitholm, Coldstream

APRIL

Monday 1 April
Berwickshire　　　　　　　　　　　Bughtrig, near Leitholm, Coldstream

Wednesday 3 April
East Lothian　　　　　　　　　　　Stobshiel House, Humbie
Peeblesshire & Tweeddale　　　　　Kirkton Manor House, Peebles

Sunday 7 April
Aberdeenshire　　　　　　　　　　Auchmacoy, Ellon
Perth & Kinross　　　　　　　　　　Fingask Castle, Rait

Wednesday 10 April
East Lothian　　　　　　　　　　　Stobshiel House, Humbie
Peeblesshire & Tweeddale　　　　　Kirkton Manor House, Peebles

Thursday 11 April
Inverness, Ross, Cromarty & Skye　　Dundonnell House, Little Loch Broom, Wester Ross

Saturday 13 April
East Lothian　　　　　　　　　　　A Blackbird Sings, 20 Kings Park, Longniddry

Sunday 14 April
Berwickshire　　　　　　　　　　　Harlaw Farmhouse, Eccles near Kelso, Roxburghshire
East Lothian　　　　　　　　　　　Winton Castle, Pencaitland
Kirkcudbrightshire　　　　　　　　3 Millhall, Shore Road, Kirkcudbright
Perth & Kinross　　　　　　　　　　Megginch Castle, Errol

Tuesday 16 April
East Lothian　　　　　　　　　　　Shepherd House, Inveresk, Musselburgh

Wednesday 17 April
East Lothian　　　　　　　　　　　Humbie Dean, Humbie
East Lothian　　　　　　　　　　　Stobshiel House, Humbie
Peeblesshire & Tweeddale　　　　　Kirkton Manor House, Peebles

Thursday 18 April
East Lothian　　　　　　　　　　　Shepherd House, Inveresk, Musselburgh

Saturday 20 April
Angus, Dundee & The Mearns　　　17a Menzieshill Road, Dundee
Dumfriesshire　　　　　　　　　　Tinnisburn Plants, Upper Millsteads, Canonbie

Sunday 21 April
Aberdeenshire　　　　　　　　　　Westhall Castle, Oyne, Inverurie
Angus, Dundee & The Mearns　　　17a Menzieshill Road, Dundee
Dumfriesshire　　　　　　　　　　Tinnisburn Plants, Upper Millsteads, Canonbie

Tuesday 23 April
East Lothian　　　　　　　　　　　Shepherd House, Inveresk, Musselburgh

Wednesday 24 April
East Lothian　　　　　　　　　　　Stobshiel House, Humbie
Peeblesshire & Tweeddale　　　　　Kirkton Manor House, Peebles

Thursday 25 April
East Lothian　　　　　　　　　　　Shepherd House, Inveresk, Musselburgh

Saturday 27 April

Caithness, Sutherland, Orkney & Shetland	16 Mulla, Voe, Shetland
Fife	Willowhill, Forgan, Newport-on-Tay
Renfrewshire	SGS Kilmacolm Plant Sale, Outside Kilmacolm Library, Kilmacolm

Sunday 28 April

Angus, Dundee & The Mearns	Forfar Open Garden, 36 Lochside Road, Forfar
Caithness, Sutherland, Orkney & Shetland	16 Mulla, Voe, Shetland
Edinburgh, Midlothian & West Lothian	101 Greenbank Crescent, Edinburgh
Fife	Willowhill, Forgan, Newport-on-Tay
Kirkcudbrightshire	Balmaclellan House, Balmaclellan, Castle Douglas
Stirlingshire	NEW 3 Southfield Crescent, Stirling

Monday 29 April

Fife	Willowhill, Forgan, Newport-on-Tay

Tuesday 30 April

East Lothian	Shepherd House, Inveresk, Musselburgh

MAY

Wednesday 1 May

East Lothian	Stobshiel House, Humbie
Peeblesshire & Tweeddale	Kirkton Manor House, Peebles

Thursday 2 May

East Lothian	Shepherd House, Inveresk, Musselburgh

Saturday 4 May

Angus, Dundee & The Mearns	17a Menzieshill Road, Dundee
Argyll & Lochaber	Achamore Gardens, Isle of Gigha
Dumfriesshire	Portrack, The Garden of Cosmic Speculation, Holywood
Edinburgh, Midlothian & West Lothian	Dr Neil's Garden, Duddingston Village
Moray & Nairn	NEW The Biblical Garden, King Street, Elgin, Moray

Sunday 5 May

Aberdeenshire	Middle Cairncake, Cuminestown, Turriff
Angus, Dundee & The Mearns	17a Menzieshill Road, Dundee
Argyll & Lochaber	NEW Ilha de Deus, Tiroran, Isle of Mull
Ayrshire & Arran	Blair Castle & Estate, Dalry, Ayrshire
Dumfriesshire	Portrack, The Garden of Cosmic Speculation, Holywood
Edinburgh, Midlothian & West Lothian	Dr Neil's Garden, Duddingston Village
Edinburgh, Midlothian & West Lothian	Greentree, 18 Green Hill Park, Edinburgh
Fife	Craig Cottage, Blebo Craigs
Fife	South Flisk, Blebo Craigs, Cupar
Stirlingshire	NEW Oakmore, Blairhoyle, Port of Menteith, Stirling

Monday 6 May

Kirkcudbrightshire	Threave Garden, Castle Douglas

Tuesday 7 May

East Lothian	Shepherd House, Inveresk, Musselburgh

Wednesday 8 May

East Lothian	Stobshiel House, Humbie
Peeblesshire & Tweeddale	Kirkton Manor House, Peebles

Thursday 9 May

Angus, Dundee & The Mearns	Inchmill Cottage, Glenprosen, near Kirriemuir
East Lothian	Shepherd House, Inveresk, Musselburgh
Fife	Edenhill, Kennedy Gardens, St Andrews

Saturday 11 May

Angus, Dundee & The Mearns	Balhary Walled Garden, Balhary, Alyth, Blairgowrie
Argyll & Lochaber	Knock Newhouse, Lochgair
Ayrshire & Arran	Underwood Lodge, Craigie, Kilmarnock, South Ayrshire
Edinburgh, Midlothian & West Lothian	NEW Regent, Royal and Carlton Terrace Gardens, 17a Royal Terrace Mews, Carlton Terrace Lane Entrance, Edinburgh
Edinburgh, Midlothian & West Lothian	Redcroft, 23 Murrayfield Road, Edinburgh
Perth & Kinross	NEW Birnam Bank Walled Garden, Birnam Bank, Birnam Glen, Dunkeld

Sunday 12 May

Aberdeenshire	Middle Cairncake, Cuminestown, Turriff
Argyll & Lochaber	Braevallich Farm, by Dalmally
Argyll & Lochaber	Knock Newhouse, Lochgair
Argyll & Lochaber	Strachur Flower & Woodland Gardens, Strachur
Ayrshire & Arran	Burnhouse, Cemetery Road, Galston
Dumfriesshire	Dalswinton House, Dalswinton
East Lothian	Tyninghame House and The Walled Garden, Dunbar
Edinburgh, Midlothian & West Lothian	Hunter's Tryst, 95 Oxgangs Road, Edinburgh
Edinburgh, Midlothian & West Lothian	Redcroft, 23 Murrayfield Road, Edinburgh
Kirkcudbrightshire	Arbigland House, Kirkbean, Dumfries
Perth & Kinross	Cloan, by Auchterarder
Renfrewshire	Highwood, off Lochwinnoch Road, Kilmacolm
Stirlingshire	NEW 18 Buchany, Doune

Tuesday 14 May

East Lothian	Shepherd House, Inveresk, Musselburgh

Wednesday 15 May

East Lothian	Humbie Dean, Humbie
East Lothian	Longwood, Humbie
East Lothian	Stobshiel House, Humbie
Peeblesshire & Tweeddale	Kirkton Manor House, Peebles

Thursday 16 May

East Lothian	Shepherd House, Inveresk, Musselburgh
Fife	Edenhill, Kennedy Gardens, St Andrews

Saturday 18 May

Angus, Dundee & The Mearns	Angus Plant Sale, House of Pitmuies, Guthrie, by Forfar
Dumfriesshire	Tinnisburn Plants, Upper Millsteads, Canonbie
East Lothian	A Blackbird Sings, 20 Kings Park, Longniddry
Fife	The Garden with the Dragon, 2, Upper Wellheads, Limekilns

Sunday 19 May

Aberdeenshire	Inchmarlo Retirement Village Garden, Inchmarlo, Banchory
Angus, Dundee & The Mearns	Dalfruin, Kirktonhill Road, Kirriemuir
Argyll & Lochaber	Strachur Flower & Woodland Gardens, Strachur
Dumfriesshire	Tinnisburn Plants, Upper Millsteads, Canonbie
Dunbartonshire	Ross Priory, Gartocharn
East Lothian	Broadwoodside, Gifford
East Lothian	Shepherd House, Inveresk, Musselburgh
Edinburgh, Midlothian & West Lothian	Moray Place and Bank Gardens, Edinburgh
Kirkcudbrightshire	Brooklands, Crocketford
Kirkcudbrightshire	The Limes, Kirkcudbright
Stirlingshire	Bridge of Allan Gardens, Bridge of Allan
Wigtownshire	Logan Botanic Garden, Port Logan, by Stranraer
Wigtownshire	Woodfall Gardens, Glasserton

Tuesday 21 May
East Lothian   Shepherd House, Inveresk, Musselburgh

Wednesday 22 May
East Lothian   Stobshiel House, Humbie
Peeblesshire & Tweeddale   Kirkton Manor House, Peebles

Thursday 23 May
East Lothian   Shepherd House, Inveresk, Musselburgh
Fife   Edenhill, Kennedy Gardens, St Andrews

Friday 24 May
Inverness, Ross, Cromarty & Skye   Gorthleck House Garden, Stratherrick

Saturday 25 May
Angus, Dundee & The Mearns   Gray Cottage, 23 Church Road, Liff, Dundee
Fife   The Garden with the Dragon, 2, Upper Wellheads, Limekilns
Inverness, Ross, Cromarty & Skye   Gorthleck House Garden, Stratherrick
Kirkcudbrightshire   Cally Biodiversity Gardens, Cally Avenue, Gatehouse of Fleet

Sunday 26 May
Angus, Dundee & The Mearns   Brechin Castle, Brechin
Angus, Dundee & The Mearns   Gray Cottage, 23 Church Road, Liff, Dundee
Ayrshire & Arran   Barnweil Garden, Craigie, near Kilmarnock
Fife   **NEW** Pitlochie House, Gateside
Fife   Earlshall Castle, Leuchars
Fife   Kirklands, Saline
Glasgow & District   Kilsyth Gardens, Allanfauld Road
Inverness, Ross, Cromarty & Skye   Gorthleck House Garden, Stratherrick
Kirkcudbrightshire   Corsock House, Corsock, Castle Douglas
Stirlingshire   Kilbryde Castle, Dunblane

Monday 27 May
Inverness, Ross, Cromarty & Skye   Gorthleck House Garden, Stratherrick

Tuesday 28 May
East Lothian   Shepherd House, Inveresk, Musselburgh
Inverness, Ross, Cromarty & Skye   Gorthleck House Garden, Stratherrick

Wednesday 29 May
East Lothian   Stobshiel House, Humbie
Inverness, Ross, Cromarty & Skye   Gorthleck House Garden, Stratherrick
Peeblesshire & Tweeddale   Kirkton Manor House, Peebles

Thursday 30 May
Angus, Dundee & The Mearns   Inchmill Cottage, Glenprosen, near Kirriemuir
East Lothian   Shepherd House, Inveresk, Musselburgh
Inverness, Ross, Cromarty & Skye   Dundonnell House, Little Loch Broom, Wester Ross
Inverness, Ross, Cromarty & Skye   Gorthleck House Garden, Stratherrick

Friday 31 May
Inverness, Ross, Cromarty & Skye   Gorthleck House Garden, Stratherrick

JUNE

Saturday 1 June

Angus, Dundee & The Mearns	West End Trio , 3 & 12 Glamis Drive and 5 Glamis Terrace, Dundee
Fife	Willowhill, Forgan, Newport-on-Tay
Inverness, Ross, Cromarty & Skye	Gorthleck House Garden, Stratherrick

Sunday 2 June

Aberdeenshire	NEW Norton House, 1 North Deeside Road, Kincardine O'Neil, Aboyne, Aberdeenshire
Angus, Dundee & The Mearns	West End Trio , 3 & 12 Glamis Drive and 5 Glamis Terrace, Dundee
Argyll & Lochaber	NEW Ilha de Deus, Tiroran, Isle of Mull
Argyll & Lochaber	Ardverikie with Aberarder, Kinloch Laggan, Newtonmore
Argyll & Lochaber	Braevallich Farm, by Dalmally
Argyll & Lochaber	Knock Newhouse, Lochgair
Caithness, Sutherland, Orkney & Shetland	Old Granary Quoy and The Quoy of Houton, The Quoy of Houton, Orphir, Orkney
Dumfriesshire	Cowhill Tower, Holywood
Dumfriesshire	Waterside Garden, Moffat
Dunbartonshire	Geilston Garden, Main Road, Cardross
Edinburgh, Midlothian & West Lothian	20 Blackford Road, Edinburgh
Fife	Lindores House, by Newburgh
Fife	Swallows Rest, Lindores
Inverness, Ross, Cromarty & Skye	Gorthleck House Garden, Stratherrick
Kirkcudbrightshire	Seabank, The Merse, Rockcliffe
Peeblesshire & Tweeddale	Macbiehill Gardens, The Walled Garden, Macbiehill
Peeblesshire & Tweeddale	Quercus Garden Plants, Whitmuir Farm, West Linton
Peeblesshire & Tweeddale	Stobo Japanese Water Garden, Stobo Farm, Stobo
Renfrewshire	NEW Barnbeth House, Clevans Road, Bridge of Weir
Roxburghshire	West Leas, Bonchester Bridge
Stirlingshire	Coldoch, Blairdrummond, Stirling

Monday 3 June

Fife	Willowhill, Forgan, Newport-on-Tay

Tuesday 4 June

East Lothian	Shepherd House, Inveresk, Musselburgh

Wednesday 5 June

East Lothian	Stobshiel House, Humbie
Peeblesshire & Tweeddale	Kirkton Manor House, Peebles
Peeblesshire & Tweeddale	Laidlawstiel House, Clovenfords, Galashiels

Thursday 6 June

East Lothian	Shepherd House, Inveresk, Musselburgh
Peeblesshire & Tweeddale	Laidlawstiel House, Clovenfords, Galashiels
Perth & Kinross	Bradystone House, Murthly

Friday 7 June

East Lothian	NEW Blackdykes Garden, Blackdykes Farmhouse, North Berwick,
East Lothian	

Saturday 8 June

Angus, Dundee & The Mearns	Balhary Walled Garden, Balhary, Alyth, Blairgowrie
East Lothian	NEW Blackdykes Garden, Blackdykes Farmhouse, North Berwick,
East Lothian	
East Lothian	Dirleton Village, Dirleton
Perth & Kinross	Cloan, by Auchterarder

Sunday 9 June

Angus, Dundee & The Mearns	Arbuthnott House Gardens, Arbuthnott House, Laurencekirk
Angus, Dundee & The Mearns	Tillytoghills Steading, Fettercairn
Argyll & Lochaber	Ardchattan Priory, North Connel
East Lothian	Dirleton Village, Dirleton
Edinburgh, Midlothian & West Lothian	Dean Gardens, Edinburgh
Edinburgh, Midlothian & West Lothian	Maggie's Edinburgh, Western General Hospital, Crewe Road, Edinburgh
Inverness, Ross, Cromarty & Skye	Old Allangrange, Munlochy
Peeblesshire & Tweeddale	NEW Srongarbh, The Loan, West Linton
Perth & Kinross	36 Muirfield, Perth
Perth & Kinross	Cloan, by Auchterarder
Renfrewshire	The Bishop's House, Glencairn Road, Kilmacolm
Stirlingshire	Thorntree, Arnprior
Wigtownshire	Castle Kennedy Gardens, Stranraer

Tuesday 11 June

East Lothian	Shepherd House, Inveresk, Musselburgh

Wednesday 12 June

East Lothian	Humbie Dean, Humbie
East Lothian	Stobshiel House, Humbie
Peeblesshire & Tweeddale	Kirkton Manor House, Peebles
Renfrewshire	Craig Hepburn Memorial Garden, Stirling Drive, Linwood

Thursday 13 June

Angus, Dundee & The Mearns	Inchmill Cottage, Glenprosen, near Kirriemuir
East Lothian	Shepherd House, Inveresk, Musselburgh
Perth & Kinross	Bradystone House, Murthly
Renfrewshire	Craig Hepburn Memorial Garden, Stirling Drive, Linwood

Friday 14 June

Perth & Kinross	NEW Mouse Cottage, Strathtay, Pitlochry

Saturday 15 June

Angus, Dundee & The Mearns	St Bride's Cottage, South Kingennie, Broughty Ferry
Ayrshire & Arran	Barrmill Community Garden, Barrmill Park and Gardens
Dumfriesshire	Tinnisburn Plants, Upper Millsteads, Canonbie
East Lothian	Inveresk Village, Inveresk, Musselburgh
Fife	Auchtermuchty Open Gardens, Fife
Perth & Kinross	NEW Mouse Cottage, Strathtay, Pitlochry
Perth & Kinross	Blair Castle Gardens, Blair Atholl
Perth & Kinross	Bradystone House, Murthly
Perth & Kinross	The Abercairny Garden, Abercairny House, Crieff

Sunday 16 June

Angus, Dundee & The Mearns	NEW Kirkside of Lochty, Menmuir, by Brechin
Angus, Dundee & The Mearns	St Bride's Cottage, South Kingennie, Broughty Ferry
Dumfriesshire	Tinnisburn Plants, Upper Millsteads, Canonbie
East Lothian	Inveresk Village, Inveresk, Musselburgh
Edinburgh, Midlothian & West Lothian	14 East Brighton Crescent, Portobello, Edinburgh
Edinburgh, Midlothian & West Lothian	Claremont, Redmill
Fife	Auchtermuchty Open Gardens, Fife
Fife	Pittenweem: Gardens in the Burgh, Pittenweem
Inverness, Ross, Cromarty & Skye	Glenkyllachy, Tomatin
Lanarkshire	NEW Covington Gardens, Covington Village
Peeblesshire & Tweeddale	NEW Kirkhouse, Traquair
Wigtownshire	Woodfall Gardens, Glasserton

Tuesday 18 June
East Lothian   Shepherd House, Inveresk, Musselburgh

Wednesday 19 June
East Lothian   Stobshiel House, Humbie
Peeblesshire & Tweeddale   Kirkton Manor House, Peebles

Thursday 20 June
East Lothian   NEW Blackdykes Garden, Blackdykes Farmhouse, North Berwick,
East Lothian
East Lothian   Shepherd House, Inveresk, Musselburgh
Perth & Kinross   Bradystone House, Murthly

Friday 21 June
East Lothian   NEW Blackdykes Garden, Blackdykes Farmhouse, North Berwick,
East Lothian
East Lothian   Congalton House, North Berwick

Saturday 22 June
Fife   NEW Kirkbrae House, Culross
Roxburghshire   NEW Southdean Mill, Southdean Mill, Chesters, Hawick

Sunday 23 June
Angus, Dundee & The Mearns   Brechin Gardens in June, Locations across Brechin
Berwickshire   The Moorhouse, Duns
Dumfriesshire   NEW The Hewke, Lockerbie, Dumfries
Dunbartonshire   NEW Brantwoode and High Glenan, 24a Queen Street, Helensburgh
East Lothian   Longniddry Gardens, Longniddry
East Lothian   Tyninghame House and The Walled Garden, Tyninghame House,
                                                Dunbar
Edinburgh, Midlothian & West Lothian   Merchiston Cottage, 16 Colinton Road, Edinburgh
Edinburgh, Midlothian & West Lothian   Stockbridge Gardens, Garden trail runs between Logie Green
                                                Gardens EH7 4HE and Royal Circus Gardens North
Fife   NEW Kirkbrae House, Culross
Fife   Earlshall Castle, Leuchars
Glasgow & District   The Gardens of Milton of Campsie, Milton of Campsie
Inverness, Ross, Cromarty & Skye   House of Aigas and Field Centre, by Beauly
Roxburghshire   NEW Southdean Mill, Southdean Mill, Chesters, Hawick
Stirlingshire   NEW Tiny Farm, St Modan's High School, Royal Stuart Way, Stirling

Tuesday 25 June
East Lothian   Shepherd House, Inveresk, Musselburgh
Lanarkshire   Little Sparta, Stonypath, Dunsyre

Wednesday 26 June
East Lothian   Stobshiel House, Humbie
Peeblesshire & Tweeddale   Kirkton Manor House, Peebles

Thursday 27 June
East Lothian   Shepherd House, Inveresk, Musselburgh
Perth & Kinross   Bradystone House, Murthly

Saturday 29 June
East Lothian   Gifford Bank, Gifford
Fife   NEW Blanerne, West Road, Charlestown
Perth & Kinross   The Bield at Blackruthven, Blackruthven House, Tibbermore

Sunday 30 June

Aberdeenshire	Bruckhills Croft, Rothienorman, Inverurie
Aberdeenshire	Middle Cairncake, Cuminestown, Turriff
Angus, Dundee & The Mearns	The Old Schoolhouse, Kilry
Ayrshire & Arran	Dalhowan Farm, Crosshill, Maybole
Berwickshire	Ruthven House, Coldstream
East Lothian	Gifford Bank, Gifford
Edinburgh, Midlothian & West Lothian	NEW Whitehouse & Grange Bowling Club, 18a Hope Terrace, Edinburgh
Fife	NEW Blanerne, West Road, Charlestown
Fife	NEW Moonzie House, By Cupar
Fife	Blebo Craigs Village Gardens, Blebo Craigs, Cupar
Fife	Craigfoodie, Dairsie
Inverness, Ross, Cromarty & Skye	7 Braes of Conon, Conon Bridge
Kirkcudbrightshire	Southwick House, Southwick

JULY

Monday 1 July

Aberdeenshire	Middle Cairncake, Cuminestown, Turriff
Fife	Willowhill, Forgan, Newport-on-Tay

Tuesday 2 July

Aberdeenshire	Middle Cairncake, Cuminestown, Turriff
Ayrshire & Arran	Dougarie, Isle of Arran
East Lothian	Shepherd House, Inveresk, Musselburgh
Lanarkshire	Little Sparta, Stonypath, Dunsyre

Wednesday 3 July

Aberdeenshire	Middle Cairncake, Cuminestown, Turriff
East Lothian	Stobshiel House, Humbie
Peeblesshire & Tweeddale	Kirkton Manor House, Peebles

Thursday 4 July

Aberdeenshire	Middle Cairncake, Cuminestown, Turriff
Angus, Dundee & The Mearns	Inchmill Cottage, Glenprosen, near Kirriemuir
East Lothian	Shepherd House, Inveresk, Musselburgh
Perth & Kinross	Bradystone House, Murthly

Friday 5 July

Aberdeenshire	Middle Cairncake, Cuminestown, Turriff

Saturday 6 July

Aberdeenshire	Middle Cairncake, Cuminestown, Turriff
Caithness, Sutherland, Orkney & Shetland	Amat, Amat Lodge, Ardgay
Edinburgh, Midlothian & West Lothian	NEW Fountainbank, 5 Back Station Road, Linlithgow, West Lothian
Fife	Crail: Gardens in the Burgh, Crail
Fife	Willowhill, Forgan, Newport-on-Tay
Glasgow & District	King's Park Walled Garden, Kings Park, 325 Carmunnock Road, Glasgow
Moray & Nairn	Cuthberts Brae, 84 Seatown, Buckie

Sunday 7 July

Aberdeenshire	Douneside House, Tarland
Aberdeenshire	Middle Cairncake, Cuminestown, Turriff
Argyll & Lochaber	NEW Ilha de Deus, Tiroran, Isle of Mull
Caithness, Sutherland, Orkney & Shetland	Amat, Amat Lodge, Ardgay
Edinburgh, Midlothian & West Lothian	NEW Fountainbank, 5 Back Station Road, Linlithgow, West Lothian
Edinburgh, Midlothian & West Lothian	Pentland Crescent Gardens, 2 Pentland Crescent, Edinburgh
Fife	Crail: Gardens in the Burgh, Crail
Moray & Nairn	Cuthberts Brae, 84 Seatown, Buckie
Peeblesshire & Tweeddale	Carolside, Earlston
Peeblesshire & Tweeddale	Glen House, Glen Estate, Innerleithen
Wigtownshire	Woodfall Gardens, Glasserton

Monday 8 July

Aberdeenshire	Middle Cairncake, Cuminestown, Turriff
Fife	Willowhill, Forgan, Newport-on-Tay

Tuesday 9 July

Aberdeenshire	Middle Cairncake, Cuminestown, Turriff
East Lothian	Shepherd House, Inveresk, Musselburgh

Wednesday 10 July

Aberdeenshire	Middle Cairncake, Cuminestown, Turriff
East Lothian	Stobshiel House, Humbie
Peeblesshire & Tweeddale	Kirkton Manor House, Peebles

Thursday 11 July

Aberdeenshire	Middle Cairncake, Cuminestown, Turriff
East Lothian	Shepherd House, Inveresk, Musselburgh
Perth & Kinross	Bradystone House, Murthly

Friday 12 July

Aberdeenshire	Middle Cairncake, Cuminestown, Turriff

Saturday 13 July

Aberdeenshire	Middle Cairncake, Cuminestown, Turriff
Angus, Dundee & The Mearns	Balhary Walled Garden, Balhary, Alyth, Blairgowrie
Ayrshire & Arran	Whitewin House, Golf Course Road, Girvan
East Lothian	A Blackbird Sings, 20 Kings Park, Longniddry
Fife	Willowhill, Forgan, Newport-on-Tay
Moray & Nairn	Sunflower Dreams, 2 Househill Drive, Nairn
Renfrewshire	SGS Kilmacolm Plant Sale, Outside Kilmacolm Library, Kilmacolm
Wigtownshire	Amulree, 8 Mill Street, Drummore, Stranraer

Sunday 14 July

Aberdeenshire	Middle Cairncake, Cuminestown, Turriff
Ayrshire & Arran	Whitewin House, Golf Course Road, Girvan
Edinburgh, Midlothian & West Lothian	Claremont, Redmill
Inverness, Ross, Cromarty & Skye	Kiltarlity Gardens, Kiltarlity, Beauly
Moray & Nairn	Glebe House, Main Street, Urquhart
Stirlingshire	NEW Oakmore, Blairhoyle, Port of Menteith, Stirling
Wigtownshire	Amulree, 8 Mill Street, Drummore, Stranraer

Monday 15 July

Fife	Willowhill, Forgan, Newport-on-Tay

Tuesday 16 July

East Lothian	Shepherd House, Inveresk, Musselburgh

Wednesday 17 July

East Lothian	Humbie Dean, Humbie
East Lothian	Stobshiel House, Humbie

Thursday 18 July

East Lothian	Shepherd House, Inveresk, Musselburgh
Perth & Kinross	Bradystone House, Murthly

Saturday 20 July

Aberdeenshire	Two Gardens in Banchory Devenick, Banchory Devenick
Angus, Dundee & The Mearns	NEW Charleston Forest Garden, 43 Gourdie Terrace, Dundee
Ayrshire & Arran	Whitewin House, Golf Course Road, Girvan
Caithness, Sutherland, Orkney & Shetland	16 Mulla, Voe, Shetland
Caithness, Sutherland, Orkney & Shetland	Auchlea, Balnapolaig Muir, Dornoch
Fife	NEW Kirkbrae House, Culross
Fife	Willowhill, Forgan, Newport-on-Tay

Sunday 21 July

Aberdeenshire	Two Gardens in Banchory Devenick, Banchory Devenick
Angus, Dundee & The Mearns	Gardeners Cottage, Fern, Brechin
Ayrshire & Arran	Whitewin House, Golf Course Road, Girvan
Caithness, Sutherland, Orkney & Shetland	16 Mulla, Voe, Shetland
Edinburgh, Midlothian & West Lothian	Craigentinny Telferton Allotments, Telferton Road, off Portobello Road, Edinburgh
Fife	NEW Kirkbrae House, Culross
Glasgow & District	NEW SWG3 Community Garden, 100 Eastvale Place, Glasgow
Peeblesshire & Tweeddale	Kailzie Gardens, Peebles
Stirlingshire	NEW 18 Buchany, Doune

Monday 22 July

Fife	Willowhill, Forgan, Newport-on-Tay

Tuesday 23 July

East Lothian	Shepherd House, Inveresk, Musselburgh

Wednesday 24 July

East Lothian	Stobshiel House, Humbie

Thursday 25 July

East Lothian	Shepherd House, Inveresk, Musselburgh
Perth & Kinross	Bradystone House, Murthly

Saturday 27 July

Ayrshire & Arran	Whitewin House, Golf Course Road, Girvan
Caithness, Sutherland, Orkney & Shetland	42 Astle, Dornoch
Caithness, Sutherland, Orkney & Shetland	Skelbo House, Skelbo, Dornoch
Fife	Willowhill, Forgan, Newport-on-Tay
Perth & Kinross	Tomandroighne, Edradynate, Aberfeldy

Sunday 28 July

Angus, Dundee & The Mearns	Brechin Gardens in July, Locations across Brechin
Ayrshire & Arran	Whitewin House, Golf Course Road, Girvan
Caithness, Sutherland, Orkney & Shetland	42 Astle, Dornoch
Caithness, Sutherland, Orkney & Shetland	Langwell, Berriedale
Caithness, Sutherland, Orkney & Shetland	Skelbo House, Skelbo, Dornoch
Fife	NEW Pitlochie House, Gateside
Glasgow & District	Strathbungo Garden, March Street, Glasgow
Inverness, Ross, Cromarty & Skye	House of Aigas and Field Centre, by Beauly
Moray & Nairn	Glenrinnes Lodge, Dufftown, Keith, Banffshire
Peeblesshire & Tweeddale	Gattonside Village Gardens, Gattonside
Perth & Kinross	Tomandroighne, Edradynate, Aberfeldy

Monday 29 July

Fife	Willowhill, Forgan, Newport-on-Tay

Wednesday 31 July

East Lothian	Stobshiel House, Humbie

AUGUST

Thursday 1 August

Perth & Kinross	Bradystone House, Murthly

Saturday 3 August

Ayrshire & Arran	Whitewin House, Golf Course Road, Girvan
Edinburgh, Midlothian & West Lothian	39 Nantwich Drive, Edinburgh
Fife	Willowhill, Forgan, Newport-on-Tay

Sunday 4 August

Angus, Dundee & The Mearns	Glenbervie House, Drumlithie, Stonehaven
Ayrshire & Arran	Whitewin House, Golf Course Road, Girvan
Dumfriesshire	Dalswinton Mill, Dalswinton
Edinburgh, Midlothian & West Lothian	NEW 77 Kirk Brae, Edinburgh
Edinburgh, Midlothian & West Lothian	Claremont, Redmill
Inverness, Ross, Cromarty & Skye	2 Durnamuck, Little Loch Broom, Wester Ross
Lanarkshire	The Walled Garden, Shieldhill, Quothquan, Biggar
Perth & Kinross	Drummond Castle Gardens, Muthill, Crieff
Roxburghshire	West Leas, Bonchester Bridge
Stirlingshire	NEW Braehead Community Garden, Broom Road, Braehead

Monday 5 August

Fife	Willowhill, Forgan, Newport-on-Tay

Wednesday 7 August

East Lothian	Stobshiel House, Humbie

Thursday 8 August

Perth & Kinross	Bradystone House, Murthly

Saturday 10 August

Angus, Dundee & The Mearns	Balhary Walled Garden, Balhary, Alyth, Blairgowrie
Ayrshire & Arran	Whitewin House, Golf Course Road, Girvan
Fife	Willowhill, Forgan, Newport-on-Tay
Lanarkshire	NEW Stobwood Cottage Garden, Stobwood Cottage, Stobwood, Forth, South Lanarkshire
Roxburghshire	NEW Southdean Mill, Southdean Mill, Chesters, Hawick

Sunday 11 August

Aberdeenshire	Tarland Community Garden, Tarland, Aboyne
Ayrshire & Arran	Whitewin House, Golf Course Road, Girvan
East Lothian	The Gardens at Archerfield Walled Garden, Archerfield Walled
Garden	Archerfield Estate, Dirleton, North Berwick, East Lothian
Inverness, Ross, Cromarty & Skye	NEW Aldourie Castle Garden, Dores, Inverness
Lanarkshire	NEW Stobwood Cottage Garden, Stobwood Cottage, Stobwood, Forth, South Lanarkshire
Perth & Kinross	Cloan, by Auchterarder
Renfrewshire	NEW North Newton Farm, Kilmacolm
Roxburghshire	NEW Southdean Mill, Southdean Mill, Chesters, Hawick

Monday 12 August

Fife	Willowhill, Forgan, Newport-on-Tay

Wednesday 14 August

East Lothian	Humbie Dean, Humbie
East Lothian	Longwood, Humbie
East Lothian	Stobshiel House, Humbie

Thursday 15 August

Angus, Dundee & The Mearns	Inchmill Cottage, Glenprosen, near Kirriemuir
Inverness, Ross, Cromarty & Skye	Dundonnell House, Little Loch Broom, Wester Ross
Perth & Kinross	Bradystone House, Murthly

Saturday 17 August

Ayrshire & Arran	Whitewin House, Golf Course Road, Girvan
East Lothian	A Blackbird Sings, 20 Kings Park, Longniddry
Fife	NEW Blanerne, West Road, Charlestown
Fife	Willowhill, Forgan, Newport-on-Tay
Wigtownshire	NEW Lutra Holt, Penninghame, Newton Stewart

Sunday 18 August

Angus, Dundee & The Mearns	Glensaugh, Glensaugh Lodge, Fettercairn, Laurencekirk
Ayrshire & Arran	Whitewin House, Golf Course Road, Girvan
Fife	NEW Kirkbrae House, Culross
Inverness, Ross, Cromarty & Skye	Old Allangrange, Munlochy
Wigtownshire	NEW Lutra Holt, Penninghame, Newton Stewart

Monday 19 August

Fife	Willowhill, Forgan, Newport-on-Tay

Wednesday 21 August

East Lothian	Stobshiel House, Humbie

Thursday 22 August

Perth & Kinross	Bradystone House, Murthly

Saturday 24 August

Ayrshire & Arran	Whitewin House, Golf Course Road, Girvan
East Lothian	NEW Amisfield Walled Garden, Haddington
Fife	Willowhill, Forgan, Newport-on-Tay
Moray & Nairn	Easter Laggan, Dulnain Bridge, Grantown-on-Spey
Perth & Kinross	NEW Auchterarder Allotments Association, Located behind St Margaret's Hospital

Sunday 25 August

Angus, Dundee & The Mearns	Forfar Open Garden, 36 Lochside Road, Forfar
Ayrshire & Arran	Whitewin House, Golf Course Road, Girvan
East Lothian	NEW Amisfield Walled Garden, Haddington
Peeblesshire & Tweeddale	Quercus Garden Plants, Whitmuir Farm, West Linton
Stirlingshire	NEW Bannockburn House Gardens, Stirling

Monday 26 August

Fife	Willowhill, Forgan, Newport-on-Tay

Tuesday 27 August

Lanarkshire	Little Sparta, Stonypath, Dunsyre

Wednesday 28 August

East Lothian	Stobshiel House, Humbie

Thursday 29 August

Perth & Kinross	Bradystone House, Murthly

Saturday 31 August

Angus, Dundee & The Mearns	NEW Carnoustie's Tropical Garden, 28 Prosen Bank, Carnoustie
Fife	Willowhill, Forgan, Newport-on-Tay

SEPTEMBER

Sunday 1 September

Dunbartonshire	James Street Community Garden Plant Sale, James Street, Helensburgh
Fife	NEW Pitlochie House, Gateside
Glasgow & District	Horatio's Garden, National Spinal Unit, Queen Elizabeth University Hospital, Govan Road, Glasgow
Kirkcudbrightshire	3 Millhall, Shore Road, Kirkcudbright

Tuesday 3 September

Lanarkshire	Little Sparta, Stonypath, Dunsyre

Wednesday 4 September

East Lothian	Stobshiel House, Humbie

Thursday 5 September
Angus, Dundee & The Mearns   Inchmill Cottage, Glenprosen, near Kirriemuir
Perth & Kinross   Bradystone House, Murthly

Sunday 8 September
Angus, Dundee & The Mearns   Braidestone Farm, Meigle, Blairgowrie

Wednesday 11 September
East Lothian   Stobshiel House, Humbie

Thursday 12 September
Perth & Kinross   Bradystone House, Murthly

Saturday 14 September
Angus, Dundee & The Mearns   Balhary Walled Garden, Balhary, Alyth, Blairgowrie
Glasgow & District   12 Chatelherault Avenue (A Soiree in September),
                                    Cambuslang, Glasgow

Sunday 15 September
Fife   Greenhead Farmhouse, Greenhead of Arnot, Leslie

Wednesday 18 September
East Lothian   Stobshiel House, Humbie

Thursday 19 September
Perth & Kinross   Bradystone House, Murthly

Wednesday 25 September
East Lothian   Stobshiel House, Humbie

Thursday 26 September
Perth & Kinross   Bradystone House, Murthly

Saturday 28 September
Angus, Dundee & The Mearns   Hospitalfield Gardens, Hospitalfield House, Westway, Arbroath

Sunday 29 September
Argyll & Lochaber   Benmore Botanic Garden, Benmore, Dunoon
Kirkcudbrightshire   Cally Biodiversity Gardens, Cally Avenue, Gatehouse of Fleet

OCTOBER

Wednesday 2 October
East Lothian   Humbie Dean, Humbie

Sunday 6 October
Fife   SGS Autumn Plant Sale at St Andrews Botanic Garden, St Andrews
Peeblesshire & Tweeddale   Dawyck Botanic Garden, Stobo

Saturday 19 October
Angus, Dundee & The Mearns   Westgate, 12 Glamis Drive, Dundee

Sunday 20 October
Angus, Dundee & The Mearns   Westgate, 12 Glamis Drive, Dundee

Saturday 26 October
Roxburghshire   Thirlestane, Kelso

Sunday 27 October
Roxburghshire   Thirlestane, Kelso

Index of Gardens

Support our charity and make a £5.00 donation today

By donating to Scotland's Gardens Scheme you will make an instant difference as it will help us to continue and improve our volunteer support and develop our garden opening programme for all to enjoy.

Please donate on our website:
scotlandsgardens.org/donate/

or scan the QR code:

Carolside, Peeblesshire & Tweeddale